To Thornton,

Happy Birthday, 1970.

Dorothy, Presley, Linda and
Presley I.

Books by Lon Tinkle

THIRTEEN DAYS TO GLORY: THE SIEGE OF THE ALAMO

THE COWBOY READER (with Allen Maxwell)

J. FRANK DOBIE: THE MAKING OF AN AMPLE MIND

MR. DE: A BIOGRAPHY OF EVERETTE LEE DEGOLYER

For Younger Readers

THE STORY OF OKLAHOMA

THE VALIANT FEW

THE KEY TO DALLAS

MIRACLE IN MEXICO

MR. DE

A Biography of
Everette Lee DeGolyer

DeGolyer liked this photograph of what he called his
"peasant's face."

MR. DE

A Biography of
Everette Lee DeGolyer

by Lon Tinkle

With a Foreword by Norman Cousins

Little, Brown and Company — Boston — Toronto

LIBRARY OF CONGRESS CATALOG CARD NO. 75–121439

01308   w0611   T11/70

FIRST EDITION

The author gratefully acknowledges permission to quote from the following publications:

Fightin' Oil by Harold Ickes (1943). Reprinted by permission of the publisher Alfred A. Knopf.

The Liberal Imagination by Lionel Trilling (1950). Reprinted by permission of Viking Press, Inc., Publishers.

The Greatest Gamblers: The Epic of American Oil Exploration by Ruth Knowles (1959). Reprinted by permission of the publisher McGraw-Hill, Inc.

Portrait in Oil by Nubar Gulbenkian (1965). Reprinted by permission of the publisher Simon and Schuster.

"Memorial" to Mr. DeGolyer by Rodger Denison in *Biographical Memoirs* Vol. XXXIII (1959) reprinted by permission of the Columbia University Press for the National Academy of Sciences.

Quotations from the *Time* article of April 3, 1944 on Mr. DeGolyer are reprinted by permission of *TIME: The Weekly Newsmagazine;* Copyright 1944 by Time, Inc.

Excerpts from "How Men Find Oil" from the August 1949 issue of *Fortune* magazine are used by permission.

Quotations from *Proceedings,* Vol. 68, Part I, published by the Geological Society of America (1957) are reprinted by permission.

Permission to reprint President Eisenhower's letter was granted by Mrs. Dwight D. Eisenhower.

*Published simultaneously in Canada
by Little, Brown & Company (Canada) Limited*

PRINTED IN THE UNITED STATES OF AMERICA

*This book is dedicated to five men whose friend-
ship E. DeGolyer greatly prized, and whose
help on this biography has been considerable:*

CLEVELAND AMORY

NORMAN COUSINS

ERIK JONSSON

SAVOIE LOTTINVILLE

EUGENE MCDERMOTT

Contents

V.   Country of the Blind

Foreword

This is a book about one of the most remarkable men it has been my privilege to know. He signed his name E. DeGolyer. Almost everyone else called him De or Mr. De. *Who's Who* and the formal records spell it out — Everette Lee DeGolyer, petroleum geologist.

He had more sides to him than an exhibit of mobiles. Put him in one setting and he could be as coldly analytical as a brain surgeon describing the difference between a synapse and a ganglion. Put him in another setting and he could be as compassionate and tender as an Irish setter in an outdoor nursery.

And he could slide from one role to the other without any perceptible grinding of emotional gears. At an informal dinner one night in New York he was the complete scientist-historian, explaining mining techniques in ancient Greece. You had to listen carefully, for he didn't waste words and he spoke with deceptive ease. What impressed you was the total lack of the extraneous or the emotional in his command of the subject. You had the feeling that every word had behind it total research. Here, you thought, was the ideal marriage of science to history. From dinner we went directly to the theater. If my memory is correct, we went to see *Allegro* by Rodgers and Hammerstein. Within five minutes after the curtain went up, De was as emotionally involved in the story as though he had lived it. His tear ducts went into action. During the intermission he dried out. He met a geologist friend in the lobby who asked a question about the oil reserves of the Persian Gulf area. Once again, De was the precise, dispassionate scientist, putting one fact down after another in proper weight and progression. When the play resumed, De surrendered promptly and completely to the sentiment of the story. He was the playwright's delight.

No man had more respect for the scientific method; yet few have gotten more mileage out of their hunches — even when all the evidence seemed to go the other way. His mind was like a spark jumping across gaps. Once, a subordinate reported that he had dug five dry holes in a field, having gone down to 12,000 feet. De told him to stay put and go down another 2,000 feet. The rest was almost inevitable. They hit at 14,000.

When I asked De what caused him to give the order to drill the additional footage, he bit hard on the end of his twisted Mexican cigar, grinned and said: "Damned if I know. I'm just lucky."

De *was* lucky; but it wasn't blind, stumbling luck. He knew every wrinkle in the face of Lady Luck as though he had drawn the original sketches. He could translate her slightest whisper into a marching order. He knew where she lived, where she kept her charms, where she went for her winter vacation. Most of all, he knew when not to press her too far. If De was lucky, it was no accident. He had bound the lady to him with hoops of steel.

Among the highlights of DeGolyer's career were his part in the founding of Amerada Petroleum Corporation; his pioneering work with torsion balances and the refraction and reflection seismographs; his leadership in the Geophysical Research Corporation, with its history-making record in Texas and Louisiana; the spectacular discoveries for Amerada in the Seminole Plateau in 1930; his work as assistant deputy petroleum administrator in World War II; his revolutionary predictions about the oil reserves of the Persian Gulf area; his various scientific medals and honors; his presidency of the American Institute of Mining and Metallurgical Engineers, and his directorships of the American Petroleum Institute and Southern Pacific Railroad.

Not so well known, however, was the nature of the man himself. Indeed, he was something of a legend in the petroleum industry, some of whose members regarded him as a combination of maverick and mystery man. This was largely due to the great deal of time he spent in pursuit of his many outside interests. He would, for example, go running off for days at a time just to track down a book by some Spanish fellow named Cabeza de Vaca.

There was nothing feigned about this side of Mr. De. He had an abiding delight in book collecting and the creative life. His own writing was a painful joy; he would spend hours on a sentence just to make sure it turned right. He filled out thousands of catalogue cards by hand in preparing his notes for what was to be the major literary effort in his life — a history of the petroleum industry — a project his illness prevented him from completing. He was an indefatigable researcher. He would hunt down even the smallest fact with a relentless tenacity generally associated with TV dramatizations of Scotland Yard.

His private library, like the man himself, was wide-ranging, well organized, primed for constant action. It is doubtful if anyone has built up finer private collections in the fields of Southwest Americana and folklore, the early exploration of America, the history of science, Charles Darwin, or Morleyana (he owned everything Christopher Morley ever wrote, some of them in original manuscript).

The collection on the history of science, running into thousands of volumes, he presented to the University of Oklahoma without condition or stipulation. "No point in giving them money or a building," he said. "They've got plenty. But did you ever know of a university that didn't need good books?"

He placed a value above pearls on good talk. He himself had a remarkable conversational change of pace; he could mix together abstract ideas, earthy illustrations, scientific data, random speculation, and droll stories. Once, after he had spent almost a week on the campuses of Harvard and M.I.T. at some geophysical meetings, I asked him if his trip had been productive. "Couldn't have been a better trip," he said, "I picked up two good stories."

He knew people all over the world — government officials, industrial leaders, fellow oilmen, scientists, writers, editors, newsmen, printers, booksellers, college presidents and professors, cab drivers, headwaiters.

I first met E. DeGolyer in Dallas in 1941. John William Rogers, the author and playwright, got permission from Mrs. DeGolyer to show me Mr. De's famous book collections. Mr. De was there and took me on a personal tour. He showed me original manuscripts of articles that had been published in my own magazine, then opened the door to a small storage closet and showed me a complete file of the *Saturday Review* since it was founded by Henry Seidel Canby, Amy Loveman, William Rose Benét and Christopher Morley in 1924.

Mr. De asked me to stay to dinner. The next day I asked him if he would like to own the magazine. We really needed help in those days: we were two months behind in our printer's bills. Mr. De held out his hand: I took it, and that was that.

"Just one condition," he said. "If you spend one damn

cent for lawyers' fees in drawing up any papers to for-
malize the deal, it's off. We've already shaken hands; that's
enough."

For fifteen years De was the owner of the *Saturday Review* and my boss. Not once in all that time did he suggest
or intimate that the editorial page or the magazine take
any turn to coincide with his own views. He gave me,
quite literally, all the freedom in the world. My main problem was not to fight for editorial independence but to justify the independence I had.

One day, I received a telephone call at SR from an officer of a patriotic organization in Dallas. He said he had
just learned that I was scheduled to speak in Dallas on the
subject of peace, under the auspices of Quakers. He suggested I withdraw from the meeting, for his group intended to picket it. The meeting seemed to him to be questionable in terms of possible subversive associations. He
pointed out politely that everyone connected with the
meeting would be in the line of fire. Since Mr. DeGolyer
owned the *Saturday Review*, my appearance might prove
embarrassing to my boss in his home town.

I told the gentleman that I hoped he would look into the
history and background of the Society of Friends, for it
was quite possible that any embarrassment over the meeting might belong to those who accused the Quakers of
subversion. In any event, if my appearance at the meeting
would be embarrassing to Mr. DeGolyer, then Mr. De
would have to tell it to me himself. I suggested the gentleman take the matter up with Mr. De.

He did so. The results were completely predictable. Mr.
De told him to jump in the lake. He then telephoned the
Quakers, asked if he could join the sponsors of the meeting, and volunteered to introduce me. He telegraphed me
saying he expected me to come to Dallas and to be sure to
stay at the house.

The moment it was announced that Mr. De would appear on the program, all opposition collapsed. There was no picket line, just an overflow crowd, many of them attracted no doubt by the prestige of Mr. De's name. The entire episode was one that would have made Mr. Oliver W. Holmes sing for joy.

It was the only time Mr. De had introduced me at a meeting, or, for that matter, had heard me speak publicly. I can't remember a more generous introduction or one that touched me more deeply. On the way home, Mr. De congratulated me on the talk and added he didn't agree with a damned thing I had said. We laughed, then spent the rest of the evening talking about the new publishing program of the University of Oklahoma Press, the need for a new history of science, and the mess the Dodgers had made of the World Series.

Mr. De died in 1956, just before Christmas. It left a terrible hole in my life. He went by the political name of conservative; but he taught me a great deal about genuine liberalism and the largeness of the human spirit. He taught me, too, not to place stock in stereotypes — whether they went by the names of industrialists or intellectuals. The *Saturday Review* would not be possible without him. Some weeks before he died he told me he got a bigger kick out of the success of the magazine, after its many years at the bottom of the barrel, than out of his biggest oil strike. I knew he meant it. He never took a cent out of SR, and when there was no longer any question about its ability to go it alone, he transferred his ownership to the people who had the responsibility of publishing it.

I felt proud to have worked for him. I felt even prouder to have had him for a friend.

NORMAN COUSINS

Acknowledgments

Although this is in no way an "official" or subsidized biography, it could not have been written without the cooperation of the DeGolyer Foundation in Dallas and of two other Dallas institutions. The Foundation, administered by Everett L. DeGolyer, Jr., houses all the papers and relics of E. DeGolyer. No restriction was placed on the author's use of these materials; indeed, every encouragement was given by the Foundation and the family to make of this as objective and impartial a study as possible. I can not adequately express my gratitude to Mrs. E. DeGolyer and her son Everett (himself a trained historian) for their intelligent helpfulness and their patient cooperation.

Southern Methodist University, where I serve as E. A. Lilly Professor of Literature, gave me two grants-in-aid and leaves of absence for work on this biography, one as a Fellow in a Faculty Seminar on Research for one year, administered by Professor Albert C. Outler and made possible by the Danforth Foundation of St. Louis. Encouragement of this project has been steady from the university's administration, as it has been from the *Dallas Morning News* (where I serve as book critic), an institution which has generously granted me much freedom in my attention to this work.

My indebtedness to individuals is so extensive as to preclude any comprehensive inventory here. This is the first book-length biography, and in a sense the first biography of any sort, of this multifaceted man, and much of my research has necessarily been "leg work," or personal interviews, from Tampico to New York, from Mexico City to Tulsa, from Dallas to Washington, D.C. Nonetheless, I have signaled in my dedication five men to whom I am profoundly grateful. Nearly as significant has been the help of Dr. James Phillips, former student of mine now librarian of the DeGolyer Foundation, and the help of freelance writer and friend North Bigbee of Dallas, who had assembled on assignment from the *Reader's Digest* a formidable cargo of DeGolyer materials and who generously allowed me to use them in his devotion to this exceptional Southwestern figure.

I should like also to make a "token" expression of general gratitude to the many friends and associates of E. DeGolyer who were unstinting of their time in the wish to be helpful on any project concerning their friend. The list is too long to detail, but I wish to sift out a few, in certain categories, as representative.

For example, of early associates of DeGolyer in Mexican Eagle and the Amerada Corporation, I am indebted for personal interviews to the late Alfred Jacobsen, who succeeded DeGolyer as president and then as chairman of the board of Amerada, to the late John Lovejoy, the late Paul Weaver, and to James Hall. In the latter case, my indebtedness is amply evident in the text proper, as is true of so many not individually acknowledged here, such as Tom Lea, Carl Hertzog, Dillon Anderson, Elizabeth Ann McMurray, William Weber Johnson, Holland McCombs and others.

Briefly, then, here are other major informants, associates of DeGolyer in Geophysical Research Corporation or Geophysical Service, Inc. or friends in the oil industry or in other of DeGolyer's interests, who have aided me much either in personal interviews or in correspondence: Clarence Karcher, Jay Hall, Wallace Everett Pratt, Eric Schroeder, John Suman, the late Lewis MacNaughton, John Murrell, Miss Dorothy Pitts, Cecil Green, Kenneth A. Burg, H. H. ("Babe") Fuqua, Harry Huntt Ransom, Stanley Marcus, the late Jack Cominsky, Bennett Cerf, Alfred A. Knopf, Neville Penrose, Claude Albritton, Max Trent, Decherd Turner, Pete Wiggins, Jake Hamon. To all those uncited, my apologies and my thanks. Justice, not to name something other, requires me to conclude finally with stating my debt to my wife, María-Ofelia, whose knowledge of Mexico (where she grew up) and its history has been of priceless service in my account of E. DeGolyer's Mexican-based apprentice years.

L.T.

Illustrations

I

Chapapote Conquistador: Christmas in Mexico

1

First Christmas in Tampico

IT WAS AN ODD PLACE for a Kansas-born, Oklahoma-reared youth to be spending Christmas day in 1909. His quizzical blue-gray eyes had mostly looked, during his first twenty years, at great plains flat as a floor, or at gully-scarred clay hills spreading to the distant horizon. The people he knew and lived with spoke the twangy English of the American Southwest.

"I was born into a red land," he was to write years later in one of the many short poems he wrote down as a kind of diary note, and after he had circled the globe seeking oil, "and I will always love a red land best." But here he was on December 25 — ten years after the twentieth century had opened — in a green land, a tropical green land whose brilliant flowers ironically offered one slight recall of Christmas back home: the thick-clustered poinsettias, named for another American, Ambassador Joel Poinsett, who had also spent a Christmas day in Tampico, Mexico — almost a hundred years earlier.

But what made Tampico most unlike young Everette Lee DeGolyer's haunts back home was its water. Cut by rivers and streams, bathed by immense lagoons, forested by giant avocado and mango trees along the water courses, the small town of twenty thousand inhabitants seemed less earthbound than afloat in the air. Even the English that the young man heard spoken in Tampico's Colonial Club, haven of the foreign population, did not sound like the English in Norman or Oklahoma City. It came from British throats, uttered in the Oxford style from the top of the head. It came from Swiss and Dutch geologists, from European engineers in the employ — as was young DeGolyer — of Sir Weetman Pearson and his mighty international business empire centered, up till now, on bridge, dam, tunnel and railway construction.

Young Everette Lee DeGolyer did not resemble the people around him in looks or in clothes or in accent. He did not, in fact, look like anybody else. Short and stocky, like many of the Tampiqueños, he had the bright ruddy complexion and blondness of the rail-thin British geologists. But he was partridge plump. Above all, he had a massive leonine head on his five-foot six-inch body, which always made him seem to fill more space than he actually did. He was immediately likable. As British colleague F. E. Wellings described him, he was wonderful company, "witty and always jovial, but nonetheless tough-minded." He did share one thing, almost a Continental specialty, with the Englishmen: he had beautiful hands. Manually gifted, like his father, he could do almost anything with them.

Still, Tampico had one thing in common with the American Southwest, the one thing that had magnetized and brought into unexpected association such diverse men as Sir Weetman Pearson and Californian Edward L. Doheny, crack Swiss geologist Dr. Theodore Erb and fledgling geologist Everette DeGolyer, Dr. C. Willard Hayes of the United States Geological Survey and the Mexican government's own petroleum expert, Dr. Ezequiel Ordoñez. Tampico had, almost as copiously as its water, oil. But this was

only a promise or nearly that in 1909. Just how much oil
became evident only another Christmas later. Meantime
the great Pearson financial empire — risked, because of the
turn of strange events, on finding oil in Mexico — was
threatened with total doom.

Oil meant wealth, and wealth seemed to have been
bursting forth from the earth all around Everette Lee De-
Golyer ever since his birth. But it had always eluded him
and his father, an inveterate prospector for minerals, who
had followed his "hobby" for twenty years as he moved
from one farm to another across Kansas and Missouri and
Oklahoma. His luck, or lack of it, kept his status as prospector "amateur" but did not lessen his steady persistence.
Meantime, to earn his family a living, he had to follow
more conventional pursuits. And yet, good luck always
seemed just around the corner. As the faraway English
poet John Cowper Powys had observed, for international
quotation, "In Oklahoma anything can happen."

First, there had been the "greatest giveaway in history,"
the Oklahoma Land Runs, starting in 1889. The United
States government had opened the Unassigned Lands, sub-
sequently Oklahoma Territory, for white settlement, with
only a token fee for large grants of land. Rome wasn't built
in a day, but a dozen Oklahoma towns sprouted tent cities
overnight. Hundreds of thousands of land-hungry Americans profited from this governmental largesse, including
DeGolyer's father.

Four Oklahoma runs took place between 1889 and 1893.
These were the dramatic ones that captured the interest of
the whole nation. After them, several minor ones occurred
as more Indian land became available by government purchase. But the race for choice land from a common starting point, a race patrolled by government agents and
opened with cannon shot, gave way to the safer, surer,

milder method of drawing lottery tickets for prestaked land. The last of the latter was held in 1901, when Kiowa holdings were offered to the general public. This was the successful one of three tries that Everette DeGolyer's father made. He drew an allotment in what became Hobart, Oklahoma. Excitement was elsewhere. John DeGolyer transferred his family soon after to Norman, seat of the University of Oklahoma, which had opened in a downtown one-story building in 1892. Ten years later the college had moved out to its present two hundred and eighty-five acres and was offering preparatory training and the first two years of college work.

And then, in the same year as the Kiowa reservation land run, the central economic event in southwestern history happened. The great spuming oil gusher known as Spindletop blew in near Beaumont, Texas — and ushered in the modern oil industry with all the inventions, from automobiles to jet planes, dependent upon it. Again the nation looked to the Southwest for news of wealth and natural resources untapped so far. What other treasures lay underneath this land, good portions of which the government had given away?

The fledgling University of Oklahoma was directly affected by these bonanza events, a result reinforced when the first Oklahoma oil pools of tremendous flow were discovered in 1905–1906 around nearby Tulsa. In 1907, Oklahoma surpassed California as the number one oil-producing state, with a total of 44 million barrels.

And that is no doubt why Everette Lee DeGolyer spent Christmas of 1909 in Tampico, a continuation — it was hoped — of the Spindletop and Gulf Coast oil treasures. For brilliant geological, and other, minds came to teach at the young Oklahoma university, which was the first in the nation to pioneer in the field of petroleum geology. Among

the exceptional students they drew was young DeGolyer.
This lucky chain of chances was the only wealth his father had been able to give him. Except an inveterate hun-
ger for exploration. It was enough.

His father also taught him how to cook. (This was to
have a curious consequence.) Disappointed in his luck at
farming, at prospecting, at land running, DeGolyer senior
set up a restaurant in Oklahoma City, then ran Delmoni-
co's in Norman while young Everette started in 1904, aged
eighteen and irregularly schooled, to work his way through
the university's preparatory school and the college.

When a chance came in the summer of 1906 to work at
camp with the United States Geological Survey, the young
DeGolyer signed on, thanks to his professor of geology,
Charles N. Gould. The student got the job of camp cook.
The next three summers — spent in Wyoming and Mon-
tana and Colorado — he was geological assistant. His skill
won the attention of a prominent visitor to the camp, Dr.
C. Willard Hayes, director of the United States Geological
Survey. In 1909, Sir Weetman Pearson appealed to Dr.
Hayes for help in the British construction firm's flounder-
ing oil explorations around Tampico. Hayes accepted, and
took young DeGolyer along with him. Hayes got to Tam-
pico in September 1909, DeGolyer on November 19. De-
Golyer was delayed because he had some courting to do.
He could not, that autumn, persuade Nell Goodrich of
Norman to marry him and go live in Mexico. But he did
not give up. He was both indomitable and stubborn.

The four summers of camp work with the United States
Geological Survey recorded more immediate success than
his courtship. He moved up from camp cook and teamster
to foreman of the drilling crew to assistant geologist. He
impressed significantly every boss he had in the four USGS
camps, and these were among the half-dozen greatest

names in American geology at the time: N. H. Darton ("the dean of reconnaissance geologists"), Dr. C. W. Hayes, Carl D. Smith and Willis Lee. At age twenty-three, DeGolyer had been watched, trained, encouraged, hired by the men with the biggest reputations in American geology, all of whom held him in affection and esteem, as their letters to him and to each other show. His virtuoso gifts at geology were immediately apparent to men in a position to recognize them. Curiously, although he had no specialized training to qualify his judgment, Sir Weetman Pearson also recognized them. He decided early that DeGolyer was his good-luck talisman, often referring to him as "my lucky charm." The second Christmas DeGolyer spent in Mexico — this time at Tuxpam — was to offer proof. Four months after the young Oklahoman got to Tampico, Sir Weetman specified to Dr. Hayes that DeGolyer was to select the next drilling site. The choice of location was crucial; the Pearson fortunes were touching rock bottom.

Sir Weetman may have been influenced by the overpowering effect of a visit he made — to reassure himself that what he had seen at Spindletop in 1901 was not a fluke — to the Oklahoma oil fields early in 1908. "The grandest sight imaginable," he wrote about his trip to the Tulsa area, "beautiful country, 2,000 rigs, 700 big tanks, and a tract of country twice the size of Paddockhurst and Dalcombe * of productive wells of magnificent oil. I marvelled." Most of it belonged, alas, to his rival, Standard Oil. And he added: "Tulsa, a delightful town, now 35,000 people, four years ago an Indian trading village, brings home to me more vividly than any imagination can, the immensity of the enterprise we are engaged upon. But

---

* Estate properties of Cowdray in Sussex; Paddockhurst, about six thousand acres, later was offered to Porfirio Díaz as "residence in exile" — he preferred Paris. Sir Weetman became Lord Cowdray in 1910.

with all its brilliant prospects, it may be there is a long road to travel before they are realized."

Once he got to Mexico, DeGolyer had plenty of time to rehearse in his mind this odd chain of events. Forty years later he summarized its beginning for his friend, Cleveland Amory:

One day in 1909 Dr. C. Willard Hayes, chief geologist of the Survey, called me to his office. I was scared. Upon my return from Colorado I had submitted my expense account. It included an item of three dollars and a half for three meals on a diner. This was well within allowable expenditure but the division chief had questioned it. He had written my immediate chief. My chief had written a letter of transmittal and sent the complaining letter on to me. I had replied according to bureaucratic protocol protesting indignantly that the money had been spent. Here the matter stood when the Hayes' call came. I presumed that I was being called on the carpet for reckless expenditure and cursed both my chiefs mentally, one for meanness and the other for weakness in not supporting me.

I was mistaken. Hayes had called me to his office to offer me a job as an oil geologist in Mexico. He had remembered pleasantly our meeting two years previously in Meetetsee, Wyoming, and had remembered favorably certain of my field work which he had reviewed at that time.

He had visited Mexico with Dr. David T. Day in mid-1908 shortly after the burning of Mexican Eagle's Dos Bocas well. While there he had met Sir Weetman Pearson, afterward Lord Cowdray, and had been engaged by him to direct the geological work of the Mexican Eagle Oil Co., Ltd. — the Compañía Mexicana de Petroleo "El Aguila" S.A., or the Aguila as it was known generally. Hayes was to send field geologists to do the work, to supervise their re-

ports, to inspect the work at least once a year and to have charge generally of geological work. There were then no restrictions against foreign work by members of the Survey and he retained his position with it.

I asked for a few days to consider the offer, spent them miserably fearing that it would be withdrawn and then accepted.

He arrived in Tampico a few days before Thanksgiving, 1909. "I had remained a few weeks in Washington to finish the map-making from the summer's fieldwork, then stopped over a few days in Norman and then came on down to San Antonio where I spent the night." He got up early the next morning, when there was just a little light, to see the Alamo. It was the first time he had ever seen the Texas shrine; he was stirred by it. "You have to see it for yourself," he said. "The Alamo is a thing you have some sentiment about; if you don't, it's just a broken-down lot of rock buildings."

He left the same morning for Mexico, traveling in what was then called a "hotel car," a pullman equipped with a buffet. In those days, one did not need passports or tourist cards to get into Mexico; at Laredo, as he later recalled, the baggage was cursorily examined and "somebody came through the car and asked you a few vital statistics and whether you were an anarchist." He spent the second night in Monterrey, leaving next morning on the early train and reaching Tampico shortly after dark. The train made stops at "just about every wide place on the road." He was met in Tampico by his friend, Edwin B. Hopkins (with whose family DeGolyer had taken his meals in Washington), and by Dr. Hayes' other young recruit, Chester Washburne. He put up at the new Victoria Hotel, run by an American widow, Mrs. Weeks.

In 1909, there was very little oil business in Tampico itself; the companies then had no big office buildings. Mexican Eagle, later to build an imposing five-story office building opposite the Hotel Imperial, had only three major European employees in their Tampico office at the time: a Scot who was superintendent and manager of the office, a Dutchman who kept books and an Englishman in charge of launches and other transportation. There were also a few clerks, British and Mexican.

Ed Hopkins was working out of the south edge of the Tamiahua Lagoon, below Tampico. After a few days in Tampico, DeGolyer left with Hopkins for the field. When they set out by launch, Superintendent Calder came down in the early morning to see them off; he told them that if the launch broke down, as launches often did in those days, they would find groceries on board which they were to break out and feed on in emergency. The launch did break down, but they were able to pull into a little estuary where they spent the night. They tied up at a bank near a little Mexican hut. The friendly natives offered them beans and tortillas and coffee; they did not have to break into the case goods. (At the end of the trip, DeGolyer's curiosity got the better of him. He took a look at the groceries. One case contained tomato catsup, another Lea and Perrin's Sauce, the third bottled vinegar.) They stopped the next morning to call at Dos Bocas, to see the crater of the great well which had come in on July 4, 1908, and burned for thirty or forty days until it was finally extinguished by the influx of salt water. The crater, all that remained, was still boiling and steaming with the continued flow of salt water, and the sulphur fumes from the accompanying gas were still so great, they blackened the silver change in DeGolyer's pocket.

Hopkins could not have chosen for DeGolyer a more

awesome introduction to the oil business. When the famous "Dos Bocas" well in Mexican Eagle's northern Veracruz field gushed forth in a triumphant roar, it was proof
that an earlier 2,000-barrel-a-day well in the same area really did herald the existence of a great pool. Unhappily,
the Dos Bocas find blew in so fiercely, the escaping gases
ignited before the boiler fires could be put out. At first the
well consumed itself so high in the air that not a drop of
oil fell to the ground. Despite frenzied efforts to save the
well, the fire could not be controlled, and the well burned
itself out. For two months the flames raged, sometimes as
high as five hundred feet above ground. Ships at sea a hundred miles away could see the plumes of flame; villagers
seventeen miles off could read at night by the glow. It was
a catastrophe for Mexican Eagle. Approximately five million dollars' worth of oil went up in smoke — the estimate
was that a million tons of oil were destroyed — and nearby
landholders whose property suffered considerable damage
brought heavy suits against the firm.

The black cloud had a silver lining. If that much oil lay
underground, Pearson decided he could risk another million dollars to locate companion wells. This had been the
history of the enterprise for six years now: solid proof that
oil was to be found, failure as yet to capture enough to
make the huge investment pay. Not to mention inconceiv-
able bad luck. Shortly after the burning of the Dos Bocas
in the San Diego field, a great fire destroyed Pearson's refinery at Tampico. A fragment of the installation was left;
just enough to leave Pearson the will to push ahead. Company workers observed that the Chief was developing
short nerves and an edgy temper. They understood and
marveled at his persistence. He would not say "yes" to
fate; his favorite word was a resolute "no." A few years
later, when young Everette DeGolyer had become invalu-

able to the firm, the Chief sent DeGolyer an autographed portrait of himself. Perhaps remembering the first days of his association with the company, DeGolyer returned the portrait with a request that the Chief write across it a message about the importance of learning to say the most difficult word in the language. Lord Cowdray complied. "Remember," he cautioned De Golyer, "that most ambitious enterprises fail for this reason more than any other, the inability to say 'no' at the right time."

Leaving Dos Bocas in midafternoon, DeGolyer and Hopkins arrived at the end of their journey by water, the little hamlet of Tamiahua, a sandspit between the lagoon and marshes. Sand was so deep in the one street of the little town that DeGolyer found it hard to walk. But he was noticing everything. He described it later: "Gaily plumaged fighting cocks, each tethered by one leg, were staked out in front of almost every door. A few scattered coconut palms curving from the sand and carrying their plumes of dark-gray fronds high into the sky and the white and pastel-colored houses stamped the scene with the mark of the tropics. An old barn of a church in front of which a great bronze bell rested on the ground gave the whole an appearance of great antiquity. Away from cities, bright lights, hotels and restaurants similar to those at home, I began to get acquainted with Mexico."

Hopkins was staying with a native Louisianan, called Don Luis Kenyon, who operated a general store at Tamiahua. DeGolyer rode out with Hopkins the first few days to see what the country was like, then he got outfitted and started his work. His "outfit" consisted of a *mozo*, or saddle boy, horses for himself and his *mozo*, and a pack animal to carry his baggage and equipment. And — at first — an interpreter.

His first assignment was a lucky one. He was to map the

Hacienda Tierra Amarilla, leased from the large landholding and prominent Pelaez family, and DeGolyer was invited to live at the hacienda. There were three sons, all near DeGolyer's age. One was a lawyer employed by the Pearson enterprises, who was a close friend of DeGolyer's all his life; another later became a famous revolutionary chieftain. DeGolyer was additionally lucky. After making a survey of the property, he made his first recommendation for locating a well; it was drilled and was, technically, successful. In time, fifteen or twenty wells were drilled on this property, but not one of them was ever a spectacular commercial success.

He moved on from there to the company's camp in the Potrero del Llano field, where the first well in that area was being drilled in. The camp at this drilling site consisted of three or four canvas "boxes," that is, wooden floors with canvas for walls except for a yard-wide strip around the middle which was screened; the whole structure was topped with a palm-thatched roof. These were very pleasant places to live, very clean. The camp had Chinese cooks and houseboys.

"I was there one evening," DeGolyer recalled, "and we were all in the mess hall having dinner when there was a terrific roar, like the blowing off of a boiler. Nobody could think what could cause such a noise, so we all rushed out. Potrero del Llano #1 had drilled itself in. It had been drilled to a point so close to the rock holding oil that the oil finally just broke through and finished the job. We saw a stream of black oil flowing up through the derrick and hitting the crown block and making two great ears of oil on each side. That was the discovery well for the field. Maybe a couple of taps more with the drill at the time the workers stopped would have brought the well in, but it came in of its own will. This discovery well, located by

Geoffrey Jeffrey, was a small well that flowed by heads and made three or four hundred barrels a day. There was no difficulty in stopping the free flow of a well of that size, just a matter of closing a valve."

It became necessary to build a pipeline to get the oil to Tampico, where Mexican Eagle had built a big refinery. The final drilling of other wells in the Potrero pool had to await completion of the line, buried just barely underground in the early days; once the oil got to Tamiahua, it had to be put on barges and hauled across the lagoon, put into a line again and pumped on to Tampico.

He had only one heroic moment in dealing with landowners. One of the company's most complicated holdings was the lease on the Hacienda of Los Horcones. Mexican Eagle had about half the vast property leased, but the titles were very confused, the family being numerous and widely scattered. On his first day of surveying there, DeGolyer received a message by courier from the *administrador* — "stay off this property." He retreated to think. He was days away from any communication with the office. He could ignore the command — after all, the company had legal access to most of the land — or he could conduct a survey surreptitiously. Unsure of what was technically right, DeGolyer decided at least not to be surreptitious. He went back next morning and set up his plane table right in the *administrador's* front gate.

Breathing fire, the latter came out and stood between the instrument and the rod, so that DeGolyer could do nothing. DeGolyer kept his eye glued to the telescope and kept waving his hand for the *administrador* to get out of the way. He did take his eye off the telescope long enough to give his *mozo*, a tough customer, a meaningful glance. The *mozo* moved in, gave Don Felicitas a slap across the

C. W. Hamilton, Dr. C. Willard Hayes, Ben Belt and E. DeGolyer, in the Golden Lane, Mexico, 1910.

thigh with the flat of a machete and said to him, "*Dice me jefe que se muere!*"

Don Felicitas moved, just as the "boss" or *jefe* had demanded. The battle was won. There was no further interference. It was a lesson in loyalty that DeGolyer remembered. The *mozo's* only job was to take care of the horses and the pack animals, of the baggage and equipment. If treated right, he could do more. DeGolyer's "baggage," at any rate, was not a burden. Although in that first year he made many long trips by saddle into the back country, forty and fifty miles inland, he carried only a clean shirt or two, some socks and underwear rolled up in a slicker and tied to the back of the saddle. On reconnaissance trips, he sometimes limited his equipment to a pocket compass, no other instruments.

His job was to ride out, on saddle horse, to inspect the Pearson leases, recommend other prospects, study well location potentials. He had three years of specialized training behind him, plus some fieldwork in the Oklahoma strikes, and his camp work for the U.S. Geological Survey. He had been trained by partisans of the "anticline" theory of oil detection, developed by, among others, Professor Benjamin Silliman at Yale after the epoch-making discovery of the Drake Well near Titusville, Pennsylvania in 1859. To this theory Captain Anthony Lucas gave credit for his even more epoch-making discovery at Spindletop in 1901. And DeGolyer's senior professor, Dr. Charles N. Gould, had one supreme axiom: "Any anticline is worth drilling." (An "anticline" is an upthrusting of rock strata, often causing a surface mound as a sign of the structure below, in whose rooflike form oil is sometimes trapped.)

For three months, battling the ever-present malaria with quinine, DeGolyer, accompanied by his plane table and a Mexican peon as guide and servant, camped out in the mountains and along the Panuco river's many tributaries. He was a brilliant mapmaker, a meticulous observer, but he indulged a whim, perhaps a lurking poetic flair, by adorning his charts and maps with stylized cattle skulls and symbolic Indian tepees. As he wrote at the time, he was powerfully excited by the work of establishing the stratigraphy of the region and by the challenge of reading the presence of oil traps in the surface topography. At least once in the first months, when overcome with tropical fever, he owed his life to the kindly and knowing care of the Mexican Indian tribes he encountered in the villages and hamlets.

He also had time to think of something else, of finishing his college education. Dr. Hayes had taken him out of college before he got his degree. This was bad, because DeGolyer was in love. "I am not going to marry you," Nell Goodrich of Norman had told him before he left for Mexico, "until you finish your college education." Virginia Nell Goodrich knew whereof she spoke. A student of the famed musicologist Fredrik Holmberg, who had created for the University of Oklahoma an exceptional school of music, she herself was teaching piano at the college the autumn that DeGolyer left to work for Dr. Hayes and Sir Weetman Pearson's Mexican Eagle Oil Company. She wasn't trying to stop his Mexican venture into fortune; she just wanted to put first things first. Her father had been a professor of mathematics at the University of Missouri; her mother had been a teacher too. Education before money.

2   Lord Cowdray in Mexico

In 1909, Tampico was not the important city it became a few years later. The only practical way to reach it was by boat from the Gulf of Mexico or by train from Monterrey, both ways long and slow and generally off-schedule. There was usually a stopover at the border town of Laredo, by train.

It was the unpredictable Laredo stopover that explained the surprising presence of the internationally famous British engineer, Sir Weetman Pearson, in Tampico. The train service and also the phenomenon of Spindletop were involved too. But whatever explained it, his presence there was of capital importance to Everette DeGolyer. Lord Cowdray was, in many respects, the most influential man in his life.

With many famous achievements behind him — dams in Egypt, the Hudson Tunnel in New York — Cowdray undertook at the turn of the century the daring enterprise of rebuilding, really reconstructing, a railroad through the jungle across Mexico's Isthmus of Tehuantepec. It was a project that, like the Panama Canal, had long haunted men's minds. A rival project of the canal, it sought a shortcut to join by practical transportation the Atlantic and the

Pacific in Central America. Oil seepages long known in the Isthmus promised cheap fuel for the locomotives. Sir Weetman's contract called for extensive allotments of land along the right of way. At first, the jungle proved too burdensome and costly to clear. Baffled and fearing failure, Sir Weetman set out in early 1901 for New York. At Laredo, the stopover lasted into *mañana*. Sir Weetman put up at a hotel to wait. It was the luckiest thing that ever happened to him.

The spectacular news of Spindletop filled the papers. A lady staying at the hotel confirmed from personal experience the wild excitement in East Texas, investors waving money in the air. Sir Weetman decided to have a look for himself. What he saw committed him forever after to oil exploration. His decision was made when he got back to Mexico, where oil seepages or chapapote (tar) patches were almost as common as sombreros.

For Spindletop had been in every way dramatic. At Spindletop, the four-inch drill pipe, swivels, blocks, and tackle were all blown up through the derrick, followed by the drilling fluid, mud, sand and rocks, and then a strong gas eruption and a solid column of oil extending far above the top of the derrick. The four-inch pipe weighed at least six tons. The derrick, sixty feet high, was thrown three hundred feet into the air.

Oil prosperity promised, likewise, to soar sky high.

Sir Weetman Pearson was not only a great construction engineer but also a financial wizard. One of the richest capitalists in England around 1900, he was famous for personally testing any risk his men might incur in the company's amazing program of construction. Pearson and Son had contracts all over the world, from Peking to Mexico City, from the Hudson and East River tunnels in New York to dams along the White Nile, from Dover harbor to ports in Malta.

Sir Weetman was himself an extraordinary character, fully as daring and bold as the enterprises he undertook. He was the grandson of the founder of the famous firm of contractors. The founder began his career as a brickmaker, moved on to small construction work. Two generations later, the grandson expanded the firm to international proportions, installing famed public works in half a dozen different parts of the world — and added its most profitable branch, oil.

For a time in the 1890's, when major engineering dreams met with failure, there always remained Sir Weetman to call on. It was, in fact, as supreme last resort that he had been summoned to save the Hudson River Tunnel project, to save the Great Canal in Mexico that freed the capital from devastating floods, to save the crosscontinent railway from just below Veracruz on over the Isthmus of Tehuantepec. In every case, he came through. In every case he tested the dangers the project involved for the working crews.

The Hudson River Tunnel feat indeed nearly killed him. Indirectly, it caused him to go to Mexico and to make the acquaintance of that master dictator and friend of foreign capital, Don Porfirio Díaz. Instead of dying in the Hudson Tunnel accident, he survived to go on to another fortune, three in fact, in Mexico. What happened was typical of the man, both in the matter of the tunnel and in the matter of luck. Sir Weetman always had it tough at first, he was always challenged to his limit and tempted to give up; he was always determined to stick a project out to the end through his indomitable will and his fear of failure.

At the end of the nineteenth century Manhattan Island simply had to have, for economic survival, either bridges over or tunnels under the Hudson River. To tunnel the river was judged by engineers more practical, certainly a good deal less expensive. The first attempt, engineered by DeWitt Haskins, ended in failure in 1882, after capital ran out and after twenty workers were buried alive in a silt cave-in. Haskins had made the first effort to use underwater a technique that had proved itself in tunneling hard surfaces, the compressed air and shield tunneling process which had been so successful in the Tower Bridge Subway. The great danger of this process, which prevented soft silt from seeping into the advancing sections of the tunnel, was the risk involved for men who had to line the walls of the tunnel with steel plates and brick while working in the high pressure pumped into the "air lock" or cave from a nearby power plant. The high pressure could, and often did, cause "the bends" or paralysis of the limbs.

When Sir Weetman took over the project late in 1889, science had not yet perfected the solution it later found. Sir Weetman, with other British engineers, devised a "shield" process to combine with the compressed air technique, but the new method raised the air temperature inside the working area to a near inferno. Something else had to be done. Sir Weetman, known for his insistence on being the "test" man in a crisis, went down into the "inferno" — and less than an hour after coming back to the surface, his body was stricken with paralysis from the waist down. Medical knowledge had devised a cure for this. He was rushed back into a medical air lock and his body was subjected to the process of gradual decompression. But recovery was slow and it took several weeks of later hospital care for the paralyzed legs to return to life.

In Sir Weetman's case, recovery often seemed doubtful and he suffered tormenting pain. His wife, luckily, was with him. She read in the New York papers advertisements

of a new "crack train" to Mexico City — the Montezuma
Express — which would transport with comfort winter-de-
pressed New Yorkers to the balmy eternal spring of Mexico's central plateau. She persuaded her husband to follow
the sun, in his convalescence. Anyway, time was needed to
devise a new shield for the tunnel work. Sir Weetman
yielded, in part, no doubt, because Don Porfirio Díaz had
already sent an agent to New York to beg the great engineer to solve Mexico City's flood problems. Sir Weetman,
like a Renaissance man, felt a compulsive need to keep a
dozen balls in the air at the same time.

The story ends happily. The engineers found a solution
to the compressed air problem. Sir Weetman Pearson fell
in love with Mexico. He accepted the drainage project for
Mexico City's precarious waters. He and Don Porfirio understood each other at sight and worked together for years
in mutual trust, in a sort of father and son relationship,
though neither was competent in the other's native tongue.
Sir Weetman, after the Hudson Tunnel was successfully
completed, converted the stinking, nearly useless port of
malaria-infested Veracruz into a great, clean, modern harbor and electricity-run modern city to give Mexico at last
a great port on the Gulf of Mexico, and hence access to the
Atlantic.

Veracruz was Mexico's gateway to Europe and hence its
principal port, but by nature it was a storm-swept open
roadstead full of sunken and dangerous reefs. Before Pearson, American, French and Mexican engineers had tried to
insure safety for ships and had made some pioneering
progress. But the town remained unhealthful, smelly and
squalid, and the harbor was still a hazard to ships that got
caught in the terrible "northers" that swept the shore.
Pearson made the harbor safe and the city livable, and

many Veracruzanos thought he had performed miracles where others before him had failed.

As for the Tehuantepec Railway, it was a dream that lasted for two centuries, before a flimsy, inefficient line was at last completed in the 1890's, but it was unable to bear heavy traffic. Worst of all the two ports it connected were not shipworthy. Disgusted, Porfirio Díaz asked Pearson to salvage the situation. But the fact of asking was proof that Díaz shared the Veracruzano belief that Pearson could succeed where others had not. As indeed he did with the railway.

Salina Cruz, located at the narrowest point of the North American continent above Nicaragua, has huge docks that remain testimony to the engineering skill of Sir Weetman Pearson, who provided a sheltered harbor of several hundred acres by making two breakwaters converge. When the competition from the Panama Canal caused the docks to fall into disuse, the harbor too fell into disrepair. At the peak of its prosperity, though, the Tehuantepec National Railway often ran forty freight trains a day between Salina Cruz and its northern terminus, Puerto Mexico or, as it is now called, Coatzacoalcos. One project was started on the completion of another, until Sir Weetman held in Mexico, for a foreigner, a position absolutely unique — as Standard Oil was to discover.

It was this venturesome, courageous, just and indomitable man, passionately attached to converting nature to man's uses, who became the greatest influence on Everette Lee DeGolyer in his most impressionable years. Until the end of his life, an oil portrait of Lord Cowdray (as he will be referred to hereafter) remained the central object in DeGolyer's office. It was the accident of oil that brought them together; it was mutual respect and affinity of char-

acter that bound them in a quarter century of business relations. Watching Lord Cowdray in London as well as in
Mexico, DeGolyer got on-the-spot lessons in how to put
together three things: great corporations, a great private
library, and money and science and imaginative boldness
into that union known as applied technology.

Nonetheless, by the Christmas season of 1909, the triumphant good fortunes of the Pearson business empire faced
doom. The most grandiose of all the Pearson enterprises —
the production and distribution of oil in Mexico — had de-
voured money for seven years without yielding a cent of
real income. Unyielding as usual, Lord Cowdray poured —
while results were still merely promising — enormous sums
of money into exploration, pipelines, tanks and refining
plants. The few meager strikes made where oil seepages
abounded in the land he held along his Tehuantepec railway venture did not amount to a drop in the bucket. The
trans-isthmian railroad was a distance of 210 miles. Lord
Cowdray needed a local, cheap, fuel-oil supply for the locomotives and for the electricity-generating plants of the
ports. This incentive was of course reinforced by the other
one of the spectacular success of Spindletop. Desperately
he turned to the Atlantic coast, to the Gulf of Mexico flat-
lands east of the Sierra Madre, reaching from the superb
Veracruz harbor on up to Tampico. There was just enough
return on the vast investments he made to spur and
strengthen his resolve never to quit a loser.

But by 1909, his Aguila Oil Company (Mexican Eagle),
its payoff reaching by now the stage of hopelessness, had
gone five hundred percent beyond his original, and always
shrewd, estimate of the amount of capital he would put in
it. He was famous for mapping out his ventures so that an
unexpected loss, if it should occur, would not seriously
weaken the company's overall financial standing. The

firm had had its share of duds. All were absorbed without serious damage. But the Mexican Eagle affair, which had captured his imagination like no other venture, was now a monumental liability. His careful early calculation had set its risk capital limit at 1,500,000 pounds sterling. In 1909, he had sunk more than five million pounds in it, a fantastic sum for those days.

No wonder his men, like Everette Lee DeGolyer, found Christmas day of 1909 depressing and bleak. Tampico had become the central office location for Mexican Eagle. It was in that area, on the basis of all that geologists knew at the time and on the basis of past experience of several other struggling oil companies in Mexico, that Pearson would have to make the strikes that could bail him out.

Captain Anthony Lucas, the mining engineer who had brought in the great gusher at Spindletop, spent 1902 and 1903 trying to locate wells for Pearson on the Isthmus of Tehuantepec. Some oil was found, but not enough for profit. Captain Lucas returned dejectedly to the States, in 1904. Pearson's British and Swiss geologists did better in the Tampico-Tuxpam region on the eastern coast. But expenses still far outran income. The American team of Dr. C. Willard Hayes and his young American geologists, recruited by Pearson in 1909, faced a grimly challenging prospect. From the start there was friction between the British staff and the American imports.

As early as 1889, two geologists in Austin, Texas, Professor E. T. Dumble and Josiah Owen, decided that oil could be discovered on a large scale in Mexico. Owen made a trip down the east coast as far as Tuxpam, sending back samples of his findings and reporting results to Professor Dumble for analysis. They were encouraged, but it was not till 1899 that they decided on practical measures. They interested President Huntington of the Southern

Pacific, but he concluded that even though oil might be found in great quantity, the fields would nonetheless be too remote from existing railroad operations in this country.

Five years later, Professor Dumble's help in locating artesian wells was sought by the president of the Mexican Senate. Dumble sent down an associate, W. P. Cummins, and made an arrangement whereby all reports would be provided in copy form for Southern Pacific. When Harriman succeeded Huntington as president of Southern Pacific, Tampico's deposits were proven, and at last Professor Dumble got the assignment he wanted. Harriman sent him as consulting geologist for Southern Pacific to select lands for the company's newly formed East Coast Oil Company.

Meantime, another American railroad "great," A. A. Robinson, had grown excited about oil seepages in the Tampico area. Robinson, who surveyed and built the Santa Fe line from Kansas to the Pacific Ocean, left this country in 1889 to become president of the Mexican Central Railway, one of whose branches led to Tampico, then a fever-ridden, malarial village beside a beautiful river and gifted with a fine harbor if sandbars could be cleared away. Robinson engineers built jetties to clear the bar and opened Tampico's port to the world. Since Mexico's coal was scarce and of poor quality, Robinson was greatly impressed with the prospect of fuel oil from the hints of oil around Tampico, revealed in the seepages. He invited two friends from the States, Edward L. Doheny and C. A. Canfield, to come investigate.

On foot and on horseback, Doheny and Canfield bought up 450,000 acres west of Tampico, then later 170,000 acres southward toward Tuxpam. The Mexican owners were astonished to be offered sixty cents an acre for what they looked on as worthless jungle. At first Doheny and Canfield prospected the Tampico area by crawling and cutting their way through the jungle; they soon announced they would pay five pesos to anybody pointing out the location of chapapote tar spots.

Doheny was already a millionaire from his California strikes. He cleared much of the jungle, built blacksmith shops, laid water lines, set up warehouses, even put in a hospital. His first discovery well was at Ebano, thirty miles west of Tampico, in 1901. The oil was heavy and of less good quality than was to be found later in the Tuxpam region. But Doheny took a gamble, and his company, Mexican Petroleum, had the audacity to build railroads and pipelines well in advance of guaranteed success. This construction, before major results of any sort, cost Doheny around four million dollars. Tampico's function as a cattle distribution point was gone forever.

Doheny's gamble paid off. In 1916 Mexican Petroleum Company produced 12,400,000 barrels of oil and sold 10,600,000 for $8,825,000. The cost per barrel, including bond interest, taxes and depreciation was twenty-five cents; the selling price was about eighty-three cents per barrel. No wonder Doheny proclaimed, in the midst of the Mexican revolution, on March 16, 1917: "I would sink all my interest on this coast ten thousand feet deep in the sea to give the good people of Mexico right, justice, and freedom in a modern system of civilization."

Doheny had prospected for gold in Mexico twenty years earlier, when he was a young mule-driver for the Geological Survey in Arizona and New Mexico. But he was an oil addict from the start. About 1895 he got a Santa Fe locomotive converted into an oil burner, one of the first of its kind. It was this demonstration of oil's use as cheap fuel that interested A. A. Robinson in attracting Doheny to Mexico in the search for oil. Robinson guaranteed Doheny

a contract with Mexican Central. He provided Doheny
with a special train for prospecting oil seepages in the
Tampico region, along the railway line. With his assistants,
Doheny would stop the train every few miles and explore
the fields on foot. A new chairman of the board of Mexican Central abrogated the contract, but Doheny had the
oil, and therefore asphalt,* so he set up a paving company
in Mexico City. Its success redeemed the loss of the fuel
contract. Doheny's company paved half of Mexico City,
then went on to Guadalajara, Morelia, Tampico, Durango,
Chihuahua and Puebla, giving those cities rank among the
best paved in the world. This, of course, was part of the
largesse of the Díaz government, under whose control all
the Doheny paving was done. Curiously, it was only after
the Madero revolution against Díaz in 1910–1911 that Doheny really struck it rich in oil. But it was really Doheny,
DeGolyer often wrote, who opened up Mexico to oil.

In 1909, Tampico was already the scene of a deadly ri-
valry. As Sir Weetman bought up more and more land in
the Tampico-Tuxpam area and got concessions to explore
national lands, no doubt from his unique relationship with
Porfirio Díaz, he began to threaten the long-standing retail
oil trade monopoly held in Mexico by the Waters Pierce
Oil Company, owned one-third by Henry Clay Pierce and
two-thirds by Standard Oil. Had Pearson aspired to be
merely a producer and not a distributor also, the Waters
Pierce Company might not have worried. Without any
great wells discovered in Mexico up till this time, they
were making their profit — they made about two million
dollars in 1908, for instance — by importing oil to satisfy
Mexican consumption, the need being around seven hun-

* Asphalt, an organic solid of carbohydrates, can be and is in great
quantity artificially produced from petroleum. It is generally found
where oil occurs, and was long thought to be produced by the drying up
of petroleum.

dred barrels of refined oil per day. But Sir Weetman started building tank ships, of 3,000-barrel capacity, for use in the Gulf as early as 1906. He obviously meant to distribute as well as produce oil. After his immense outlay of capital and time he meant to get his money's worth, including the lion's share of Mexican consumption. He defended the latter aim on the charge that Waters Pierce was abusing its monopoly by charging excessive prices; the country would benefit by competition.

The two companies played a cat and mouse game, attempting negotiations that came to nothing and seemed staged primarily in the hope of secretly discovering each other's trump cards. The competition quickly became cutthroat. Pearson set up fifteen depots in principal centers, sought contracts with leading merchants, ordered a fleet of tank cars for transport. To get this retail trade, he had to import oil from Texas; he wasn't yet producing enough to count.

Waters Pierce could afford to wait, though price-cutting tactics were promptly used. Its overall strategy was to wear Pearson down by making him sell his imported oil at a loss he could not long sustain. By March 1910, four months after young DeGolyer went to work for him, Pearson had lost 50,000 pounds on his retail trade. Waters Pierce knew that if he didn't find his own oil in Mexico — which looked less promising every day — he must soon or late admit he was beaten. It was a very anxious time.

For a young man who had started out to make himself a mining engineer and who was now caught up intimately in this complex drama of international financial giants, it was a startling and strenuous apprenticeship, and a thrilling one. The rewards of success, of real success, would obviously be very high.

How much did the young Americans under Dr. Hayes

know about the fight? Their business was to ride out over the country, mapping the leases and making recommendations for drilling sites. But they could not have ignored the battle had they wanted to. Rumors multiplied, press attacks upon Pearson and Mexican Eagle were appearing simultaneously in American, Mexican, French and English newspapers. Pearson claimed he was shadowed everywhere, that his telegrams were intercepted. He trembled at the press stories that stated his enterprise "was doomed to failure, that it was losing enormous sums." He knew the latter statement was true, but he still did not believe the former. There was one personal show of confidence that must have touched him. The opposition tried to make trouble in Washington because Dr. Hayes, still connected with the United States Geological Survey, was working for Pearson. Dr. Hayes resigned from the Survey and became a vice-president of Mexican Eagle. His faith was not just in "the Chief," as everybody called Lord Cowdray, but also in Mexican oil deposits. He could not forget that a really great well — the Dos Bocas — had been discovered forty miles below Tampico in 1908.

Like his boss Dr. Hayes, DeGolyer too had faith. Being a resolute man, in the middle of 1910 he decided to make a supreme act of faith in himself, in his bride-to-be, in the future of Mexican oil and Lord Cowdray's enterprises. He simply took, more or less, French leave from his work and made a swift trip back home, unannounced except to Ed Hopkins, to get Nell Goodrich to marry him. Having endured the separation and the torment of jealousy as long as he could, he showed up in Norman in early June. "I don't think he even troubled to get formal permission," Nell DeGolyer recalled, "he just announced he was coming to get me and left. It was perhaps the only reckless thing De ever did in his life. He got me."

He met Nell Virginia Goodrich (she was called "Nellie" in those days) after he enrolled as a "prep boy" at the University of Oklahoma. She was one month and two days younger than he. With his irregular schooling, he was just starting college about the time Nell Goodrich was garnering her first degree. She took a bachelor of music degree in 1906, and her B.A. the following year. In addition to teaching in the university's school of music, she helped out as assistant in the German department. One of the students of German in the autumn of 1905 was Everette DeGolyer. She graded his papers. He made an A.

Their romance was no secret. The college yearbook, named "The Mistletoe," awarded DeGolyer a prize one year for being a "five-hour gate swinger." His reward, according to "The Mistletoe": "just another spoon-case." But it turned out to be more than a matter of "spooning" (a delicious word that has fallen obsolete in the glossary of courtship). It was the real thing.

Nell DeGolyer was a small, curly-haired blond with periwinkle blue eyes. She had a peaches-and-cream complexion and a radiant beauty, but she also had a mind to match DeGolyer's. Above all else, she was spirited and fiercely independent, exactly like her gate-hanging beau. Had she been inwardly the china doll she seemed to be on the outside, she would not have interested him enough for the venture, rare for a young couple in those days, to leave home and go live in a primitive area of a foreign land. But as he often said in later life, she had more strength to cope with life than even he. "She has always made large decisions," he told this writer in 1955, "without a trace of nervousness or fear."

Nell Goodrich DeGolyer was the oldest of six children,

four of whose lives were bound up with the geological
ferment in Oklahoma. She and her sister married geologists; two of her brothers became geologists. At the time
the University of Oklahoma was the first and only university in the nation to sponsor geological training with direct application to the problems and needs of the infant
petroleum industry.

Her father settled in Norman because it was a college
town. Dr. Goodrich practiced dentistry. Both parents,
however, having at one point been teachers, were firm and
businesslike in regard to habits of study. After clearing the
table and doing the dishes, the six children then propped
their schoolbooks on the dining room table and went to
work. "We were not allowed to quit," Nell DeGolyer observed, "until we had finished our homework. Maybe that's
why I was able to enter the University of Oklahoma at the
age of fifteen, which again is why I was grading German
papers, as assistant in the department, when De enrolled
for his first course in German. All my life I've had to put
up with people saying to me, 'Oh, I hear you were your
husband's teacher.' Well, I wasn't, but I got so tired of this
hint that I was older than he that at last I would just answer, 'yes, because De was slow and stupid.' At any rate,
in my family education was an ideal and all of us finished
college, a rare thing in American life in the early part of
the century."

She had met DeGolyer when he entered the University
of Oklahoma preparatory school. "He suffered," she said,
"at being a 'prep boy' at his age and I looked down on him
at first; but only because my friends teased me for having
a 'prep boy' as my friend. This didn't last long, the teasing.
He was so full of humor that he could win the friendship
of anyone he wanted to. He and my mother were friends
from their first meeting. He was a poor boy and had to

work his way through college but my mother always said there was no need to worry about De, that he would manage. And indeed when he returned to Norman to complete his degree after eighteen months in Mexico, he was the richest student in school. Even mother hadn't expected anything like that but she took pride in seeing her judgment proved."

The marriage took place in the morning in the Goodrich home, the rites performed by the pastor of the Methodist Church where Nell Goodrich had been the organist for several years. She appeared in the university yearbook identified as a member of the faculty. DeGolyer had not finished his degree. But his salary had jumped from $150 a month (United States Currency) to $175 per month, so he was at last making more money than she. And he had one great practical advantage over her: he now spoke Spanish like a native and she knew scarcely one single word. Just about all Norman bade them good-bye at the Santa Fe station. It was June 10, 1910. For the first five hundred miles they would be riding over a flat land; after that, the tropics.

The ceremony had to be in the morning so the young couple could catch the afternoon train to make connections with the Montezuma Express, the train that carried Lord Cowdray and his wife on their first and fateful trip to Mexico. It was only when they were on the train that Nell DeGolyer was struck with the enormity of the change in environment that her marriage was going to cause. Every blow of the whistle, forlorn as it sounded, evaporated over the nearly empty southwestern countryside and signaled her farther removal from home. She noticed that an old nervous affliction was assailing her as she looked down at her arms and saw red splotches begin to appear. She asked herself, "What on earth will De think of me?" and

Nell Goodrich DeGolyer as a student at the University of
Oklahoma.

promptly regained control. The nervous bumps disappeared and she didn't even have to have a good cry. Would there be a piano in Tuxpam?

Nell Goodrich had other thoughts about her new husband's recklessness when she got to Tuxpam. "I could tell you enough to make your hair curl," she recalled. "De had made no arrangements, none at all, so we went to the village hotel. I suppose you'd call it that. There were cots, like army cots, in the room we got; below it was the early morning marketplace. Every kind of bug known to man shared the room with us, and it seemed that all the mosquitoes in Mexico were in convention there. No screens for the windows, although we did have little mosquito nets which the mosquitoes took as a challenge. I think I cried all the first night. There was no electric lighting, just candles as I remember. If we hadn't spent all our money, I would probably have started back home the next day. It was exciting to set out to live in a foreign country for the first time — but I had no idea how primitive it was going to be. And De had got so used to it, he was no longer aware of it."

But the shock wore off and the charm set in. They moved over to an immense room on the second floor of a house that overlooked the single street in the town and also the river. The room was so big, each of the four corners had its own identity. One was De's office, another the bedroom, another the kitchen and dining room, and the fourth a sort of parlor. Together, they went down to the marketplace to buy food (it was a short trip!), and discovered and enjoyed many exotic things they had never eaten before.

Nell DeGolyer was, for the natives, a curiosity; she was very blond and seemed to be the only woman in town who wore or had a hat. She finally had to abandon it to prove she felt no stigma in being blond. The DeGolyers went to the Sunday night band concerts at the plaza with another American couple (the husband was an engineer) who had a little boy about three. This youngster invariably got lost; the little Mexican children would bring the American towhead back to Nell DeGolyer, deciding he belonged to the woman with the blond hair.

Although DeGolyer never carried a gun in Mexico, Mrs. DeGolyer was a bit afraid while he was away during the week. He got a pistol for her and she kept it under her pillow. Sometimes, on going out, she would carry it in her handkerchief. But she never knew whether De had loaded it or not. "I didn't even look to see," she confessed. "I was afraid of it, I just carried it; it was some comfort to think others might be afraid of it, too."

3

Second Christmas:
Potrero Del Llano #4

PERHAPS the arrival of the American team had nothing to do with it particularly, but soon after the dismal Christmas of 1909 the winds of fortune shifted for Mexican Eagle. They began to blow most favorably.

Early in January of 1910, the first success came, minor

but immensely promising. At Tanhuijo — thirty miles north of the port of Tuxpam — an eighty-barrel-a-day well came in at a depth of only 115 feet. This was followed with another promise the next month, when British geologist Geoffrey Jeffrey brought in the first well in what was to become the great Potrero del Llano (Pasture of the Plains) field. The famine promised to turn into a feast. In short order, several more wells came in in the San Pedro field. There was nothing yet sensational, but the long years of anxiety seemed over. Lord Cowdray's nerves and temper regained their old calm. It was not clear that the nine years of exploration and organization would prove themselves in a great bonanza — only a sensational strike could achieve that — but it did seem clear that Mexican Eagle would not lose the Pearson fortune.

It took another Christmas, plus two more days, to make clear that the venture, far from losing a fortune, would make Lord Cowdray another one, his greatest of all.

On December 27, 1910, the company at last really hit pay dirt. The fourth successful well in Potrero del Llano field, the famous Potrero del Llano #4, came in like a raging monster. It even put the dramatic splendor of Spindletop in the shade. The greatest oil well yet discovered in the world, it has remained the champion of all time in productive yield, reaching to more than a hundred million barrels before playing itself out, eight years later. This single well qualifies as "major" in itself. (The standard gauge for an oil field to qualify as major is that it produce a hundred million barrels of oil during its lifetime.)

The decision to drill on the location DeGolyer chose was made in April 1910. The site, in the state of Veracruz, was about forty miles northwest of Tuxpam. The exact site for the well was about twenty to twenty-five yards from the banks of the Buena Vista, twenty miles above the point where this small tributary joins the larger Tuxpam river. Drilling began on the ninth of June; a depth of 1,856 feet was reached by July 23. Operations were then halted, to await pipeline facilities, until the twenty-third of December.

When drilling recommenced on December 23 to enter the Tamasopo limestone beds (the parent strata of Mexican petroleum), signs of gas and oil were immediately anticipated. But none were forthcoming, so despite instructions, the drilling crew had not placed a drilling valve on the wellhead by December 27. The bailer * was being used, and when oil was struck during the night at 2:00 A.M., the bailer was thrown clear of the well. The oil itself rose in a gigantic black plume to a height of 250 feet, the spray and the gas rising even higher. The vegetation for a radius of about a mile around the well was rapidly and thickly coated with oil.

Potrero del Llano #4 was located by Everette Lee De-Golyer, when he was only twenty-four years old. It was not his first nor his last success for the company, but it was, of course, his greatest.

(All his life DeGolyer kept a fist-sized piece of the rock that was blown out as a souvenir.) Neither he nor Lord Cowdray was in the field when the great strike cascaded in. Lord Cowdray, whose sons Clive and Harold were learning the family business in Mexico, was with his family in Mexico City, where the Pearson Casa was as much a showplace as the Lord Cowdray Hospital now is.

DeGolyer was spending the Christmas week, his second in Mexico, working with Dr. Hayes, helping acquaint the new general manager of Mexican Eagle, Robert Sterling,

* A long cylinder lowered into the well hole — after other tools have been temporarily removed — designed to allow water and rock samplings, or "cuttings," to be bailed or scooped out, in order to help identify the formation being drilled.

with the company's properties. Their trip brought them to the Potrero #4 camp a day or so before the well came in. Actually, there was some concern about the well's success. It had been drilled already to a depth as great as that of the other two completed wells but had not yet reached the oil-producing rock, the Tamasopo limestone. Ben Belt, later vice-president of Gulf Oil Corporation, was the resident geologist at Potrero.

In this unelated or anxious mood, Dr. Hayes and Messrs. Sterling and DeGolyer continued their tour by packsaddle until they could take the narrow-gauge railroad out to the Furbero field, farther south. About thirty miles from Tuxpam, they received word that Potrero #4 had come in, indeed had blown in, and was flowing wild. Nonetheless, they went on to Furbero as planned. But second word reached them there that #4 was not a well like the first two discovered in the field — it was still flowing wild and the estimate (too low) was that, far from three to four hundred barrels a day, it was making at least sixty thousand. In this crisis, Sterling abandoned the acquaintanceship tour and left *pronto* to take charge of the efforts being made to close the monster.

Dr. Hayes and DeGolyer were summoned to Mexico City. They had a two-day horseback ride over the face of the Mexican plateau before they could reach the train to take them into the capital. They found Lord Cowdray at the railway station. He was leaving to be on the ground at Potrero personally and to take charge himself of closing the great well.

DeGolyer, who had got to the capital with nothing but field clothes — khaki riding breeches and boots — discovered that he and Dr. Hayes were invited to have lunch with Lady Cowdray. DeGolyer tried to beg off, but Dr. Hayes was adamant. It was, he said, like a court command. DeGolyer was the fair-haired boy, but he had no inkling of it. Hayes would not excuse him.

Early next morning, DeGolyer hastened to the famous emporium, El High Life, still operating in the city, and bought a new suit for the luncheon he didn't care to attend. It would be his first experience of the "high life," he thought wryly as he bought the clothes.

The luncheon was a plush affair. Sir Reginald Tower, British minister to Mexico, was present, as was the governor of Mexico's Federal District. After the lunch, the latter took young DeGolyer on a tour of the city in his big car, one of the first in Mexico. Dr. Hayes, as it turned out, did not attend the luncheon. DeGolyer, thinking of Hayes' unwillingness to get him out of it, was so indignant he forgot to wonder whether or not he was using the right fork. Many years later, prodded by Cleveland Amory about his recollection of the occasion, DeGolyer guessed that Dr. Hayes was leaving all the limelight to his young protégé. He said: "I didn't realize then that I was at that time the fair-haired boy. As I look back at it, I know now that I was. Fortunately for me, both Lord Cowdray and Dr. Hayes thought I was one of the prime factors in a success that was beyond anything that anybody could have dreamed of."

It was a week after Potrero del Llano #4 blew in before DeGolyer got to the scene. Following the Chief, he went by train from Mexico City to Tampico, then down the lagoon by launch and on to the camp. Life in the Potrero camp was fearfully rugged. The well was still flowing wild. Everybody's clothes were ruined; a mere ten-yard walk, or dash, spoiled a suit. The company brought in thousands of quickly bought suits of the cheapest Mexican kind; these could be had on application, but their fit was usually grotesque and nothing could stay clean in the oil-drenched air. The little river, Buena Vista, which ran past the well flowed oil so thick on the surface that no water could be seen between its banks. It joined the Tuxpam river, which in turn was covered with oil six inches deep clear out to the sea. At Tampico, a hundred miles away by sea, the beaches were covered by oil, oil which probably traveled two hundred miles by water before it got there.

DeGolyer stayed in camp for a couple of weeks. At the moment, his chief task was to help construct flumes * in the Buena Vista river. Only the air-surface oil would burn; the flumes were designed to rush the oil through so fast that the flames could not follow up the flume. The local Mexican authorities ordered all *administradores* of haciendas to bring all their able-bodied men and to report to the company for work assignments on the flumes, and on the dams. DeGolyer's "old friend" from Los Horcones, Don Felicitas, arrived with a score of men. DeGolyer also helped organize the "chow lines" to feed the thousands of pressed-in-to-service help, mostly with bean-filled tacos, each worker taking a tortilla in each hand and proceeding by tables where beans from huge pots were spooned onto the tortillas. Coffee was available in big five-gallon tins; a thirsty worker went up and drank from the tin until pulled away by others behind him.

Next, Cowdray dispatched DeGolyer to help an expert engineer named De la Suerta, to pick a route for a new pipeline to Tuscumbar. Since DeGolyer had already made a topographic survey of the country around, this posed little difficulty. It did have a hazard. They decided the line should avoid the town of Tuxpam; this required crossing the river twice, from the north side to the south and then back again to the north.

Arrived in Tuxpam, DeGolyer immediately bought the

---

* Chutes or troughs normally used to carry water but, in this case, oil.

best new clothes he could find, having happily at last escaped the oil-soaked camp. Then he engaged a man with a
dugout canoe to row him over to the south side of the river
to locate a good river crossing. The Tuxpam was, of course,
still covered with oil, half a foot of it as surface, and the
river was nearly as broad here as the Hudson. DeGolyer,
sitting on a box in the canoe, suddenly realized his Indian
pilot was drunk. He looked at the slick oil, he looked at his
new outfit, he looked at the drunken Indian. He was seized
with anger, made an unwitting quick movement — and
promptly fell out of the canoe. Fished back in, he was
speechless with anger. "But I realized even while I was in
the oil and water," he later reported, "that I couldn't in
any way blame the Indian. It had been my own fault —
just falling out of the canoe, and that was all there was
to it."

He didn't even have the comfort of being able to tell
Nell DeGolyer about it. She had left Tuxpam a month or
so before Christmas for a trip back to the States. With De
working out in the field all week long, returning to town
only for the weekends, she was hungry to see her family
at Christmastime. So, she missed all the big excitement,
save by letter. For her, a part of the excitement was that
Lord Cowdray, seeing daylight for the first time in his
Mexican oil operations, agreed that his "lucky talisman"
should return to Norman to finish his education.

Once Potrero del Llano #4 blew in, there was not time,
nor inclination even, for Christmas season holidaying.
Lord Cowdray, and his son, had rushed up from Mexico
City in mingled joy and fear. Lord Cowdray remembered
the million-dollar fire that had destroyed his San Diego
field gusher "Dos Bocas," two years before.

Potrero #4, a real giant, gave no sign, as the daily drilling had progressed, that any usual precautions would be

necessary. From past experience, the boilers had been placed far away from the well, behind a thicket. DeGolyer had given instructions to install a drilling valve, but the drillers postponed doing so while waiting for signs that would indicate such need. The drillers were taken by surprise. The first thought of the driller in charge was to race through the thicket to extinguish the boilers, whose fires — supplying the engine for the drilling machinery — were always a supreme danger in the first moments. This time there was no ignition from the boiler fires. The driller got to them before the flowing oil risked being set alight. But there was another major problem. How to cap the flow of oil spurting forth under such tremendous pressure? It took Cowdray and his engineers sixty days to close down Potrero #4's record-breaking flow. In the meantime catastrophe threatened, as six million barrels of oil went to waste, most of it flowing down the nearby Buena Vista river. Ten or fifteen miles downstream, the oil caught fire. Immense black clouds that looked alive in their fierce menace rose to mountainous height. The horizon was an inferno of flame. The anxiety was almost unendurable — would the fires travel back upstream to the well?

Lord Cowdray directed the erection of earthen barricades, working himself and his men without letup. He directed setting up camps for thousands of Mexicans from the neighboring villages, recruited for the work that had to be done. Most of them gave up after one week, quite understandably; another thousand had to be recruited at once. He directed the construction of a great basin which succeeded in impounding three million barrels of oil that were salvaged in the two-month crisis.

The well itself was resisting capture like a wild animal. It spewed forth noxious asphaltic gases that defied the crews trying to cap it to work more than a few minutes at a time. Despite devices improvised on the spot to protect eyes and throats, the engineers and their assistants had to work in five minute or so relays, desperately forcing into final place an invention made on the spot and which came to be known as the "Bell Nipple." This solution was the idea of a Texas driller who remembered somewhat similar devices used to cap small wells back home. Skill and courage and endurance at last won out. It was as Lord Cowdray later said, the "supreme moment" for Mexican Eagle; a two-month ordeal for all concerned.

From Mexico City, Cowdray sent a note seventeen days after the strike. "Mr. DeGolyer," he wrote in longhand, "word has reached us that your dam is not holding very well. If the current where you are damming is too swift you had better select a point where it is slower, trying to fell the trees so they will fall where you want them. It requires a little engineering study to get the dams just right to serve the proper purpose. Mr. Weaver and about 100 men are on the way towards La Ceiba and will put up dams there also, fighting the fire bit by bit to hold it in check. Lord Cowdray."

Another note, undated save for "Camp. 2:15 P.M.," reveals other problems the gusher spawned: "Mr. DeGolyer: Many thanks for your note just to hand. The men will not be paid today. Advise them that the authorities tell us the men must remain at work until the fire is extinguished and that we must not pay them till then. Otherwise the men will leave. They can have some payment on account but we must hold the regular pay back. What rate of flow have you in the 80-feet length of flume and what width is it? Make the best terms possible with the woman feeding the men. Fifty cents a day for 3 meals per man should be a fair charge under the circumstances. But do the best possible threatening that you will ask the *rurales* [local policemen] to see that she feeds the men and have the local *jefe* or judge tell us what we must pay her. This only if she be too unreasonable. Cowdray."

Leakage from the first capping was considerable; an improved replacement was installed two months later, in March 1911. Once again the workmen had to battle the poisonous gases that escaped, very few being able to avoid the painful inflammation the fumes caused in the eyelids. The standard remedy for soothing relief turned out to be a slice of raw potato held against the shut eye. At all times, Mexican Eagle had doctors in the field, but the potato slice was more effective than medicines or chemical solutions.

Potrero #4 was too valuable not to inspire every sort of protection. The management decided to build a concrete house on a little mound just over the head of the well to nullify risk of fire from the lightning storms that plague the Tampico-Tuxpam Gulf of Mexico area. This "house" was equipped with steam pipes inside in order to surround the wellhead completely by steam during the violent storms. Potrero had no derrick then. Part of the derrick had been blown away when the oil gushed forth, the rest had been removed to allow installation of the Bell Nipple.

The concrete safeguard did double duty soon after the beginning of the Mexican revolution. Rebel activity in the area grew so alarming that in November 1913 Mexican Eagle decided to shield Potrero #4 even more. The concrete shelter was filled in with reinforced concrete, leaving open only a small aperture through which the valve spindle could be manipulated. Potrero seemed to be safe from nature's violence, from being set afire by revolutionaries, from being dynamited by the warring parties of rebels and federalists.

Soon after, in 1914, other dangers threatened. A half-dozen surface seepages began to surround the well, creat-

ing fire hazards and the prospect that pressure underground was dispersing and destroying the pool. Several
theories were advanced to explain the new problem and
to dispose of it. One was that the installation of the concrete house had damaged the Bell Nipple and that a great
quantity of oil was escaping and flowing back down alongside the casing. The only way to repair the installation was
to remove the concrete pillbox and all its reinforcement.
Once again, mechanical genius was required to overcome
the difficulties of controlling the oil flow while a new cap
was gradually and intricately put in place.

The maneuver, laborious and involved, was approaching
success when, on August 14, before the new device was finally installed, a tropical storm hit the coast. Lightning set
fire to gas escaping from the well, now deprived of its concrete shelter, and once again Potrero #4, just as when it
first came in, lost about three million barrels of oil to fire.
Despite every conceivable maneuver, including the use
of foam-producing mixtures expressed from the United
States, it took six months to get the well again under control, this time under the direction of T. Wayland Vaughan,
who later became director of the Scripps Institution of
Oceanography. Once again, the response in human courage and skill was heroic. It was doubly difficult during the
second great fire because most of the seasoned workers —
the large corps of drilling-experienced Texans — had been
compelled to get back across the border by Woodrow Wilson's "Intervention" in Mexico's revolution.

But victory was won by March 1915. Potrero began once
more to yield its annual average of around fifteen million
barrels a year. For comparison's sake, note that the one
great spectacular strike in the Golden Lane before Potrero, Doheny's Casiano #7 (and it was considered a
champion when it came in in September 7, 1910; called at

the time "the greatest oil producer of the world"), yielded about half that annual amount in its first three years. Potrero #4 went to salt water in December 1918, after eight years of dramatic life and a total yield variously estimated from 120 million barrels to 140 million. (A barrel is normally forty-two gallons.)

Potrero was the first "wild" well of great capacity to be successfully controlled. The fact that it rebelled a second time made it doubly picturesque in oil history. But economically the significance of this great strike is suggested by still another statistic. The competition that oil now represented for coal as fuel is clearly seen in this statement by Dr. I. C. White in 1912: "The cost of the oil to the Mexican Petroleum Company [Doheny's], delivered on board to tank steamers at Tampico, is slightly less than 14 cents per barrel of 42 gallons, and the cost of transportation from there as far north as Boston is only about 20 cents per barrel." And: "Three and a half barrels of this oil equals in heating value a ton of good coal."

Where would all this oil be used in 1910? Luckily, the internal combustion engine saved the day. When Potrero #4 came in, the automobile census in the United States was 458,000 passenger cars and 10,000 trucks. But thanks to cheap fuel and great highway-building programs, by 1920 the census showed for all types of motorcars a leap in one decade from half a million to the 1920 official figure of 10,463,295 vehicles.

Five years after the discovery, DeGolyer (then in the New York office of Pearson's) sought exact data on the well. By that time, Potrero #4 had produced about one-third of all the oil found up to then in Mexico. In 1915, there were about fifteen fields in Mexico and about seven hundred wells. In his own scrupulous calculation, "the measured production of the well to the end of 1915 was some 42,275,342 barrels; estimating a flow of 110,000 barrels per day during the sixty days that the well flowed wild when it first 'came in,' we have an additional 6,600,000 barrels and I have estimated the oil lost by fire and waste between August 1914 and March 1915 as 2,400,000 barrels which certainly seems conservative enough, giving a total production of some 51,275,242 barrels up to January 1st of the present year (1916). In a report which I am writing for the Company as of date July 1st, I have included with this an estimated production of 7,800,000 barrels for the first half of this year, giving a total of July 1st of 59,075,242 barrels."

He sent this calculation for scrutiny to geologist T. Wayland Vaughan, then working for the Aguila company at Tampico, who had been in charge when the fire broke out at the well in 1914. DeGolyer's accompanying letter observed, "I am very much interested in an estimate of the total production . . . from a scientific more than a commercial standpoint . . . I am trying to arrive at a figure as a basis upon which to estimate the space which must have been left in the oil-bearing rock by the oil which has been produced." He adds that since he has himself arrived at "a rather large figure," he wants Vaughan's criticism of its exactness.

Vaughan found that DeGolyer was underestimating Potrero's production. Supplying all relative data in his reply, Vaughan ups the accurate total as of July 1, 1916, to the figure of 68,032,745 barrels. The well had another two and a half years of "dry" oil production to go before salt water set in.

Forty years later, DeGolyer — having since brought in many another well, not to say field — tended to strike a casual and cavalier attitude toward history-making Potrero #4. Here is a typical reply to the many queries about

E. DeGolyer takes his ease at his most famous discovery, the Potrero del Llano #4, near Tuxpam, Mexico. Associate geologist Leon
Russ in back.

it that kept coming to him, this one in a letter to J. E. Jan-
ney on January 7, 1954: "There really wasn't any particular thing required for the location of the Potrero #4 well
and the fact that it was such a large well was as much a
surprise to its locaters as to the world in general. Two
wells, the discovery well being located as a result of seepages, had already been drilled, each of them small wells,
say 300–400 barrels daily. After the completion of the first
two wells, several wells were drilled to the limestone but
not 'drilled in' pending the completion of pipeline facilities. As the pipeline was approaching completion the first
well to be deepened was #4 since it was in the best mechanical condition. It had been drilled to sea level depth
as greatly or slightly greater than that of the completed
wells when without any warning it came in, making at the
rate of 100–110 thousand barrels daily. I am afraid that
this account is not of much value to you but that is the way
it happened." When he chose, DeGolyer could be a very
laconic man.

No allusion to the drama and, of course, no mention of
his second-ranking feat in Mexico: location of the discovery well of the great Naranjos pool, a real wildcatter on
ground where no oil had yet been proven, a pool which
produced more than 90 million barrels in the year of its
peak production.

It is worth noting that the first really impressive well in
Mexico, Doheny's La Pez #1 located in the Tampico-
Tuxpam area in 1904, had a production rate of one million
barrels a year. But as late as 1917, Doheny was still scorn-
ful of the usefulness of geologists in locating oil wells, an
attitude which DeGolyer's whole career, more than that of
any other single petroleum pioneer, was to belie. In 1918,
DeGolyer noted that the Mexican Eagle Oil Company was
then producing petroleum at the rate of approximately 30

million barrels per year "from wells the location of which was based on the geological studies of the writer."

When the deafening roar from the uncontrolled flow of oil was at last silenced, Lord Cowdray could take his ease and assess his empire. Potrero del Llano #4 meant salvation. Mexican Eagle was now one of the most promising financial ventures in the world. As expected, other major wells began to come in. So, in 1911, Lord Cowdray named a new chief geologist for Mexican Eagle, after giving him a leave of absence to get his college degree. In his twenty-fifth year, and a newlywed, Everette Lee DeGolyer found himself in a foreign land to be the head of exploration, since as the new chief geologist he was also responsible for securing leases and lands, for one of the world's greatest oil companies.

In this heady situation, Nell DeGolyer reminded her husband of his promise to finish his education. Perhaps she spoke to Lord Cowdray. The company gave him leave in the spring of 1911 and the DeGolyers returned to Norman where he completed the requirements for his B.A. degree that summer; his thesis, chief requirement left to fulfill, was on "Metamorphosis in the Coals of Anthracite and Crested Butte Quadrangles, Colorado." Lord Cowdray added to DeGolyer's salary "the sum of $345 gold, which it is expected will cover all your expenses whilst you are taking your degree, as an appreciation of your good services."

4

Daily Life of a Geologist in the "Golden Lane"

BEFORE WORLD WAR I, the two wonders in the world of oil production were the two fields along the Louisiana–Texas Gulf Coast and, farther down the Gulf of Mexico, the Tampico-Tuxpam region. The latter, sometimes called the Panuco area from the major river of the region, comprised two fields itself: 1) the "south field," extending from the coast and about a mile wide inshore; and 2) the Tapila-Panuco-Ebano fields, south and a bit west of Tampico, seventeen miles in length, varying from a mile to four miles in width, in front of the Sierra Madre range. The geologists felt sure at the time that the oil cavities, trapped in fractured limestone, were all to be found on the coast, east of the mountains. In Mexico, this left a great deal of unknown and unexamined terrain all the way from the northern border at Matamoros on down to Yucatan.

It was a rough, harsh country to map and to explore, afflicted with swarms of mosquitoes, with ticks in the grasses, snakes in the cactus — especially rattlesnakes — moccasins in the streams, bandits along the trails. It was sparsely populated, the scattered settlements being largely *rancheros* or an occasional hacienda where some lordly inheritor of a Spanish land grant lived in baronial splendor from the labors of a submerged peonage. It was a far cry from going to college in, say, Oklahoma. But it was into this empty land that DeGolyer and such young associate American geologists as Edwin B. Hopkins and Chester Washburne had to ride out on burro and with mulepack to gauge and measure and estimate the surface signs of oil potentiality.

It was a lonely life. The geologist did not operate from camps, as the drillers did; he was expected to go out alone, to survive, to live off the country. There was no question of using automobiles, which were nonetheless providing the mainstay of oil consumption. The first automobile to appear in Tampico arrived in 1911. There were very few roads where it could be used. Prospecting still had to be done on horseback. When your horse was stolen, as it usually was, you turned to the burro or the mule carrying the saddlebags and the tent for the pitched camp.

And yet there were rewards. If you were working near the shore, food was no problem. There were millions of the delicious Gulf oysters to be had merely by scooping them up. If you were inland, the occasional hamlets observed the centuries-old tradition of offering hospitality to any stranger — and you might get shrimp cooked in banana leaves, or the standard tamales and other corn and meat dishes. The people, most often of Indian stock, were eager to help the stranger; it was a relief from boredom. And as DeGolyer discovered, they could lead you to oil seepages and to curious rocks.

He was a great collector of fossils, both out of curiosity and from a feeling or flair for systematic codification of knowledge. Writing came easy to him, and he took copious notes, perhaps because he was already a great reader. He developed a fascinated interest in the Spanish conquests in the New World. As early as 1910 he was sending back fossil specimens and Spanish books to his college teachers.

He admitted later, in a letter to his friend W. E. Wrather, "We didn't know much about the stratigraphy in those days, practically no paleontological work had been done. . . . Under C. Willard Hayes, who became vice-president in charge of production for the Company, we were very much entranced with the possibilities of interpreting geological structure from physiography and land form."

It was pioneer work, which was one of its charms, a chance to do what had never been done before. If it required pluck and skill and courage to devise a way to cap a well like Potrero #4, it took even more to "scout" this land alone and make studious reports and recommendations whose testing would require the outlay of thousands, perhaps hundreds of thousands, of dollars. The search for data, for information, had to be conducted under primitive conditions. No commercial railway ran near the oil fields.

The prospector, like the crews at the wells, was dependent on mule transport. The boilers transported to a drill site required a team of twenty mules, and in the frequent quagmires the crew itself had to help shove and push. The prospector had one animal, at most two. The crews, in the established camps, lived in portable frame dwellings, which were really primitive shacks, fitted with numerous bunks. But the geologist slept out, on his field trips, under his tent and was his own cook. He was always welcome, however, at the camp of any company, his own or a rival, in the fraternity of the oil game. There he could count on food and a bunk overnight, as he traveled on his lonely way. He would be plied with questions, of course; everybody was in the market for tips and clues, which might be sold or traded for similar information. You had to learn to be close-mouthed. DeGolyer learned it. At least his friends in later life observed that it was a talent he practiced in a superior, even a superlative, way.

The young American geologists had an advantage over many of the English and European scientists. The Americans had ridden horses since childhood and had usually dealt with the maddening stubbornness of mules. The Texas saddle was in general use, and the Americans were accustomed to it. They all traveled light, their only instruments a hand compass, a prismatic compass, pocket lens and geologist's pick or hammer. A few lucky ones had, like DeGolyer, a plane table. Dr. Erb, the famous Swiss geologist, was envied for his pocket range finder.

If the geologist had a Mexican guide and assistant, he had to deal with the spirit of *mañana*. Up at the crack of dawn and ready to work before the heat of the day set in, he was frustrated by his missing *mozo*. The *mozo* had probably waked at dawn too, but in the land of *poco tiempo*, he found it good, as in the Mexican saying, that God had given us the night to sleep in and the day to rest in.

Once DeGolyer's reconnaissance trip had got started, it meant long days in the saddle. There was much walking, however, up hills in search of outcropping and to high points in order to check positions. Before the afternoon light vanished, he had to seek a place to pitch tent and, if possible, to find a watercourse that might yield fish for dinner, in case he had seen no suitable wildlife to shoot during the day. A lucky stop at a ranch meant usually a chance to sleep on a cot, though sometimes DeGolyer, like the others, had to sleep on the floor. At least at a ranch, one was sure of tortillas, black beans, meat (often dried) and eggs. Most of the fare was so heavily seasoned with chili peppers that the Europeans didn't know whether they were eating the food or it was eating them.

Water at the ranches was usually in short supply. The nomad geologists relied on coming across a clear stream to stop for a swim or to wash clothing. Beards were the rule, for shaving, on reconnaissance trips, was too inconvenient. The height of luxury was to carry along a case of beer, to relieve the monotony of drinking boiled water. Whiskey, of course, had its partisans. Strangely, there were not too infrequent encounters in the small villages with Europeans or Americans who had settled and intermarried in Mexico because they liked the free and pioneering life. Such encounters could and did provide guides and useful connections.

The work was strenuous. DeGolyer often had, in the course of an exploration, to creep along riverbanks bristling with thorny plants that stuck or stung. At day's end his clothes were torn to tatters. And the chief curse of the country, for the geologists, lay in the ticks that clustered everywhere. The small, brown, flat insects were inescapable — the best way to remove them from the skin or clothing was to chew gum and with it stick the insects and pick them off. If they got into the skin, they were treated with a bit of tobacco leaf soaked in the Mexican brandy, *aguardiente*. The danger was that they could cause fever.

A seepage of oil or gas to the surface, a chapapote patch, was still the tried-and-true indication of promise. Sometimes the seepages were literally pools, deep and broad enough to trap animals, even animals as large as cows. The grapevine of rumor, so rampant around Tampico and Tuxpam, had miraculously spread to the hinterland and the backwoods. The natives guarded the big seepage sites, wanted to exact money from the geologist who proposed to study them. Any questions from the "foreigner" met a stone wall of silence and secrecy. It was a problem, for these important clues had to be mapped and charted, their relationships in location carefully analyzed and studied. The geologist usually came through with a fair sum of money. It was worth it. This led to the disclosure of other seepages — for a price.

These contacts had their dangers. If after the departure of the stranger, the town suffered a misfortune — from drought to storms to yellow fever — the traveler became the scapegoat cause of it. The next geologist to pass through had a rough time of it. Once DeGolyer, smitten with fever and half-unconscious, barely made it to the edge of a little village before falling off his horse. The kindly natives took care of him and cured him in two days with their local herbs and folk remedies. There was a gay and companionable departure, with well wishes and congratulations all around. A week later, as he afterward learned, nearly the whole town was extinct from a scourge of cholera. Folk medicine had been of no avail. Though still grateful, DeGolyer decided never again to go that way.

Anyway, these pioneers took enough risks as it was. The trails they followed often disappeared into trackless wastes. They rarely came upon the clean, decent, lovely little towns that dotted the Mexican landscape farther south, nearer Veracruz, nearer the thickly populated Central Plateau, little towns where pleasant hotels and smiling, happy people were to be found.

And so it was a pleasure to get back to Tampico, where the elegant and agreeable Colonial Club with its handsome veranda had been founded in 1906, where the Sporting Club offered horse racing and other diversions, where civilized talk was again available. It was a pleasure in fact to reach one of the drillers' camps, where the workers, mostly Americans, demanded and got excellent and abundant food. Or so it seemed to the pilgrimaging geologist, who shot his own wild turkey or deer when he was lucky enough to find any. And for the young DeGolyer there was the pleasure of writing up his copious field notes. There was a historian in him, later to find expression in an astonishing number of contributions to learned journals. All his life he semed indifferent to power, which was easily in his reach, concentrating rather on knowledge and its diffusion.

On January 13, 1913, First Vice-President C. Willard Hayes on stationery letterheaded Compañía Mexicana de Petroleo "El Aguila," S.A., announced to DeGolyer that his salary had been raised to "12,000 per annum." On June 13, 1913, a letter from London signed merely "Cowdray" said to DeGolyer in Tampico: "On Dr. Hayes' recommendation I have much pleasure in advising you that we have decided to grant you a bonus consisting of 600 shares in the Aguila Company as a mark of our appreciation of the able manner in which you have carried out the duties of your department in the past twelve months, and of the keen personal devotion which Dr. Hayes tells me you have shown in the interests of the company.

"If you will advise me of the name of your bank to which these shares should be sent, I will have them forwarded for safe-keeping."

On the preceding September 9, 1912, the company had given its young chief geologist an earlier bonus of 250 shares. The letter was marked private. In seven years, from 1906 to 1913, DeGolyer's salary had jumped from $50 per month with the United States Geological Survey to $1,000 a month with Mexican Eagle, not to mention various bonuses. (Economists estimate that pre-World War I salaries should be multiplied by ten for current equivalents.) Here is how his salary rose with Mexican Eagle: in 1909 (when first employed), $150 gold; increased on August 1910 to $175 gold; increased on January 1, 1911 to $200 gold; a year later, January 1, 1912, $600 Mexican; raised July 1, 1912 to $800 Mexican, and then on January 1, 1913 to $1,000 Mexican. The Mexican "dollar," or peso, was worth approximately fifty cents, American coinage, at the time.

DeGolyer tried to keep a touch of British reticence in his pride over the success. He wrote W. L. Gregory on May 14, 1913: "The loading station of Tuxpam is putting about a million barrels a month into the ships and is generally one grand success. Tuxpam is loading more oil into the ships than all the companies together are loading out of the port of Tampico. Not bad, eh what?"

Tuxpam was the dock area for oil from the Potrero and Los Naranjos pools, both DeGolyer discoveries. In 1913 crude oil was selling for $3 per barrel, so the Tuxpam dock was handling about $3,000,000 of oil per month.

5   Richest Student on the O.U. Campus: His Background

DeGolyer's associates were astounded when he took time off in 1911 to go back to the University of Oklahoma to get his degree. By all signs, Mexican Eagle was on its way to becoming the richest oil enterprise in the world, which in fact it was between 1914 and 1919. But DeGolyer's decision is not hard to explain.

Oil in the United States had become practically synonymous with Oklahoma. The great Glenn Pool, twelve miles south of Tulsa, was a national sensation when it was discovered in 1905. It was the predecessor to other spectacular strikes which made Oklahoma literally the oil capital of the nation for about two decades. It made sense for DeGolyer to observe what was happening back in the States. It made sense to take a college degree when he was so close to finishing the required work and when only a small percentage of the population had one. In Tampico and elsewhere in Mexico, DeGolyer had made friends with highly trained European men whose distinction might well have made him keenly aware of his own scattered education. And DeGolyer was a man in love with learning. As we shall see later, very few professional or businessmen of his time had so close and intimate a connection with the academic world as DeGolyer had in the last thirty years of his life.

After Potrero #4, DeGolyer could suppose that he had proved himself as a geologist. But we must turn back to his early years, to his heritage, to discover why he had to return, almost compulsively, to the university in 1911 to prove himself again. His was a fiercely competitive nature; he relished situations in which he had to "test" himself against fate, against nature, against others.

It so happened that in his first year at the university DeGolyer had profited from that sovereign experience any fine university can offer, the collision of a great, original teaching mind with student minds full of response and hungry for ideas. This teacher was Vernon Louis Parrington whose three-volume *Main Currents in American Thought* remains a significant achievement in American scholarship, though now outdated. Parrington was himself a pioneer in a pioneer school. Both in his teaching and in his personality he was a searchlight on clear values for some of the most distinguished men the state of Oklahoma ever produced.

Of this teacher, Lionel Trilling in 1940 observed: "It is possible to say of V. L. Parrington that with his *Main Currents in American Thought* he has had an influence on our conception of American culture which is not equaled by that of any other writer of the last two decades. His ideas are now the accepted ones wherever the college course in American literature is given by a teacher who conceives himself to be opposed to the genteel and the academic and in alliance with the vigorous and the actual." Then noting the weaknesses of Parrington's thought, based on an overly simple distinction between "reality" and "mind," Trilling adds: "his best virtue was real and important — he had what we like to think of as the saving salt of the American mind, the lively sense of the practical, workaday world, of the welter of ordinary undistinguished things and people, of the tangible, quirky, unrefined elements of life. He knew what so many literary historians do not know, that emotions and ideas are the sparks that fly when the mind meets difficulties." *

Parrington was fully aware from personal experience of what happens when the mind meets difficulties. His idea of what education was did not precisely match that of the administration of the University of Oklahoma. He was judged too individualistic. He was condemned for drinking beer with his students. He was fired in 1908, but went on to the University of Washington and to the ultimate ac-

---

* The latest serious study of Parrington's once immensely influential work is Richard Hofstadter's *The Progressive Historians* (Knopf, 1968). Professor Hofstadter, incidentally, cites the same passage from Trilling's famous essay.

colade of a Pulitzer Prize for his master work. In the history of southwestern universities, the firing of teachers who later and elsewhere achieved great distinction was almost a standard pattern down till World War II.

What Parrington gave his students in Oklahoma, plus perhaps a fondness for beer, was a love of literature and reading and a great respect for the life of the mind. Several alumni who underwent his influence were later to make, ironically, sterling endowments and gifts to the university that kicked him out. Among them was Everette DeGolyer, known in his senior year but not before as "the richest student on the campus."

From 1904 until 1909, the young and fast-growing University of Oklahoma was the real anchor in Everette Lee DeGolyer's life. In addition to Vernon Louis Parrington, he had great teachers also in his major subject, geology. It was a familiar joke on the campus in those days that geology professors Gould and Woodruff could teach their students to find oil under any rock in Oklahoma. It wasn't that easy, but any tribute, generous extravagance deducted, to Woodruff and Gould seemed deserved. Their department was one that had put the fledgling university on the map. In 1906 Professors Gould and Woodruff persuaded the administration to create a post of geology assistant, the salary to be fifteen dollars a month. They chose as the first assistant of the department student Everette Lee DeGolyer. His job was to label and classify rocks and material the professors had gathered in summer work in the Texas Panhandle. Credit for the discovery of Panhandle gas and oil is usually given to Professor Gould.

Dr. Gould came to the University of Oklahoma in 1900 — the same year as Parrington — and began his instruction in geology in the one-building university in what was still not a state but Oklahoma Territory. When the Indian and

Oklahoma territories were joined in statehood in 1907, Dr. Gould had won so much prestige that he was able to write into the State Constitution a provision for the formation of an Oklahoma State Geological Survey, of which he served as a director from 1908 to 1911. In the autumn of 1908 he gave Everette DeGolyer a job with the unique state survey as assistant geologist. DeGolyer kept his official identification card all his life, but he kept the job only a few months, leaving it for the United States Geological Survey, at the insistence of Dr. Woodruff.

The university had a one-man cyclone as president, David Ross Boyd. His ideas on education were modern and aggressive. He was determined to make the new 285-acre campus a botanical delight and a pleasure to the eye. Thanks to his foresight, the University of Oklahoma has one of the most beautiful campuses in the land, featuring seventy-five different varieties of trees. The mood on the campus was electric. The Twin Territories, Indian Territory and Oklahoma Territory, were about to be joined in statehood. The future — political, social, economic — was all to be made more or less from scratch.

At college age, Everette DeGolyer was short and stocky, ruddy and round in face, companionable, cheerful and chaffing, and not inclined to take himself too seriously. Even then he had the effortless gift of winning friends; he was elected president of his freshman class. There were sixty-one entering freshmen at the University of Oklahoma in 1905. He was secretary of the debating group, the Forum, and a member of the Engineers' Literary Society. He pledged Kappa Alpha and was a loyal "brother," obviously happy in group activity. Four years after his graduation, he remained actively concerned in helping other "alums" keep the chapter shipshape, financially and otherwise. He had, early, an executive's fondness for clean desks and smooth organization. He never outgrew his sense of loyalty to his fraternity associations and he kept his closest friends, rare thing, for a lifetime.

He loved to read. He kept in mind the prospect that he might turn to newspapering. Under the influence of one of his closest college classmates, George B. Parker — who later became editor in chief of the Scripps-Howard newspaper chain — he nearly turned to journalism. He worked hard, like Parker, on the student paper.

DeGolyer once told William B. Ruggles of Dallas how his luck worked in passing a math course at the university. He had been away and missed a number of classes. The stern but considerate professor called DeGolyer to his desk after the last class of the semester.

"If you want to even pass this course, DeGolyer," the math instructor said, "you'll absolutely have to make an A on the final, nothing less."

DeGolyer was surprised. He thought he had been doing average work.

"Is it really that bad?" he asked.

"Yes, that bad."

DeGolyer knew he couldn't learn the whole course in the remaining night before the final examination. He had to concentrate. His only chance, he said, was to outguess the teacher. He picked out fifteen theorems or problems, committed them to memory during the course of an all night session. He won. The teacher gave ten problems, all ten in the fifteen DeGolyer could reproduce from memory. He didn't get an A as final grade but he did pass the course. Typical of him, he did not panic, or work consumingly without plan. He took time out to think, made a decision, stuck to it. It was this pattern, this habit, no doubt, that gave him that air of confidence and calm, low-pressure self-control that many of his associates regarded as primary in his temperament. In times of storm, one of his favorite remarks to the bothered was "Don't let it throw you." A good horseman first of all looked to keeping his seat, no matter what his mount might be doing.

Back in Norman at the university in 1911 DeGolyer could see before his own eyes what had not been so evident in Tampico. The motor age had arrived. America was rapidly "going on wheels." Petroleum products had opened a new economic frontier. The native American venturesomeness, so central in Parrington's explanation of American thought, was again vindicated.

Perhaps the "venturesomeness" was both environmental and inherited. Certainly, Everette DeGolyer's European forebear had come to America out of the same motivation. The founder of the DeGolyer line in this country was a Frenchman, with Swiss-German stock on his maternal side. Four generations later, venturesomeness was the chief trait of Everette DeGolyer's father, as of himself. Everette DeGolyer always spoke of the French and Irish ancestry on his father's side and of the Swiss and German on his mother's. (Both lines arrived in this country before the Revolution.) DeGolyer usually said of his forebears: "The men in both lines have been for the most part farmers."

Jacques de Golier, son of Antoine de Golier, was born in Paris in 1726, under the reign of Louis XV. Fifty years before the birth of Jacques, LaSalle had climaxed his explorations for Louis XIV in the New World by his last and fatal expedition to the mouth of the Mississippi, which he had already claimed for France when he descended the river from northern French ports. By accident or design in 1685 he sailed four hundred miles west of the Mississippi to found a French settlement on the Texas Gulf Coast. There is much evidence that his secret purpose was to take over from the Spanish the gold and silver wealth of Mexico. In this he failed, but his example became a model for adventurous French youth.

Jacques de Golier first trained for the priesthood but apparently did not have the vocation. Son of a nobleman, he left home and school against his father's opposition in order to join the French army. He was promptly sent to Flanders in the campaign Louis XV was leading against Great Britain and other nations in the War of the Austrian Succession, terminated by the Treaty of Aix-la-Chapelle in 1748. Jacques de Golier was twenty-two, and hungry for adventure; he emigrated to French Canada when his regiment was dispatched there after the Treaty. In Canada he became an excellent ice skater and carried messages from Quebec to French outposts to the west on the St. Lawrence. On one such sortie he was taken prisoner by the English but managed to escape, making his way into Massachusetts, where he decided to stay. In 1754 he married Miss Jane Hatch of West Stockbridge, Mass. The couple later moved to Columbia County in New York and then to Tryon on the Mohawk, thirty miles from Albany. As though war were his true vocation, he served two years in the American Revolution and his three eldest sons fought in it likewise. He nearly rounded out a full century of life, dying in Washington County, New York, at age ninety-seven.

He named one of his sons for his father; Anthony De-Golier (the name now spelled most often with a "y" rather than "i") moved westward to Ohio in 1806. Anthony's son Jacob pushed further westward so Jacob's son John, fourth generation of the family in the New World and the father of Everette Lee DeGolyer, was born at Napoleonville, Indiana on January 26, 1859. But he too continued the migration westward and took a bride from the next state,

Narcissa Kagy Huddle, born in East Saint Louis, Illinois. She and John DeGolyer were married on April 17, 1883 at Iuka, Marion County, Illinois. When their first child was born three years later — on October 9, 1886 — the family's westward movement had accelerated, not waiting on the next generation. Everette Lee was born in Greensburg, Kansas. His father was farming a homestead but his inveterate interest was in mining. He was on the trail of zinc and lead, said to abound in Kansas.

This homestead in Kiowa County of western Kansas, chosen in the summer of 1886, was the westernmost point in John DeGolyer's roamings. He was a restless man. Only a year before, he and his brother Lee had built a two-story house (it is still standing) in Oxford, Kansas, but John DeGolyer, fiddle-footed, soon wanted to move on. He had tried farming, mineral prospecting, U.S. Government service when he carried the mail on horseback, general store business in Oxford, Kansas — he still couldn't find what he wanted to do. He didn't tarry long in Kiowa County when he discovered his homestead was located in an 1880's version of the 1930's "Dust Bowl." The drought was unusually severe. Farming was futile. To make a living, he and his brother opened a café in the neighboring community of Greensburg, "The German Restaurant." But he took as an omen what happened to the sod shanty he so hastily erected on his homestead in the autumn of 1886. A cyclone struck the section a few weeks after Everette Lee was born. It tore the roof from the sod house — but left intact the part where mother and baby lay. John DeGolyer moved on as soon as he could. The escape was narrow.

His equity in his homestead was worth about an even trade for a team of horses and a covered wagon. In 1889, John DeGolyer made the trade, loaded his family and his furniture into his new wagon, harnessed up his new team

— and started back east. By "east," he meant only Missouri. Joplin was booming as one of the world's great centers for zinc and lead mining. This was his new destination, at age thirty. His wife was twenty-one.

His son Everette was demanding and positive. The little boy was so accustomed to being rocked to sleep every night, his father had to stop the wagon, unstrap the rocking chair and pause beside the road while the mother rocked the baby to sleep — either this or be tormented for hours with the baby's outraged howls.

Their return eastward brought them to the Joplin area in August 1889. John DeGolyer, ever in search of free land, left his family awhile in 1889 to make the run, from a point near Wellington, into the Unassigned Lands of Indian Territory. He must not have liked what he saw or got, for he was soon back in Marionville, Missouri, where he ran a restaurant. Everette's sister, Edith Christine, was born there August 29, 1890. Two years later at Aurora the couple's third and last child was born, Homer Lewis De-Golyer, on November 13, 1892.

What the Gold Rush in California in '49 and in Colorado in '59 had done to magnetize the ambitious, lead and zinc did on a smaller scale in Missouri after the Civil War. Great strikes in each metal had been made in the thirty-mile crescent of mineral wealth around Joplin Creek a decade before the war broke out. Once the war was over, miners and prospectors poured into the area. By 1870 there were more than five hundred new miners, usually bringing their families with them, in Joplin alone. Here was the chance to make great fortunes with small equipment, and on "handkerchief-size" plots of ground.

All a man needed was a pick and a shovel, a windlass and ore bucket, a hand drill and a bit of blasting powder.

By the time John W. DeGolyer got to the area, Aurora was enjoying a boom (which played out, alas, in a few years) that in 1887 seemed to rival the vast deposits around Joplin. Metal was accepted currency; miners went to the grocery store with a barrow of lead to exchange for food. Kids gleaned metal from the wasteful methods and rushed to exchange it for candy. Although the Crescent had its "Wild West" period of saloons and dance halls and gambling fever, the area was a "family" community. Churches and schools sprang up early. Young Everette Lee DeGolyer got his early schooling in Aurora and then, through the second year of high school, at Joplin. He was a poor boy surrounded by ample evidence that some people did strike it rich. He decided he would be a miner. When he later entered the University of Oklahoma, his mind was made up. Mining was to be his career.

The coming of the railroads to Joplin had sparked its prosperity. Nonetheless, the next few years of John DeGolyer's life find him steadily on the move. He tried Marionville and Aurora and Joplin, he tried again to get a stake in Oklahoma in the Cherokee Outlet Land Run of 1893, but again did not stay, tried Oklahoma City, and finally got his parcel of Oklahoma earth at the new town of Hobart in the 1901 lottery distribution of the Kiowa-Comanche Reservation surplus. It was his third try in the Oklahoma land runs. Again he turned back to the restaurant business in Hobart, all others failing. A handbill advertising the Blue Point Chop House, Phillips and DeGolyer, Props., still exists. There was a poet about somewhere. On the back, filling the space of a present-day credit card, appears an acrostic describing the unexcelled cuisine of the Blue Point.

The first school in the new community of Hobart was established in January 1902. Young Everette Lee DeGolyer attended it, for his third year in high school. From Hobart the family moved on for a time to Oklahoma City, then twenty or so miles south to Norman, where Everette entered the University of Oklahoma "prep school" in 1904, for the first stable period in his life.

John W. DeGolyer was a man of rare charm and he was usually thought to be typical of his French heritage. He was as "gay as a grig," extremely sociable and had the gift of gab. He was resourceful and steadily optimistic. His marriage to Narcissa Kagy Huddle was proof of the appeal of opposites. Though she was nine years younger than her ebullient husband, she was the calm and sobersided member of the couple. Her Pennsylvania Dutch ancestry showed in her thrift, her sense of duty and her devotion to work. As her daughter-in-law once observed, "she was a wonderful woman but beside her husband she seemed to lack humor." Her son Everette always thought he resembled his mother in appearance. From her, he would say, "I got my peasant's face." He described himself so often as having a "peasant face," that friends decided he was not being facetious. But the truth was, few men have ever had such a leonine and authoritative countenance, at once full of amused tolerance and good nature and yet aristocratically arrogant. Though he was a small man so far as height goes, his lionlike visage with its well-kept shock of thick silky hair (not wiry or bushy like a "peasant's") in its massiveness left the impression of a large man.

As the father supported his fluctuating career in the zinc and prospecting business by running restaurants here and there, the mother inevitably came to lean more and more on her son Everette as the man of the family. DeGolyer senior had with all his charm, one unfailing talent: he was able to keep almost unblemished a record of never starting any business enterprise that didn't go broke. It didn't seem

Everette Lee DeGolyer, in grown-man's necktie and collar, towers over his "baby" brother and sister, Homer and Christine. Taken about 1895 in Joplin, Missouri.

to matter; his family loved him and even the serious Dutch wife laughed at misfortune. She would take in sewing and young Everette would find odd jobs, even stay out of school for part of two years, in 1902 and 1903, to work and add to the family income.

Perhaps young Everette glimpsed the fact that his father suffered in his prospecting career for lack of proper training. At any rate, he stubbornly pursued his much interrupted education. He got another boon from his difficult boyhood and youth. One job he got in Hobart — he was then fifteen — was in a china shop. It stuck in his memory and he spoke of it often in later years. "I would look at all those gifts and art objects which I thought then were the height of luxury and I used to wonder if I would ever be able to own any myself. I remember I really studied them, which I suppose was a substitute way of possessing them." Adds Nell DeGolyer: "He must have studied them. I guess we have bought at least fifty sets of dinnerware and I never chose a single one of them. It was always De who chose and he had a sure eye for quality."

After meeting Nell Goodrich, his greatest stroke of luck in college, no doubt, was being recommended for summer work with the United States Geological Survey by Professor Gould. It was a humble start. The contract for employment, on Department of the Interior letterhead and dated June 1, 1906 at Laramie, Wyoming, reads: "You are hereby appointed cook [this word typed into the mimeographed form] in the U.S. Geological Survey and assigned to the party under the charge of Mr. N. H. Darton." Darton was a big name. DeGolyer, looking back, judged him one of the great geologists.

The salary was to be fifty dollars a month, plus travel and miscellaneous expenses. But DeGolyer was more than cook. He found himself "plotting" coal lands as Darton

sensed his gifts. The summer over, Darton sent the bud-
ding geologist and camp cook a note: "I was greatly
pleased with our field experience this summer and hope
that we may renew our relations in the future." After that,
DeGolyer was promoted the next summer to field assistant,
and went with a team to plot coal fields in the Big Horn
Basin in Wyoming, this time under the direction of Professor Woodruff. His salary was ninety dollars a month.
Again he pleased his seniors. In November he was even
called in as consultant on coal properties by an investment
banker in Denver, James R. Thorpe. Mr. Thorpe, a loyal
Princeton man, thought the young consultant too good to
be wasting his time in the youthful University of Oklahoma. He gave DeGolyer a volume of *Princeton Stories*
and volunteered to help the young man spend his junior
and senior years at Princeton. He paid him thirty dollars
for the consultation. The fee helped the young consultant
pay his room and board at his college address, the Kappa
Alpha house.

The third assignment worked like a charm. His success
with the summer geological survey in 1908 led him to
Washington during the winter of 1908–1909, interrupting
his college career. Carl D. Smith, of the USGS, directed the
summer work at Fort Peck Reservation in Montana and at
Fort Berthold Reservation in North Dakota. Smith encouraged his bright young field assistant to prepare for civil
service examination, and meantime — with Woodruff — got
him a job in the Washington office, preparing maps of the
previous summer's work. Briefly, while waiting for this assignment to go through, DeGolyer worked independently
early in the autumn, mapping areas in northeastern Oklahoma for the proud new state's own Geological Survey.

And after the third summer camp, Woodruff also began
to plan, paternalistically, DeGolyer's career. Woodruff, a

bit of a slavemaster and a stickler for form, wrote DeGolyer that he should aim at permanent connection with the USGS. For this, he would have, of course, to pass a Civil Service examination. Trying to persuade DeGolyer to come to Washington for the Civil Service examinations of the spring of 1909, he pointed out in several letters that "Dr. Hayes has a very favorable opinion of you." Even better, on November 5, 1908 he was able to write DeGolyer, confidentially and "unsolicited," that DeGolyer is to be offered a job in the USGS Washington office. He urges the young man not to pass up the chance. "If your life work is to be geology or mining engineering, this is the best opportunity which has come to you, or will come in the near future. I do not see how you can afford to miss it."

In December, DeGolyer took the final step. He accepted the job and went to Washington. He impressed Dr. Hayes even more. And the pressure that his mentors, Woodruff and less persistently Carl Smith, put on him led ultimately to his being selected by Dr. Hayes for the work in Mexico.

Having boned up for the Civil Service test all winter, DeGolyer took the examination in Washington on April 7, 1909. He wanted to qualify as an "Assistant Geologist, USGS." He realized the irregularity of his education when he made a rating on the tests only two and a half percent above the required average. However, it was the matter of foreign languages that pulled his grade down. His showing in French and German dipped below the average almost disastrously — but he came through brilliantly in "general geology and mineralogy" and redeemed the foreign language showing by a very high rating in the category of "Essay, including English and drawing." But his average was only seventy-two. The usual grade, however, was between seventy and seventy-five.

There is a lighthearted and kidding legend in the oil fraternity, still in circulation, which attributes DeGolyer's early success in the United States Geological Survey in part to the fact "that he knew at just the right time to find some cold beer for a field-weary, dust-laden and thirsty boss." This talent may have helped, but there is plenty of evidence that it was reinforced by other gifts. William B. Heroy, a longtime friend whom DeGolyer persuaded to join the PAW in 1941, categorically states that DeGolyer told him that the story of producing spring-cooled, cached-away beer for Dr. Hayes was a fiction. What really happened, according to Heroy, was this: Dr. Woodruff asked his young assistant to drive the buckboard to the train station to meet Dr. Hayes and bring him out to the camp for his inspection trip. DeGolyer accepted with delight, and asked Woodruff what Dr. Hayes was like. It was clear that the straitlaced Woodruff — who tolerated neither smoking nor drinking in his camp — had reservations. Dr. Hayes was, like DeGolyer indeed, a convivial man.

Driving back from the station, DeGolyer noticed that Dr. Hayes was searching one pocket after another with growing alarm. "Forget something?" he asked.

"My tobacco," said Hayes, an inveterate pipe-smoker. He added some comments about the curse of being without smokes.

"Don't worry," replied DeGolyer, "I have plenty of cans back at camp. I can keep you supplied."

"You don't have any on you?"

"No, sir. Out of deference to Dr. Woodruff."

"I admire discretion," said Dr. Hayes, "but don't carry it too far."

"Only a few more minutes," said DeGolyer, smiling, "and then I can hand the can to you."

DeGolyer told Heroy that he had never seen a man enjoy tobacco as much as Dr. Hayes enjoyed his pipe that night. Or any man dislike it more than the helpless Woodruff.

One thing DeGolyer did learn superlatively well from his summer training was to map country expertly. His boss at the 1907 camp was Professor Woodruff, a rather fussy and overly meticulous man who nonetheless steadily praised DeGolyer's work and steadily gave him missions that called for technical skill. (Despite this, you still hear oilmen who assert that DeGolyer's early training was that of a student camp cook who could, admittedly, bake fine bread.)

When the offer came to join the staff of Dr. C. Willard Hayes in geological exploration for Mexican Eagle, the young DeGolyer was faced with several choices. The new immense boom in Oklahoma oil and the independent surveys he had conducted in the autumn of 1908 in the northeastern part of the state inevitably encouraged him to think of a future in which he would be an oilman on his own. Then there was the matter of completing his college education — the Civil Service examination had dramatized his deficiencies, the gaps to fill in. He wanted to get married.

Cautiously, he applied to the proper division, the bureau of Economic Geology of Fuels, USGS, for a leave of absence to work with Dr. Hayes in Mexico. The furlough was granted by the geologist then in charge, M. R. Campbell, who told DeGolyer in his letter that "upon your return you will be eligible for employment at any time within three years." This security arranged, DeGolyer prepared for the trip south of the border, his first visit to a foreign land. "I have always precisely dated my decision to become an oil man," he later wrote his friend Wallace

Pratt, "as November 19, 1909, the day I arrived in Mexico." It was a crucial decision.

He could also date from that season the beginning of some of his lifelong friendships with geologist colleagues. DeGolyer had a genius for friendship, although he was always a man of rather exclusive temper, as is true of anyone who distinguishes his friends from a vast fraternity of acquaintances. Edwin Hopkins became not only his closest friend for a long time but also a valued business associate. Hopkins too, this early, was dreaming of going into the oil business on his own.

The Tampico oil fraternity was in fact abuzz with bright young minds. Among some of the dozens of young geologists who served their apprenticeships there and later rose to the heights in American enterprises were Wallace Pratt, Hopkins and Washburne, Ben Belt, Paul Weaver, William Buckley, John Muir, Fred Hall, Leon Russ, Robert Nock, C. W. Hamilton, E. L. Ickes, Burton Loomis, Harve Loomis, Frank Clark — great names later with Humble, Gulf, Texaco, and others.

The DeGolyers, both now with proper diplomas, were back in Mexico by midsummer of 1911. There was no doubt that he was now an oilman, not the mining engineer he had planned to become. He assumed his post as chief geologist. The couple lived now at Tampico, a much bigger town than Tuxpam. In a way it was a sad return. The tropical climate of the Tampico-Tuxpam area was to take its toll. They lost their first child, a son, stillborn. Nell DeGolyer's mother had gone down to be present at the birth. "Such a beautiful child," she said. A simple stone marks his grave in the shadow of the Golden Lane oil fields.

The DeGolyers lived in Tampico in a comfortable, one-story house of *mampostería*, flush on the street and about a block from the company offices. It was sparsely but tastefully furnished, perhaps the most conspicuous decoration being two maps of the Tampico oil fields — DeGolyer kept one on the wall by his bed and the other in the living room. They left Tampico before the company laid out for its staff the beautiful residential area still known as the Colonia Aguila, whose houses are now occupied by Pemex (Petroleos Mexicanos) executives.

To American friends back home who wanted to invest in the Tampico boom DeGolyer was frank. After securing permission from Dr. Hayes to release information, he wrote one inquirer from Oklahoma City: "The average of commercially profitable wells in Mexico is not much over one well to every five holes drilled." He estimated the cost of a 2,200-foot well, including new machinery, at $20,000 (American currency).

The language barrier precluded for many of the foreign wives in Tampico any real friendships with the native society. But as everywhere rituals and ceremonies developed, the chief one being to sit and sew or gossip in the jasmine-scented, bright-flowered main plaza every afternoon. Then there was charity work, supported by bazaars and amateur theatricals, organized through the church missions, the Episcopalians and Methodists and Presbyterians all having centers. Nell DeGolyer played the piano at the Methodist mission — sometimes for a native marriage delayed till a boom money period allowed the father to legitimize his children attending the wedding. She also gave piano lessons in her home — the DeGolyers lived in the heart of town on La Calle de las Damas — to daughters of her friends. Her piano, a rosewood beauty, was ordered by her husband from a dealer in Mexico City.

The ladies organized a club to help distressed compatriots, vaguely called the Women's Chapter. It fell to Nell

DeGolyer's lot to become president of it at age twenty-four. As she recalls, most of her duties involved difficulties among the American drillers and their wives, or other women, with some attention to alcoholics. With Mrs. Hodgson, wife of the doctor from Alabama who ran a little combination hospital-mortuary-drugstore, she helped out as nurse on demand or kept the children of sick mothers. "But it was a quiet and very pleasant life," she recalls. "You had to be wary and shut all your windows whenever you went out if you didn't want your belongings to be fished out on the end of long poles. But that was part of the general mood of treating life as a game."

Nonetheless, Nell DeGolyer planned to have her second child in Mexico. In the second months of her second pregnancy in 1913 she fell ill of a first-class case of malaria. Dr. Hodgson, the Alabama-born doctor who became a close friend of the DeGolyers, advised her to return to the States. Mrs. Hodgson seconded him. A pregnant woman could not take the quinine cure without grave danger. So in May 1913, Nell DeGolyer left Tampico to return to Norman. Her malaria was cured with serums, and in December she gave birth to a daughter, Nell Virginia. That autumn Woodrow Wilson had warned American citizens to get out of Mexico. Four months after young Virginia's birth, Everette DeGolyer himself had to leave Tampico.

DeGolyer demonstrated early a trait on which nearly all testimony is in total agreement, that of picking out the right men for the right assignments and receiving thereafter their absolute and spontaneous loyalty. None of his associates surpassed James H. Hall in admiration for the "boss."

Now living in retirement near Dallas, Hall is a man of far-ranging mind and prodigious memory. Born in Missouri, he went to live in Mexico at age eleven when his lawyer father went to the city on business and decided to make his career in the country. Bilingual, Hall was hired at age eighteen as a stenographer by Dr. Hayes and De-Golyer, through an employment agency in Mexico City, where he was visiting at the time. Hall soon became De-Golyer's assistant in the leasing and lands department.

Hall comments, after having made a later big success with the Texas Company: "Any value I ever had to anyone was built on the methods and practices I learned during the less than three years' association with Mr. DeGolyer as his office flunky and land man. Everyone who ever worked with Mr. DeGolyer would have been proud to have gone into business with him. He was acquisitive but not avaricious. He enjoyed money but was adjusted to it, and even much later when he became wealthy he never paraded his wealth." DeGolyer was reading in Tampico every book on geology he could get, Hall says: "and he read them with a damn sight better understanding than could any student who had never been on a derrick floor when the bit hit the basalt."

Of DeGolyer's eating and drinking habits, Hall said: "Mr. DeGolyer lived every minute. He liked good food and good drink. He was never a glutton and alcohol was no problem for him. His confinement to long hours of office work made him tend to obesity, but he fought it and was just as self-disciplined in that as he was in many other things. Some people hold that you are not intoxicated as long as you can still wiggle a finger. I have seen DeGolyer drink without stint but I have never seen him when he ever needed anyone to help him get home."

Another oilman who knew DeGolyer well in the early days, H. H. ("Babe") Fuqua, famed geologist for the Gulf Oil Company, confirms Hall's observation about the confining office work in Mexico. Fuqua says DeGolyer was, however, by nature meticulous and that he enjoyed being attentive to details and paperwork. But, adds Fuqua, "De-Golyer had the mind and spirit of a general; he was from the start a strategist and a tactician. There was nothing about him of the drill sergeant. He was tough, but frankly so and invited the same attitude toward himself. He did not, as many have done, tack a lot of hides to the wall in his climb to success."

The tempo of life below the border was slow by American standards. The first thing the Yankees had to learn was patience. As James H. Hall remembers, DeGolyer "had the greatest fund of patience in a man with a lightning-quick mind that I ever saw. If it meant success in a business deal or some competitive enterprise, DeGolyer could call up an indestructible calm. I was always amazed at how he could remain unruffled in a crisis. He simply had what it took, and everybody recognized this. From the start, Dr. Hayes relied on him more than anybody else. That early he was already a man of compelling authority. And he was a compulsive reader of everything. He gave the same attention to contracts and lease arrangements that I remember he gave to a Shakespeare jag he went on. He expected me to do the same and I had to devour Shakespeare, although like the famous lady I too found his works awfully full of quotations."

Patience was required above all in regard to transportation, mostly managed on muleback or on ponies. DeGolyer ordered some horses from Colorado. Railway service was very limited. To get from Tampico southward to the oil fields of the Golden Lane, little motor launches crossed Lake Tamiahua in an all-day-long journey. After landing, flat cars pulled by mules ran up to the Tanhuijo and Potrero fields. But there was one swift launch which crossed

Tamiahua in only three to four hours. At most, five company men "rated" the use of this speedy express; DeGolyer was one of them.

An early assignment he had was to lease the Los Horcones ranch adjoining the Potrero del Llano (Pasture of the Plains) hacienda. For this feat, DeGolyer had to deal with some three hundred kinsmen or so, each of whom owned some piece of the land. With great patience, and the help of Hall and other staffers, he pursued the problem until it was all satisfactorily arranged, primarily with the intent of protecting Potrero.

Curiously, another project after the department of lands and leases was added to DeGolyer's domain, took him to a Confederate colony that had been established after the Civil War below Tuxpam, one of the few Confederate refuges in Mexico that survived. Here less patience was required to complete the deal. According to Hall, DeGolyer was clearly determined to see "that Mexican Eagle got its share of the white bread, but he was equally determined to be clear about it and trustworthy. He was calculating, he would calculate ahead to the end of the road, but once he gave his word he was absolutely reliable."

Mexico was now producing about eleven million barrels of oil yearly. The average in 1908 had been four million. In 1911 the Mexican yield was about one-fourth of the world's production. The first automobile, a great augury, was negotiating the few asphalted roads in Mexico. Much more of an omen, the new Mexican revolution of 1910 — which was to depose Cowdray's dictator friend, Don Porfirio Díaz — began to spread its grip to the oil fields and their foreign masters.

6

Mexican Revolution and Mexican Eagle

T HE WIND THAT SWEPT MEXICO," as Anita Brenner christened the Madero revolution of 1910–1911 which terminated Porfirio Díaz's thirty consecutive years of practically one-man rule of Mexico, could only portend trouble for the foreign companies that had poured amazing sums of capital into the modernization of the country. While Díaz had achieved remarkable betterment of Mexico's material condition — in roads, railroads, harbors, manufactures, electricity, telegraph lines, etc. — he had rendered the nation a haven for foreign capital while neglecting the impoverished lives of the peons, the education of the natives, the misery of the masses. The financial health of Mexico existed for the benefit of the few.

The easiest charge the rebels could bring against him was that he had allowed foreign capital to exploit the natural wealth of Mexico. Whether the gains had been mutual seemed unimportant to Díaz's opponents when the eighty-year-old was reelected to serve his seventh term as president in 1911 (he had long ago changed the non-reelection law in his favor). His opponents were terrified at what conditions might be when the aged hero of the long-ago fight against Maximilian could not himself rule any longer. Would Mexico become a pawn of foreign interests?

Francisco Madero's "democratic" revolution gained so much support that Díaz decided to resign in face of the inevitably successful rebellion. His resignation was signed as of May 15, 1911. The next day he left the country forever. (One of the four foreigners taken into Díaz's confidence to arrange secretly his leaving the capital — to take ship for Paris at Veracruz — was Lord Cowdray's right-hand man in Mexico, the exceptionally tactful and astute John B. Body.) Madero took over the government, formalized his power by an election, but was liquidated by one of his aides and rivals, Victoriano Huerta, in 1913. Woodrow Wilson refused to recognize Huerta.

E. DeGolyer's decision to concentrate his work in the United States after 1914 (he was then only twenty-eight years old) stems from this nexus of very complex circumstances. Chief of these, of course, was the Madero revolution which in toppling Don Porfirio Díaz initiated the most dramatic and continuing political reform that our century has seen in this hemisphere. In its aspirations and its stated program, this revolution in favor of the people had its logical and idealistic defense; in its execution it was, at least until the advent of Lázaro Cárdenas in 1936, a largely sordid record of assassinations, banditry, selfish plunder, betrayal and daily anarchy. These are harsh words, but they may be tempered by the recognition that Mexico was not alone responsible. Germany, Japan, Great Britain, France and the United States were all intervening in surreptitious ways and for their own selfish purposes. They all wanted, some desperately needed, that oil. The Mexican Revolution became a pawn in the larger power play of impending World War I.

International subsidy, or bribery, made an irresistible temptation for the warring Mexican generals — Huerta, Villa, Obregón, Zapata, Carranza — and the oil industry degenerated, in the accusation of William F. Buckley (an American lawyer for oil companies in Tampico and Mexico City) into a kind of "business-by-corruption." With the rival Mexican generals grabbing for ultimate power by new taxes and levies on the foreign oil interests, there was of course no other way to survive. The gentle and ineffectual rich liberal, Francisco Madero, had unleashed a storm he could neither stomach nor control. He was cruelly assassinated in 1913. The Huerta forces which took over announced that he was shot "while trying to escape."

The United States could not stand by, remembering the Monroe Doctrine, while rudderless Mexico threatened to become the prey of European or Asiatic nations. It could not exist peacefully with the rest of Latin America while alien governments were heating up the incurable fear of Yankee Imperialism. Madero was elected while Taft was in office. Taft left the problem of the revolution to the new incumbent. Woodrow Wilson thought, and rightly, that Huerta had become the agent of the diehard Díaz foreign concessionaries. He decided to back the campaign of Carranza in the struggle for the presidency, although for a long time Wilson felt, as he said, that "Villa is the safest man to tie to."

His intervention, to dethrone Huerta, went a good deal farther than advancing "loans" to Huerta's rivals. Two specific examples, occurring both at the northern and southern limits of the famed "Golden Lane" of oil harvest, inflamed the fear and the anger of the Mexican people. Foreign agents were quick to supply propaganda about the American "invasion" of a newly liberated land.

The first was at Tampico in March 1914. Six months earlier Wilson had told the Congress that Huerta would be eliminated by popular action of the Mexican people, and he had steadily refused recognition of the Huerta regime, contrary to other foreign governments. While Tampico was under attack by the Carranza rebels in March of 1914, some Marines from an American gunboat outside the harbor took a launch upriver and entered the prohibited zone. They were promptly arrested by officers of the Huerta Federals. Taken to military headquarters, they were questioned but not imprisoned, then released and, before any demand was made, the Huerta commander presented his apology to Admiral Mayo, in command of the American squadron. Mayo demanded that the apology be made tangible by a Mexican salute to the American flag; Huerta's man countered by suggesting a double ceremony in which the American navy would likewise fire a salvo in honor of the Mexican flag. Mayo refused.

The "Tampico flag incident," interpreted in the States as an "insult to the American flag," was one surface justification for a much more serious matter at Veracruz a month later. On April 21, 1914, Woodrow Wilson had Secretary of the Navy Josephus Daniels instruct Admiral Fletcher to take the port of Veracruz in order to prevent delivery of a cargo of arms for Huerta due to arrive that evening on a German ship. Fletcher executed the order, took possession of the ship *Ypiranga* (ironically, the one on which Díaz had made a swift escape to Europe when he was challenged by Madero), and bombarded the city. One hundred and forty-five Mexicans were killed, 256 were wounded. But it is false to assume that this was a reprisal for the Tampico insult to the American flag. Wilson was motivated by three aims: 1) He really thought he was helping the Mexican people in their revolution by thwarting Huerta; 2) he was serving notice that too many affronts and indignities had been served on Americans in Mexico and on our government; 3) he wanted specifically, of course, to disarm the Huerta faction so Huerta would be compelled to retire. Whatever his intentions, the Mexican people were united in their suspicions of the "big bully to the North." Wilson put more sticks under the fire by stating publicly that the United States meant to teach the Mexican people to "elect a decent president."

For Americans in Mexico the situation was acute, but particularly so for Americans like Everette DeGolyer, working for a British enterprise. In DeGolyer's case, the situation was all the more baffling because Mexican Eagle was caught by the Madero revolution in an embarrassing plight. Lord Cowdray was one of Díaz's favorites; Mexican Eagle had important concessions from the Díaz regime (according to Anita Brenner in her study sympathetic to the revolution, "incredible concessions"); and the firm had a number of the old Díaz "reactionaries" as its company officials. With traditional British acumen, the company was able to walk a very narrow chalk line and was able to get important concessions from the Carranza regime (1914–1919) which were denied the American companies. Small wonder, then, that in 1914, Mexican Eagle instituted a policy of "all-English management" in its top posts. Unlike the American oil companies, Mexican Eagle had big Mexican business in refined oils and gasoline and fuel oil, a fact that gave the revolutionaries pause.

The so-called Tampico flag incident was a comedy of errors, a tragic comedy in a way, a veritable tempest in a teapot. Woodrow Wilson meant well but he was lamentably ill informed on conditions in Mexico. He transformed a very minor event, along with two other perfectly explainable accidental offenses and also exceedingly minor, into an "affair of honor." He decided that Huerta was treating the United States with "studied contempt." He was willing to risk war to punish one unyielding opponent, although he managed with his usual flair to clothe his impractical diplomacy in the garment of idealism. In his own mind he was perfectly sincere, but to the realistic Mexicans his decision to invade Veracruz was another example of what they called Yankee "hypocrisy."

To his credit, he thought he could order the American fleet to take over Veracruz without loss of life. To his credit, he was appalled when the Mexican soldiers offered opposition. Though he was perhaps the best-educated mind ever to serve in the White House, he was terribly ill informed on many practical matters.

His scorn for Huerta was unrealistic. The wily old general played his cards expertly. It was he who insisted that, when Wilson would not accept official apology for the arrest of the American sailors in Tampico as adequate and demanded a twenty-one-gun salute to the flag, the salute be mutual and simultaneous to both flags by both nations.

Admiral Mayo, commanding the fleet lying outside Tampico harbor (meant to be a reminder to Huerta of American military might), had no doubt that Wilson would choose Tampico, not Veracruz, as the point of attack. He, the American consul, the American colony, all were persuaded by April 20 that the navy would land at Tampico. The American colony, however, by no means sanctioned the plan and met to protest bitterly its government's indifference to them and their exceedingly valuable properties and investments. It turned out the government did protect them but not in a way they expected. When news of the invasion at Veracruz reached Tampico, rioting began. Consul Clarence Miller, who may have supposed that all Americans there risked death, persuaded Admiral Mayo to enter the river and take out the refugees, but a British admiral offered to take ships up the Panuco, flying British and German flags, to avoid Mexican fear that American ships might not be entering for rescue but for military action. Miller rounded up every American he could locate, all unaware of what their government planned. They supposed they would ride the waters outside the harbor until the confusion ended and peace was restored. To their astonishment, and against the wishes of many, they were delivered to Galveston, where the government provided transportation to homeward points for those who had left Tampico so hastily they had no money. The protests were bitter. Wilson thought they would all be grateful, just as he was unshakably certain that the Mexican people would cheer him for ridding the country of Huerta, regardless of the cost to their pride and dignity.

The American people, poorly informed, approved Wilson's action. If our flag had been insulted, why, the Mexicans responsible should be punished. Wilson also clearly knew, of course, what was good for the Mexican people much better than they, or any of their leaders, did. He would compel them to have free elections and choose good men. Just as in America.

Three months after the invasion, Huerta resigned the presidency and went into exile. The Mexicans got, but did not choose, Carranza as president, after a devastating civil war between him and Villa and Zapata and others.

President Carranza's revised national constitution (1917) immediately extended Mexican sovereignty over all mineral rights, including oil. Porfirio Díaz had altered the Juarez constitution to grant oil rights to owners of the surface. The Carranza constitution prepared the way for the ultimate appropriation of foreign-owned oil properties under the government of Lázaro Cárdenas in 1938. Everette DeGolyer was later to play a role in that settlement. He knew the problems at first hand, and he knew they were not simple.

The revolution at first seemed to the foreign colony in

Tampico a lark. It was an adventure for the young Americans who had never seen battle. The Aguila building provided a good observation post. When the rebels first tried to take over the city, DeGolyer learned it was more than a scrimmage. The Federalist defenders brought a gunboat up the river and began firing over the town at the rebels camped on the opposite side. The bullets made an arc over the town plaza, then expired futilely in the lagoon. The Aguila staff, from roof and windows, followed the bullet trajectories as though they were turning their heads to watch the ball in a tennis match. DeGolyer was in the company of Blas Rodriguez, expert Mexican lawyer who handled company business. They were on the top landing of an outdoor stairwell. As their necks moved to watch the shots, DeGolyer's pork-pie hat was blown off his head. He reached down to pick it up. It had been creased right through the crown by a bullet. An inch or so less margin and it would have gone right through his head. The spent bullet became a *recuerdo*, as the Spanish say. "My only claim to heroism in the revolution," DeGolyer would explain later.

The reality of the revolution was plain when the rebels camped along the pipelines and demanded a fee for letting the oil go through. It was their quickest way to finance a war. Still, in the recollection of James H. Hall it was all fun and games until Woodrow Wilson landed the Marines at Veracruz. After that, S. Pearson & Son had to decree that Americans on its payroll must disappear for a while until the trouble blew over.

In the late afternoon of the landing, James Hall learned about it as he was returning to the Aguila building in Tampico and saw a big crowd milling around the police *cuartel* of the main plaza. They were reading something; he pushed through to see what. Discovering in the posted notice such phrases as "the Colossus of the North" and "the Defiling of the Sacred Soil of Mexico," he quickly stopped reading and made his escape. There was as yet no hostility or even discourtesy on the part of the Mexicans. Even when a crowd gathered in front of the American consulate, Consul Clarence Miller appeared on the balcony to speak to them with no sense of danger in the air.

But that night a mob stirred by impulses of excitement and loot roved the streets shouting "*mueren los gringos*" ("death to the gringos"), and threw a few rocks through doors and broke the windows of the corner drugstore, Sanborn's, branch of the famous emporium operated in Mexico City by the American family of that name.

As looting threatened, however, the captain of a German cruiser, the *Emden,* which had been lying in the Panuco river for some time, sent a squad of fully armed marines ashore. Their officer went to the commandant of the garrison and told him that unless order was restored in thirty minutes, the Germans would do it themselves. Order was restored.

Next morning the American consulate notified the American colony to go to the wharf to be transported to ships lying off the mouth of the Panuco; no baggage was needed for this was to be only a day's removal from land for safety. Other plans intervened; Hall's ship, the collier *Cyclops,* weighed anchor that very afternoon and put to sea. Refugees crowded its deck and had to sleep there that night, as they learned they were bound for repatriation in Galveston, thirty hours away.

Because of the quarantine against yellow fever, however, the passengers could not land for six days, the required time to lapse. Despite pressure, Governor Colquitt refused to lift the quarantine for the refugees. When at last allowed to land, unwashed, unshaven and picturesque, they were offered free transportation to any place in the United States. Hall and five other of DeGolyer's men learned he had arrived with a paymaster — Mexican Eagle was to give each a month's salary. DeGolyer invited Hall to continue to New Orleans, where other Aguila American personnel were to be paid off, having been refugeed to that port on other ships. DeGolyer himself was to continue to Cuba where geologist Ben Belt was stationed for the Pearson firm. Hall was not to work for DeGolyer again until World War II, in the Petroleum War Administration, but he did return to Tampico, where he made a successful career with the Texas Company.

It was a most troubling time for Mexican Eagle. The wells were continuing to multiply, a steamship subsidiary had been organized to deliver the oil all over the world in twenty new tankers, the stock market was extremely favorable to Aguila shares — but the revolutionaries were rumored to be making plans to take over the fields. Worst of all, most of the drillers and oil field workers where experience or skill was required were Americans working for the oil companies.

Ironically enough, world oil consumption was at a peak. The war would make production indispensable. Oil was too precious for any risks. In time the rival factions realized this and allowed the golden egg to go unbroken, merely levying demands or "ransoms" that involved the sharpest dealing on the part of all concerned. Mexican Eagle managed to supply the British navy with 200,000 tons of oil in the first two years of World War I.

The refineries and the wells were kept in production. But the exploring geologist, riding out into the country alone, no longer had any work he could do. There was safety, of a sort, in the office at Tampico, or at the riverbank refineries or in the camps at the wells. Even these pockets of security were menaced, as the rival generals fought battles over possession of the stored-up fuel supplies, of the railroad and pipelines, of the right to practice levies on the oil companies.

For example, here is a telegram Dr. Hayes sent in November 1913 to Lord Cowdray in London: "The rebels promise protection, provided we contribute 100,000 dollars Mex. and monthly payment equal to the Federal tax. Pumping stopped pending reply. Threaten destroy property if demands refused or if we request Federal aid. Rebels appear entirely competent carry out promises and threats. Cable instructions."

All Cowdray could do was to give absolute bargaining power to his aides on the spot. Both British and American naval forces were in Tampico Bay, but their governments limited help to asylum for the women and children and those who sought the safety of going aboard.

The oil camps were pillaged for food, horses and guns. General Aguilar, however, who brought a thousand men into the area to occupy the Tampico fields, tried to preserve order. Nonetheless, a number of company men were kidnapped and some were shot. For the time being, Mexican Eagle's American geologists were of more use writing up reports, back in the States, than risking death in the bandit-ridden leased lands.

At any rate, DeGolyer and other Americans on the Eagle staff had peculiar problems when the American government ordered its citizens to leave Mexico in April 1914. They had loyalties torn between company and country, they had less reason than the English to be willing to compromise with the confiscatory Carranza decrees, and in any event oil prospecting for new wells was for the moment at a standstill. They went home, keeping, however, a company connection. Cowdray had no intention of losing a young man like DeGolyer. So, the youthful geologist who had brought in the world's biggest well was assigned to prepare a full report on the company's holdings. This could be written in a year, say, back home in Oklahoma.

There were other things, of course, in DeGolyer's mind. For a long time, he and his closest friend, Edwin Hopkins, had spent after-company hours pondering the oil situation back home. Hopkins insisted that they make a break. He and DeGolyer could do for themselves what they were doing for others. Hopkins had the added motive that he detested Mexico and hated having to live there. Maybe the time had come.

Robert Nock, a British subject working for S. Pearson and Son in Tampico, later became DeGolyer's secretary. Just after the American departure from Tampico in 1914, Nock sent the following letter to DeGolyer dated July 22, 1914: "It was indeed with much concern and regret that I learned of your not returning to continue in charge of the Department of Geology and Lands, not only personally but also for the fare of the remaining staff, and for the disappearance of that high concordant feeling which existed amongst your former employees in this company. The Department and part of its old staff will remain but I am sure the old spirit of loyalty will go. I have heard from one or two sources that you will probably have as ultimate headquarters an office in New York."

The grapevine, as usual, was prophetic. What Nock did not know at the time was that he too would have an office in New York, that when he got married there, the DeGolyers would send him a magnificent silver gift from Tiffany's, that when he died DeGolyer would write to Mrs. Nock as moving a letter of condolence as any widow could ever hope to get.

7

World War I and Oil — and Oil Careers

At the time of the American exodus in 1914, James Hall remembers, most of the Americans on the Aguila office staff expected to be given a month's pay and released. Speculation was rife about what would happen to the American geologists. Hall was back in Tampico by November of that year. The gossip among the Americans still there was that DeGolyer had been given the year-long report to write on the theory that the company would thus be in possession of all he knew, and then farewell to him. The talk could not have been more wrong. As Hall remembers, Aguila confidence in DeGolyer's gifts and talents was so strong that soon speculation turned on how big a "kitty" the firm had entrusted to DeGolyer to use in exploration on his own. The figure, not verifiable, ran from one million to five million. Perhaps it was only rumor; the point is that the firm of S. Pearson & Son meant to keep him. Or perhaps the rumor arose as plans for the formation of the Amerada Company with a New York home office finally crystallized with the close of World War I. Lord Cowdray had no intention of losing DeGolyer; but he had to temporize, and he could not at the moment keep an American in Mexico as his number one man.

While DeGolyer was mastering his trade in Mexico, two events of major significance in oil history had happened in his home state of Oklahoma. One was the notable decision of the Oklahoma Supreme Court in 1911 which compelled ultimately the dissolution of the Standard Oil monopoly in the United States. The practical effect of the ruling was to disperse and spread skills and knowledge and to create many new opportunities in the oil game.

The other was the wildcatting success of the great Cushing field in Oklahoma, which likewise greatly enlarged the ambitions of independent operators. Until the Cushing (a town midway between Tulsa and Oklahoma City) bonanza of 1912, most of the successful oil exploration in the country had been conducted by corporations with large resources. Cushing proved that the little man could also make a killing.

Back home also, the relatively new vocation of oil geologist had begun to gain prestige. The great Cushing field was regarded as a triumph of structural drilling. Fifty miles west of Tulsa, Cushing yielded so many fantastic gushers that Oklahomans claimed it had made a crop of one hundred millionaires, including such picturesque characters of the industry as Tom Slick, Josh Cosden, Charlie Wrightsman and John Markham. The Texas Company took the hint, and by the time young DeGolyer returned from his five-year stay in Mexico, had added a geological department with DeGolyer's old mentor and boss, E. G. Woodruff, in charge. Rough though it was to leave the scenes of triumph in Mexico, it was a good time to get back to the States.

It was to this climate of the oil business in America that DeGolyer returned when the revolution drove Americans out of Mexico. This situation tallied exactly with his inclination to go into the business for himself, which his friend

Hopkins had been urging. But while there were duties and loyalties to be reckoned with before he could think seriously about that, he could not remain unaware of or indifferent to the prospect.

His first duty after the April 1914 exodus was to make a preliminary study of oil prospects in Cuba, on assignment from Pearson's Foreign Department. After a brief stopover there, the investigation to continue at length later on, he was summoned to report in June to the London office for talks with Lord Cowdray. Dr. Hayes likewise was called to London. Proceeding from Galveston to Cuba, DeGolyer made arrangements to meet his wife and their six-month-old daughter in New York, from whence the family would sail for England. It would be their first trip abroad.

The trip was to be memorable in a number of ways. The DeGolyers were guests of Lord Cowdray and his family for "polo week." Echoes of the great homes they visited are to be found in the houses the DeGolyers built later at Montclair and in Dallas. For Mrs. DeGolyer, the outbreak of World War I in August meant a dangerous return for herself and the young baby Virginia — on a Canadian boat that traveled with darkened portholes. On the day the war was declared, Everette DeGolyer was in Paris, on his way for the first of several futile oil explorations in Spain. He never got to the border. He was mistaken in Paris for a German, and only by resorting to Spanish was he able to persuade the authorities that he was the American oilman recently domiciled in Mexico that he declared himself to be. He was allowed to return to London, where he and Dr. Hayes remained awhile in talks with the management about the future.

Most importantly, perhaps, DeGolyer fell for book collecting in London that year. It was from that summer that he dated his collecting mania, and specifically from a lucky purchase, or so he thought at the time, from Hatchard's in Piccadilly. For three pounds he got a copy of the first edition of Dickens's *The Pickwick Papers*. "This was really a pretty important book," he said later, "because on the frontispiece the engraved signboard over the inn had Tony Veller instead of Tony Weller, the proprietor. That made it *the first, the first*, and all that sort of thing. That got me started and I went along from there."

For proof of the independence and decisiveness — and perhaps stubbornness — of Everette DeGolyer's mind, few episodes of his life are more revelatory than his resolution of the perplexing career options after the 1914 sundering of his immediate usefulness in Tampico to S. Pearson and Son. Obviously, the firm was not going to release for reasons of temporary political pressures such men as Dr. Hayes and DeGolyer. But the problems of war were not merely local; Europe, sitting on a powder keg, would shortly be drawn into the first "world war." Naturally, De-Golyer drew a careful bead on his complex situation. Whatever the firm offered him might not now provide the best available future.

Both Hayes and DeGolyer hoped that company plans to investigate China might be ready. The intention was there, as they discovered, but the long groundwork of negotiations was far from completion. Nonetheless, Dr. Hayes was encouraged to get a staff and equipment prepared for the China venture with departure date hopefully fixed for late September. Meantime, DeGolyer was dispatched on the Spanish mission which the outbreak of war on August 1, 1914 abruptly halted before he ever got to the Pyrenees. Everything seemed to explode simultaneously, including ultimately the China venture.

Lord Cowdray had long wanted to drill the known oil deposits in the English Midlands, a project made all the

more desirable by the wartime need for oil. At best, however, the maneuverings required would demand a long period of overcoming red tape and British hostility to such a
threat to the landscape. Apparently DeGolyer was urged
to join the team for this potential exploration, headed by
Dr. A. C. Veatch, but he had other things in mind. As he
noted, he wanted at last to set up his own home in his own
land and to experience a regularity of domestic life. And
above all, his home state — Oklahoma — was "one of the
greatest oil regions in the world" at that time. He didn't
have the capital to launch his own firm; he didn't want to
make a final break with so great a company as Pearson's.
The ideal would be to persuade Pearson's to back him in a
subsidiary enterprise in the United States.

DeGolyer often told friends in later life, asking for his
secret of success, that one thing he recommended was his
own lifetime practice, namely, never to attend an interview with superiors without giving them something to
think about. But the summer of 1914 was much too difficult for Lord Cowdray to be in a receptive frame of mind.
His immediate concern was to secure for His Majesty's
Government the biggest, swiftest surplus of oil then possible, from proven fields. This was not the time for him to
experiment. As indeed, the stalling of the Chinese project
showed.

Dr. Hayes was able to salvage a part of what his gifted
protégé wanted. DeGolyer would be stationed for a time
in Oklahoma — but not officially locating oil prospects. In
London, Dr. Hayes prepared a "Memo for Lord Cowdray
and Lord Murray: re E. L. DeGolyer," dated July 29, 1914.
The recommendation was long and fully detailed. In summary, it proposed two duties for DeGolyer until Mr. Body
should arrive from Mexico for a conference in September;
while waiting, DeGolyer was to study northern Spain un-

der the instructions of Lord Murray and would also fa-
miliarize himself with the Foreign Department's files re-
lating to the Caribbean region. As soon as possible after
Mr. Body's return to England, DeGolyer was to return to
Mexico "to complete the urgently required geological work
in the Northern fields, and to put the Geological Department in such shape that it will not require his immediate
personal attention." Dr. Hayes estimated this might take a
year or eighteen months. All instructions would come from
Hayes, as all reports would be made to him. The memo
adds, DeGolyer "will be furnished with office and residence quarters in the Aguila Building as formerly." (The
second floor, used for dwelling, was commonly called "The
Royal Suite," reserved for Mr. Body. The Americans were
on the third floor.) Other duties were added: "DeGolyer
will also act as Chief Geologist to the Oil Fields of Mexico
Company [a recent acquisition] and to the Cuban Oil
Company," and his services were to be available as required in the Foreign Department's activity in the Caribbean region.

One key recommendation deserves to be quoted in full:
"In view of the fact that the Aguila Company has completed its active campaign for the acquisition of oil lands,
and that the general features of the geology of northern
Veracruz, insofar as they have a bearing on the occurrence
and distribution of oil, are familiar to all operators in that
region, it is recommended that Mr. DeGolyer be permitted
to publish a paper giving the scientific results of his investigations since he has been in the employ of the Aguila
Company. This is in the interests of the promotion of geological science and of Mr. DeGolyer's professional reputation." Dr. Hayes guaranteed that nothing would be published in any way detrimental to the company's interests.

So the autumn of 1914 found the DeGolyers established

in their own home in Norman, at 531 University Boulevard. For the first time, he and his wife could make plans to live like a normal American family. This prospect, he wrote Dr. Hayes, was basic in this wish to stay in the States. He bought up a dozen lots of land, invested thirty thousand dollars in the Norman Building and Loan Association, acquired a farm outside town for his mother and father.

It was a happy time, despite the uncertainty of the future. What he was doing was writing a book. He envisaged a report, he wrote Dr. Hayes, of seventy-five thousand words and with forty or fifty maps. The report would incorporate all that the company had discovered about the geology of the Tampico-Tuxpam area; it would include the history, with the precise factual data where possible, on all the oil fields and oil wells drilled in Mexico; it would be indexed and cross-indexed for maximum use of the firm, including descriptions and assessments of all leases and land. He wrote to Dr. Hayes: "I have furnished a very nice office in the house and am getting student typists for several hours each day. I have also arranged to secure the use of a suspension pantograph . . . in the engineering department of the university. The more I go into the matter of a final report the more pleased I am. I hope to make it my swan song in Mexico."

The company had allowed him to keep, on company payroll, the services of a Tampico associate, Charles Hamilton. Neither one could stand to stay out of the Oklahoma ferment; in October they invested mildly in some wildcat leases in southern Oklahoma.

DeGolyer arrived in Tampico on October 2, 1914, to spend a week gathering materials he needed. Next day he wrote Dr. Hayes: "I am allowed inside the offices of the department of Geology and Lands on sufferance, Hallatt being in charge. Everyone was glad to see me, the anti-American business having burned itself out. As far as I can make out, the Crusade was started by Phillips, aided and assisted by H.B.M. Consul. Vaughan and Ryder seem to have checked the silliness as soon as possible and a number of Americans are being employed at present in all of the departments. . . . I need my working hours here to get what I want." About the political and economic situation, he wrote: "It looks like the country would go over to Villa. The oil business is absolutely dead. The Constitutionalists have decreed that no more land transactions can take place. Everything is at a dead standstill."

Dr. Hayes, now in Washington, was too ill to be of much help. He was still hoping the Pearson's Foreign Department would send him out with a crew to investigate prospects in China. But he notified DeGolyer in December that "the Chinese negotiations are proceeding very slowly and it will be months before work can be undertaken."

In reply DeGolyer makes two suggestions for work in the States, feeling certain that oil will be found along the Rio Grande and that the Big Horn Basin of Wyoming offers great possibilities. But he adds dolefully that the Foreign Department "will hardly be interested."

But in December, he complains again to Dr. Hayes that the Tampico office is hostile, or at least indifferent, to his requests for information. There was obvious jealousy that he was enjoying such a plush assignment as oil historian. Hayes was well aware of it. Both Lord Cowdray and Mr. Body got complaints because the work was being done in the States rather than in Tampico. Wrote Hayes: "It is evident our friends in Tampico have been busy — they are after your goat. Please send me hereafter a weekly report."

But the progress was sure. Nonetheless DeGolyer was plagued by two worries. He wanted to get back in the field, so he asked Dr. Hayes to arrange for him to be sent to Cuba again in the summer of 1915. And he worried about what he would do after the report was completed. He hoped to be through with it in less than a year. What then? "I am most anxious," he wrote Dr. Hayes, "not to waste any great amount of time for something to turn up, even on the company's payroll, as I think it would result in disadvantage and injustice both to the company and myself."

His steady love for the academic life impelled him at one point that spring of 1915 to consider taking up residence at Yale or the University of Chicago for further research in the geology of oil. Characteristically, he assures Dr. Hayes that "I am really interested in the subject of the geology of oil from more than a financial standpoint and I hope some day to be one of the authorities on the subject." Carried away with this dream, he suggests that it might be wise for the company to put him on a retainer fee and give him a partial leave of absence.

By May he had completed seventy-five thousand words of the report, the length of an average book. It was done in very great detail, including the tabulation of the results, to the fullest extent of the knowledge available, of every well ever drilled in the Tampico-Tuxpam area. A major problem remaining was the index and the cross-referencing. By the time he set out for Cuba, accompanied by Mrs. DeGolyer, the greater part of the work was done. The Cuban summer work would have no sequel, for the results were entirely negative.

During that summer it became evident that Dr. Hayes, who had undergone several operations since 1913, was a stricken man. His cancer was incurable. Mr. Body therefore instructed DeGolyer to send the reports on Cuba directly to his office in London. Returning from Cuba by

way of the firm's New York office, DeGolyer stopped in
Washington to visit with Dr. Hayes. It was obvious that
his longtime "boss" would not be able to resume his business duties. For DeGolyer this meant a new relationship
with the firm. He had to make a momentous decision. It
was a confused time for all concerned.

At last he formulated a long statement for Mr. Body and
mailed it from Norman in November 1915. Pointing out
that he has never had a formal contract with the firm save
for the first year, only verbal agreements since then managed by Dr. Hayes, he now feels the need for a precise arrangement. Moreover, since the report on Mexico is all
complete save for details to be filled in, there is the question of the future plans for him. After stating his great satisfaction with the way he has been treated ("much better
than could have been expected"), he confesses that he is
disturbed by what the war has done to the projects of the
Foreign Department and what the political disturbances
in Mexico have done to the work in that country. Then he
comes to the heart of the matter: "There are also some
very attractive opportunities for work in my profession
with companies on this side at the present time. Consequently, should work be so tight that there is no opportunity to give me further assignment I shall have no difficulty in making other arrangements. . . . I should like
more than anything else to continue with the Firm, but I
feel I shall be doing both the Firm and myself an injustice
unless the matter is settled at the present time for some
years to come. . . . I trust that I have not bungled this
letter so badly but that you will understand that I desire
to define my position rather than change it."

In 1916, his old mentor, Dr. Hayes, died. DeGolyer was
on a trip to Tampico at the time. He wired Mrs. Hayes his
condolences and told her, "I feel as one who has lost a fa-

ther." Among the encounters of his life, the one with Dr. Hayes had been one of the luckiest. Hayes had given him confidence in himself. "I admire your discretion equally as much as your scientific judgment," Hayes once wrote him, adding that of the latter he had "the highest possible opinion." The death of Dr. Hayes symbolized the end of Mexican investigation as the central concern of DeGolyer's oil career, just as the encounter with Hayes in 1907 had initiated it. A month later, the firm set up DeGolyer in a new relationship, one he requested. DeGolyer's new status, conditioned by the world war and the local revolution, was defined to his satisfaction in a memorandum headed "Tampico, March 13, 1916 — Geological Department, Aguila Company." It contained eight clauses or provisions.

His new title was double: "Consulting Geologist to the Aguila Company, and Geologist attached to the Foreign Department, S. Pearson and Son, Ltd." His office was transferred from Tampico to New York City. His duties were carefully defined: "to occupy himself for the majority of time during next year with the Mexican work . . . making regularly two trips to Mexico each year," making reports both to the Tampico office and to Messrs. Body and Ryder in London. His reports would outline work for Mexico in conjunction with the Tampico office's approval. In addition, he was to supervise personally the work in the Furbero field as local conditions allowed its development and was to revise personally plans for larger pieces of work such as the Amatlán-Chinampa work just started and the Tlacolula work planned. To his office in New York, the geologist directing fieldwork in Mexico, Paul Weaver, was to make reports and memos in duplicate, plus such drilling data as DeGolyer might request. An interesting duty is outlined last; DeGolyer is to investigate "the forms of organization of the large oil companies in the United States for recommendations about efficiency and better use of applied geology in the fields."

Well, he was to have an office in the States — but he still wanted to do geological fieldwork there, too. He persists, trying to persuade Dr. Veatch in charge of the Foreign Department, getting nowhere. Rather sharply, he writes Mr. Body six months later of his dissatisfaction. He thought, he said, that his opportunities for the future lay with the Foreign Department but by October of 1916, after talks with Dr. Veatch, he states categorically that in view of the plans Dr. Veatch is making, "I am quite convinced that I shall be able to do better for myself working quite independently." He explains that this decision has nothing to do with Dr. Veatch personally, whom he admires and would be pleased to work for, but entirely with "the opportunities in America." "I am resolved to profit by some of them if possible." And, alas, he adds, Dr. Veatch does not have these prospects in mind at all. A solution is hinted at: "It is my intention to spend the greater part of my time in actual fieldwork in the areas mentioned, but I shall have to do consulting work for other interests to some extent in order to make running expenses." He speaks of other offers made to him, but "I should prefer, however, to act in actual as well as nominal consulting capacity to the Aguila Company." In other words, he would like to tell the Foreign Department where to venture in the United States. Very laconically, he concludes: "The gist of this whole letter is that I plan to do some work in attractive areas outside Mexico for myself and that I expect to continue in Mexico preferably for the Aguila Company. I am consequently putting the matter up to you. . . . May I ask you to cable as soon as you have reached a conclusion regarding this matter in order that I may arrange my own affairs promptly. I am hoping that the proposal made may be acceptable to the firm."

To an outsider the "proposal made" does not seem excessively detailed. Anyway, before it reached London, Mr. Body had dispatched a wire calling DeGolyer to London for a conference with Dr. Veatch. DeGolyer wired back that he had sent a letter — on the most recent sailing of the *Adriatic* — raising the question of his continued employment, and therefore, once the letter was received, the trip might not be necessary. Lord Cowdray himself answered this wire, on October 21, stating that the letter had not been received, and he added: "But you are with us and we can not contemplate your leaving. Hence come England. Cowdray."

DeGolyer was playing his cards close to his chest. He waited and watched. On October 24, Mr. Body wired that the letter had at last arrived and that DeGolyer would receive a reply within ten days. "Meanwhile don't go outside Aguila interest. Body."

On October 30 DeGolyer sent a wire to inform Dr. Veatch that he had finally decided to stay on this side, awaiting the firm's decision about Mexico. (Since Veatch had once again tried to lure DeGolyer to a post in the London office, the cable also carried a perfunctory "Thank you opportunity offered.") It was Mr. Body, not DeGolyer, who then crossed the ocean, apparently on decision of the Chief. DeGolyer got this wire on November 4: "BODY SAILS MONDAY   ENTIRELY HOLD YOUR HAND UNTIL HAVE SEEN HIM MUST NOT LEAVE US   COWDRAY."

The interview did not satisfy DeGolyer, as he wrote Dr. Veatch on November 22. "As you know, Mr. Body has arrived, and brought letters from the Chief which were extremely flattering and complimentary, but did not touch directly on the business I had in mind. We have held a number of discussions, confined of necessity to generalities, and I have promised to visit Mexico, leaving here on

about the 25th of December, returning during the latter
part of January and going over to England. . . . The
whole matter, I suppose, will be settled when I am in London." And with relentless determination he adds that he
will try to interest Dr. Veatch in the Gulf region when he
sees him then.

The Tampico visit stretched on into late February. De-
Golyer stood firm. He wrote Mr. Body on February 17,
from Mexico, asking for decisions on several points — and
offering a few himself. First of all, "Dr. Veatch's offer for
me to come to London as his assistant, while very flattering, is not acceptable." Secondly, he insists that his proposal is simply that he retain his present position in Mexico *and* investigate the Gulf Coast region for the firm.

In his evolution as a geologist, DeGolyer had come by
now to his basic belief, namely that the detection of salt
domes was the key to finding oil. He felt certain that the
Texas and Louisiana Gulf Coast had the salt domes. He
was pitting his knowledge now against that of any other
expert. (Of salt domes themselves, more will be said later.)
He defends his determination to investigate the Gulf Coast
in his letter to Mr. Body: "I feel quite like a dog at times
in insisting that I will not take up the proposed London
position, as it seems somewhat ungrateful on my part." But
he nonetheless asks permission to undertake, instead, a
study of the Gulf Coast region. He also requests, for his
New York office, fuller reports from the Tampico staff.
There remains the matter of going to London to see the
Chief. DeGolyer is positive: "As I have previously stated
to Dr. Veatch, Mr. Ryder and yourself, I plan to spend
most of my time on work in which I will have an interest
in the United States and South America . . . and while I
expect to go to London, as I have promised to do, I have
in mind only the securing of a final decision with regard

to the proposal made and the defining with exactness of my relation towards the Firm, should they wish me to retain my present position toward Mexico and the Aguila Company and should the Firm wish to examine the Gulf Coastal Region of the United States."

Mr. Body, also in Tampico at the time, drafted a memo to settle matters for a while. Although DeGolyer was to leave "in the next few days" to carry out a commission in the Honduras as outlined by the Foreign Department, he would upon his return spend two months in the Gulf Coast states — to prepare a report for presentation to Lord Cowdray for determining whether or not the firm would go into the oil business in the United States' Gulf Coast region. The memo also states that "the Chief will determine this summer what will be definitely and mutually settled between yourself and the Aguila Firm and S. Pearson & Son, Ltd." He adds his own wish that De stay with the company: "It is my earnest desire, in which I am sure the Chief concurs, that you continue as Chief Geologist of the Aguila Company."

The drama of decision, after months of conferences, had a happy ending. Lord Cowdray steadily opposed having his firm enter the United States and declared during the summer an unqualified rejection of that part of the plan. But it was agreed by July that DeGolyer would devote half his time (six months of the year) to work as consulting geologist for Aguila, having the other half free "to do geological work and enter into the oil business to any extent at any other point."

There was, of course, a stipulation that DeGolyer would not take up any work or personal interest in Mexico except with the company's consent. But at last, if only part-time, he was in business for himself. Now, to investigate those salt domes. Three things were needed: knowledge, money and special scientific instruments.

II

From Pick and Hammer
to Seismographs

8

Home Life
and Book Collecting

THE DEGOLYERS moved to New York in 1916 during the wartime housing shortage. They lived for a while in a hotel, searching all Westchester County fruitlessly to find a home. Nell DeGolyer was expecting her third child and at last was too fatigued to look farther. Then, through friends already living in New York, they heard of a place in Montclair. "You go by yourself," she told DeGolyer one Saturday afternoon, "I'll agree with anything you decide on."

He took the train, got out and sought the real estate agent. There was indeed a new house going up, practically finished. DeGolyer went up the hill with the agent, inspected the property and made an arrangement to return the following Saturday to conclude the deal, without fixing on the final price. His need was dire. All their furniture, which they had brought up from Norman, was in temporary storage. The warehouse warned them they would have to move the furniture out at once because the place had been requisitioned for army needs. DeGolyer was in no position to bargain over the cost of a house.

The following Saturday afternoon he got out at the Montclair station, where he had two appointments. One was with the agent whose office was a block or so away. The other was with a moving company, whose drivers had the DeGolyer furniture in their van. He talked with the truckers, told them to follow him without seeming to do so, gave them a couple of dollars to go have a beer, once they had located the house, before coming back.

He got into the agent's car and they started up Watchung Road. The agent noticed the truck, wanted to let it get ahead, but was baffled at the driver's reluctance to pass. He spoke to DeGolyer about it. "They are certainly behaving in an odd way," he observed. A little further on, he stopped his car. The truck stopped behind him.

"What do you think of that?" he asked DeGolyer.

"Oh," came the reply, "probably those boys had a little too much beer. Let's push ahead and stop worrying."

When at last they stopped in front of the house and the truck suddenly speeded ahead, the agent said, "I'm sure glad to get rid of them."

"So am I," agreed DeGolyer, and got ready to bargain.

"I'll stick around awhile," said DeGolyer when the deal was made, and he owned the house and keys.

"Take your time," the agent encouraged, "I'm in no hurry."

The truck hove into view.

"My furniture," DeGolyer explained. "I couldn't wait another day to find a place to store it. Forgot to tell you that."

When he found voice, the agent asked DeGolyer, "Where did you say you're from?"

"Oklahoma."

"Well, I see," said the agent. "This is the first time I ever did business with a wild man from the West."

The wild man from the West was decisive, as another anecdote shows. Still remembering, maybe, his wondering as a boy working in a china shop in Hobart, Oklahoma whether he would ever be able to own such beautiful objects, he haunted Tiffany's when he first went to New York. On a Saturday afternoon off, he found there a piece of sculpture he coveted. It was made for him. It was called "The Prospector." About two feet high and two feet long, it was a bronze by Solon Borglum, brother of Gutzon. Two creatures were dramatized, a patient horse standing beside his owner, a prospector seated on the ground mopping his hot brow with his bandana in the shade of his weary mount. In one hand, the thick-bearded searcher held his wide-brimmed "panning" hat. The sculptor had captured a moment of pause, of rest, of wonderment — but not of defeat. There was the solitude of the desert but no hopelessness. DeGolyer found himself tingling with excitement. The statue spoke to him in a private and special way. There were memories of his own, memories of his father who had always called himself a "zinc man." And there was this troubled current moment, when DeGolyer was striking out for himself as a prospector in part. As an oil consultant he would finance his own "wildcatting." Caution won the day. No need yet to spend six hundred dollars on a statue.

But he couldn't stop talking about it when he got home. "You go back Monday and get it," Nell told him.

He had an appointment on Monday with a man who wanted some potential oil property evaluated. It turned out not to be a major job, but it would take several days.

"What will your fee be?" the client asked.

With one thing on his mind, DeGolyer answered with lightning speed, "Six hundred dollars."

"Fair enough," the gentleman replied, as DeGolyer wondered whether he had sold himself short. The moment the man left, DeGolyer sped over to Tiffany's. The Borglum sculpture was still there. He bought it. It stayed with him the rest of his life as a particularly prized possession, as a reminder of many things, including the effectiveness of a quick, instant answer. It was the DeGolyers' first objet d'art, and it started a habit that lasted a lifetime.

DeGolyer, following his spell of book collecting on their first trip to London, took delight in the wealth of book shops in New York, a real boon for an inquisitive mind from the frontier. In London, Lord Cowdray had asked his young American guest in 1914 to pick out a book from the Cowdray library as a souvenir of the visit. DeGolyer made tentative selections of volumes he hoped might not be missed. Cowdray pressed him to take something of real worth. "It will be to remember me by," he insisted. "What I'd really like," DeGolyer at last confessed, "would be anything from Dickens." Cowdray handed him a first edition of *David Copperfield*. Along with Dickens, DeGolyer began to collect two other favorites of his, Kipling and Hardy. His letters to friends — and he was an unflagging correspondent — begin to abound in discussions of current books and information swapped about book dealers.

A poor boy while in college, where he shared what he called a "Sunday" (or going-out) suit with a roommate, he also picked up in London, or at last was able to indulge, a taste for elegant dress, getting some suits made at Norton's. Soon after moving to New York, he began going to Brooks Brothers for his clothes, and maintained a bandbox appearance the rest of his life.

Even at home he always looked as though he were expecting company and in the hot summers of Texas and Oklahoma, he refused to yield to the local custom of going coatless in the dog days. His wife would insist he pay attention to comfort, but he stubbornly held to propriety, a word that did not otherwise impress him very much. At any rate, his clothing bills were impressive. He spent in

one month at Brooks Brothers, shortly after the family settled at Montclair, as much as a new Ford cost him f.o.b. at
Norman, Oklahoma. Few men nowadays spend on clothes
in a month the cost of a Mustang.

Business ties of course brought him frequently to Norman, for Oklahoma was then the center of the nation's,
and the world's, oil production. He also retained a nostalgic yearning to keep alive the memories of the good old
college days. Just as he had sent out letters from Mexico
urging his Kappa Alpha brothers to contribute money to
the Norman chapter and to convene in annual meetings,
from New York he kept in touch with what he called "the
old crowd," and helped organize informal and unofficial
alumni reunions at some point during the football season.
Never much of an athlete himself, although he had kept a
home tennis court in Norman and later took up golf, he
loved sports and was an avid fan all his life.

Their second daughter, Dorothy Margaret, was born the
year they moved east, in 1916. At home, Everette DeGolyer insisted on reading aloud to his wife columns he admired in the genuinely great New York newspapers of that
day. He developed an especial fondness for Don Marquis's
"Sun Dial" pieces in the old *New York Sun,* ardently
praised his "Old Soak" and *archy and mehitabel;* later, he
delightedly followed the *New York Evening Post*'s Christopher Morley. He was a book collector who really loved to
read.

Ben Belt, Tampico aide out of the University of Oklahoma's geology department, sent DeGolyer some Conrad.
Of DeGolyer's reaction, Ben Belt made an interesting comment: "I cannot say that I am surprised that Conrad's descriptions affect your nerves. Perhaps after all, in order to
read Conrad one needs to be living in the dreamy atmosphere of Mexico, and under the lazy influence of the trop-

ics. At all events you were much more fortunate in the selection of books you sent me, and I have almost changed your position in my scheme of things from that of the man who was my first boss to the man who introduced me to 'Old Soak.' "

Under the influence of his friend William E. Wrather, famous geologist for the Texas Company, DeGolyer turned his reading and his collecting to the American Southwest, particularly books about Indian tribes and their conflicts with the whites. This remained an enduring interest, but DeGolyer broke away from it for a while. He announced gleefully to Wrather in a letter of July 1, 1924, "I have been on a bad book-buying spree recently, but having escaped from your influence, I have gone back to my old loves in the way of first editions. The prize acquisition was a set of the first and second issues of the first edition of each of the two volumes of Lamb's *Essays*. They cost rather a pretty penny but will probably ultimately be worth it. I also picked up a book, two books in fact, that would interest you. They were Herman Melville's *John Marr* and *Timoleon*. They were published in '88 and '90 in editions of twenty-five copies each. I just missed getting these two books about two years ago when I saw them in a catalogue at $25.00 each. The result is that they cost me about four times that much now."

The book collecting urge was thriving. Before sailing for London on the *Majestic*, August 16, 1924, DeGolyer wrote to Wrather that he was saving his money for another book-buying spree abroad. He contends they both get outwitted by the rare-book men. "Perhaps," he writes, "Mrs. W. is right about the mutual support we have to give each other in order to mutually bear up under the sufferings inflicted by book dealers." He chides Wrather for telling his wife "too much" about his book purchases, claiming "I sneak my books into the house and 'tell 'em nothing,' aside from the occasional insinuations that after I am dead and gone and all stocks, bonds, etc. and such other fripperies are found to be worthless, all that they will have to do is to sell my library for half what it has cost me and they will be able to spend the rest of their lives in ease and luxury."

He wasn't simply collecting books, he also gave them away.

One beneficiary was fellow Oklahoman and oilman, Charles Wrightsman, who misinterpreted one gift package as an early Christmas mailing. "No," DeGolyer wrote back, "the Surtees books were not intended for Christmas. I am glad you liked them. I have read all the books and have them. I think *Mr. Sponge's Sporting Tour* is my favorite. Surtees was a horseman, first, last and all of the time, and I believe the Jorrocks books were his whole literary output. He wrote only because he wanted to talk about horses . . . I was delighted with your Kipling's *Dipsey Chantey*. To tell you the truth, I had never seen a copy. Somewhat boastingly, I must say that it is now in proper company."

Obviously a Dickens enthusiast would be fond of Surtees, whose books anticipated *The Pickwick Papers*, but DeGolyer's tastes were exceedingly varied. His London "book-buying sprees," which were yearly, reflect his professional interest in science and notably in geology, his continuing interest in Mexico, his growing fondness for the American West as literary material and his attachment to London. In 1921, he bought from bookseller Francis Edwards such special items as *The Autobiography of an English Soldier in the U.S. Army* (published in 1853), Bullock's *Six Months in Mexico* (published in 1824), Fr. Padilla's *Santiago de México* (published in 1648), and Garcilaso de la Vega's *Royal Commentaries* (edition of 1688).

Anything about Mexico — geology, church history, biographies, personal memoirs, folkways — interested him. As early as the trip of 1920 he began searching for lives of the leading military and political figures, including biographies of Juárez, Iturbide, Santa Anna, Maximilian and others. Some of the items he wanted took a great deal of searching. The Edwards firm wrote him triumphantly in 1921 that after more than a year they had at last been able to turn up a copy of the obscure Lyon's *Residence in Mexico,* which had been published in 1828. No wonder he and Wrather wept crocodile tears over their costly hobby. One bill for DeGolyer from Edwards in 1924, for five books only and all connected with Mexico, totaled ninety-one pounds.

He was becoming known as a book collector and as an aficionado of Spanish colonial history. In 1928, he was invited to prepare the short, very short, biography of Santa Anna for the fourteenth edition of the *Encyclopaedia Britannica.* He was accustomed by now to see his words in print, with a long and already impressive record of papers on geology and oil. But he had qualms about nonspecialized writing. Sending his manuscript to William B. Parker, a leading spirit in the Hispanic Society of America, DeGolyer commented modestly: "Enclosed find my effort at a sketch of Santa Anna. It is not satisfactory, that I realize. The fact of the matter is that it is very unsatisfactory, but how in the world we could cage a bird of such rare plumage in five hundred words I do not know. I have not written this as I wanted to, but rather to meet what I thought were requirements."

Consulted by Parker about the amount of space to be devoted to Mexican historical figures, DeGolyer advised three groupings. "First, Hidalgo, Juárez and Díaz. Of second rank, I would place Iturbide, Santa Anna and Maximilian. In third rank I would place Morelos, Limantour, Madero, Bustamente and Victoria." A fourth grouping, he suggests, might include another hundred.

For some reason, the enigmatic, puzzling Santa Anna — never satisfactorily portrayed by any biographer, according to expert Latin American historian Henry Bamford Parkes — greatly intrigued DeGolyer. Four years before the *Encyclopaedia* article, Parker had proposed to DeGolyer collaborating on a full-length study, but the latter declined. "I have presently become so interested in the old '*sin vergüenza*,'" he wrote, "that I should like to continue for a while to see what I can do with it myself. I am negotiating with William Baker Stevens for his Mexican library, and yesterday afternoon went up to his place to look it over. It is a wonderful library and would be a perfect Eldorado for anyone working on Santa Anna. It contains three pamphlet lives of the old scoundrel, as William Baker says, one for and two against, and some files of old Mexican newspapers which are practically unreplaceable. However, the library is quite bulky and will probably require the purchase of a bigger house for my family to live in."

That problem was soon to be solved. Nonetheless, as DeGolyer says to Parker, "the great amount involved is very considerable. The problem of this library is quite difficult. It is one of those collections made by William Baker — who is a very discriminating collector — over a long period of years, and is worth almost anything to a person who is really interested and wants the material, and it could not be replaced for money, but would be worth about what old paper pulp is worth to anyone not interested." DeGolyer *was* interested. A week later, March 6, 1924, he bought it. And he writes Parker about this and about Santa Anna: "I have about come to the conclusion that there is no more

The DeGolyers did not always live in the Southwest. They built this house in Montclair, and in all lived about two decades in the East, 1916–1936.

interesting figure in American history than our General. He appears a perfect rogue, judging by almost any ordinary canon of criticism. Yet his constant comebacks indicate that there was something about him out of the ordinary. There is no lack of picturesque detail as to his colorful and erratic activities."

But at the same time, DeGolyer was equally absorbed in the lives of Coronado and Cabeza de Vaca, two far greater men. Of these, he was to write later, but with scrutiny of their routes of exploration — still inexactly established — rather than scrutiny of their personalities. For him as for others since, Santa Anna's character remained a bafflement.

And so his book interests fused in collecting and reading and in writing. And he could splurge on books as well as on oil prospects. On June 2, 1924, he paid five hundred dollars for a copy of the first edition of Stevenson's *New Arabian Nights;* a month later, July 1, he paid the same for *A Child's Garden of Verses.*

Not all his exchange of letters with W. E. Wrather concerned the business of book collecting. Having built one house in Norman, Oklahoma, in 1920, he enjoyed the experience so much that he scheduled a much larger enterprise for a new dwelling in Montclair. He was fascinated with building and had within him the soul of an architect. He wrote Wrather on October 1, 1925: "We are in the throes of planning a new house. Nell has gotten together a plot about 210' x 350' or some such matter near the top of Watchung Mountain some 600 feet above sea level, and we are hoping to build on it this fall and winter. Sort of an attempt to establish an ancestral family home for the De-Golyers, I imagine."

There were now four DeGolyer children: Virginia Nell, Dorothy Margaret, Cecilia Jeanne and Everett Lee Jr. A standing family joke was that the children doubly enjoyed Christmas — in their own right and in the great excitement of going out after dinner on Christmas Eve to help Daddy do his belated Christmas shopping. Still it couldn't have been so tardy as all that. He wrote Wrather three days before Christmas in 1926: "More rugs and finer houses for the ladies. Them's my sentiments."

The house at number 179 Watchung Road was a fine one indeed. With a conscious wish, no doubt, to establish himself in the style of his British mentor, DeGolyer built a baronial mansion in the Tudor manner, at a cost of about two hundred thousand dollars. But in a feature befitting a petroleum pioneer the house had a "rock garden" including many fossils and souvenirs of a quarter century of collecting. As early as 1910, DeGolyer was sending back from Mexico rocks to J. W. Dall and to Professor Cummins for analysis, but also from the collector's urge for appraisal.

One thing he missed in New York from his Tampico days was Mexican food. Chili flavored sauces, made from the dozens of varieties of tame to people-eating green and red peppers, he often claimed superior to curry or any other international seasoning favorite. In time, he was to launch his own small factory to produce that olive oil-soaked Mexican favorite among peppers, *jalapeños*.

Although he was writing to such college friends as "Deke" Parker (later to become executive director of Scripps-Howard newspapers), Lloyd Curtis, Frank Long, George Cline Smith, and others of the need to hold the old campus together, DeGolyer was maturing his thoughts about college education. Professionally, he specifically regarded his own meager training in higher mathematics and in physics as gaps he had to rectify on his own; he began to ponder the problem of friendships achieved at the cost of study, the problem of college considered as a lark.

From the vantage point of an industry that would have more and more to rely on precise scientific knowledge and from his encounters with highly trained men in his profession, he was led to comment to T. Wayland Vaughan in 1918: "It is rather amazing the amount of time one spends in such a school [the University of Oklahoma] and the very little that he accomplishes. The condition generally grows worse from year to year with the further development of the social life of the community, until it really represents a round of fraternities, social diversions and athletic occupations with hardly enough study to dignify the use of the term." Vaughan, another United States Geological Survey man who also worked for Mexican Eagle and who later became president of the Scripps Institution of Oceanography, was in entire agreement, but mostly blamed coeducation.

But in another way, and perhaps just as shrewdly, De-Golyer was alert to the "social development of the community." He was never a "loner," as was his great associate whom he knew in Norman as early as 1916, J. C. Karcher, or such Tampico geologists as Ben Belt and Paul Weaver. Part of his talent, as nearly everyone observed, lay in his easy gift for friendship, or as Wallace Pratt characterized him at the time, "a sort of truculent gaiety."

With the shutdown of Mexican oil exploration, DeGolyer found himself a celebrated young geologist, well regarded and well rewarded. From his sense of realism rather than from modesty, he acknowledged to himself, as he did all his life, that he played in luck. The word had for him almost a talismanic import. To find oil, he often said, you needed both skill and luck — but, for sure, skill alone would not suffice.

Nearing thirty upon his return to the States, he lacked

the big money needed to finance himself as a prospector or "wildcatter." What he had to sell, at the moment, was his reputation, perhaps even his lucky star. But deep down he knew he had something else marketable, his certitude that salt domes guaranteed far and away the most promising geological formation for the scientific detection of oil pools, or "traps," as he would have put it. But this certitude required both scientific testing by scientific instruments and scientific documentation. However attracted to the classroom DeGolyer was for theoretical study, he was more magnetized by the direct scientific experience and experiments in the field. To be a consultant looked like the ideal prospect: his royalties on successful finds would build up the capital he needed if he were to operate later as an independent, and his income from appraisals would also subsidize his search for facts about salt domes.

One of the first things he had observed in Mexico was the importance that the European geologists working for Mexican Eagle paid to discovering salt domes. The presence of these structural or stratigraphic traps could only be detected, with the geological information and tools then available, by surface indications. A rounded, unexpected hummock or hill pushing its way above the surrounding land was the usual sign. The upthrust of a salt "stalk" or "lug," pressured miles underground away and above the long-ago-deposited mother salt bed, managed to pierce the earth's crust and create a swelling, like a blister, on the land's skin. Within these arched folds and bucklings of subterranean strata, oil and gas and water were presently trapped. With his alidade and plane table and graduated or stadia rod — that is to say, the traditional tools of above-ground surveying, the special small telescope of the alidade mounted on the tripod drawing or plane table, and the graduated rod — the geologist might locate such mounds. But it would take the development of geophysics to detect the far more numerous "deep-seated" domes underground that never pierced to the visible surface.

At any event, young DeGolyer was well aware that the Mexican Eagle geologists were out to map and survey their lands as sleuths on the track of salt domes. He knew at once that Sir Weetman Pearson pinned his faith on the salt dome theory. The evidence was as plain as day. Sir Weetman had promptly engaged the great man of Spindletop, Captain Anthony Lucas (later a hero for DeGolyer, too), to inspect Mexican Eagle's holdings in the Isthmus of Tehuantepec. After two years of only meager results, Captain Lucas returned to the States, defeated or at least discouraged.

There is the highest irony in the fact that Pearson's next great American geologist recruit was Dr. C. Willard Hayes of the United States Geological Survey. In 1900, three months before the Spindletop gusher, Dr. Hayes took an assistant along to visit the oil prospecting around Beaumont. Eagerly, Captain Lucas, who had already drilled one "duster," or hole as dry as dust, sought out the expert to compare notes. Dr. Hayes, with all the support of his eminent office, was positive. He saw no logic whatsoever in Captain Lucas' theory about the relationship of oil pools to salt domes. Admittedly, Captain Lucas, who was after all a mining engineer if not a geologist, knew more about salt domes than anybody in the United States. But, said Hayes, there was no precedent in oil history for finding oil by Lucas' theory. Hayes reminded Lucas that only forty miles away, the city of Galveston had spent a million dollars drilling a hole to 3,070 feet and "not one drop of oil was recovered or even smelled." Hayes saw no oil future for the coastal Gulf plains, even if "mother" salt beds had been laid down there, and later overburdened by other sedimentary deposits, millions and millions of years ago. Lucas said the Galveston experiment was not analogous. Its aim was to find a source of fresh water; above all, it was not located at the site of a dome structure.

It was the second time Captain Lucas had cold water thrown in his face by experts. An even more knowledgeable man than Dr. Hayes gave Lucas the same negative report in the summer of 1900. Captain Lucas and his Beaumont associate, Patillo Higgins (who had been crusading unsuccessfully for ten years to get the Beaumont dome explored and drilled), sought support from the then greatest oil company in the world, Standard Oil. The company's field expert, Calvin Payne, had started as a driller and wound up as one of the highest paid men in the business. He was familiar with the earlier oil success in Texas, that at Corsicana, and had advanced money to Corsicana's famous independent producer, J. S. Cullinan. But Payne was skeptical, brutally so in fact, about hopes for Spindletop. He told Lucas that in all his travels over the globe — studying oil in Russia, Rumania, Sumatra, Borneo, the United States — he had never seen any conditions that paralleled the surface indications at Beaumont in which Captain Lucas placed his hopes and his analysis. "I do not believe," he said, "there is any chance here for oil in paying quantities." Lucas, a Dalmatian soldier of fortune from the Old World, might have yielded to despair but for the stubborn faith of his American wife and his implacable partner Higgins. But the testimony of two such experts as Dr. Hayes and Calvin Payne was searing.

The irony, of course, came full circle — in the geological, not the money aspect — years later when Dr. Hayes' protégé, DeGolyer, chose a site for the first geophysical oil explorations in the world. By 1922, the proper instruments had been developed and perfected. DeGolyer selected

Spindletop dome for the experiment — and proved Captain Lucas correct in his theorizing, as correct as the 1901 drilling had proved him about the presence of oil. It wasn't just luck that brought in the well that changed the world and put America on wheels. It took knowledge and vision.

Both Captain Lucas and Higgins had knowledge and vision. Patillo Higgins was a self-educated and gifted eccentric; Captain Lucas was a trained mining engineer. After a stormy youth, Higgins surprised the Beaumont community by settling down, even teaching in the Baptist Sunday school and taking his class on picnics to Spindletop Springs. One-armed, but nonetheless a famous fighter, he had a talent for both mechanics and business. Intrigued by the sour wells at Spindletop, he wrote the United States Geological Survey for material on geology; he was soon prophesying the presence of oil on the mound. Leading citizens backed him, but the first tries were failures. The money played out. He placed an advertisement in a manufacturing journal, offering to lease or sell acreage in this sure-fire oil prospect. He got one single answer, but it was the right one. It came from Anthony F. Lucas of New Orleans.

A Slav trained in mining engineering and a commissioned lieutenant in the Austrian navy, he became an American citizen on a visit to an uncle in Michigan, who had changed his family name of Luchrich to Lucas. Anthony Lucas prospered as a mining engineer, married Miss Caroline Fitzgerald of Macon, Georgia, moved to Louisiana where he explored salt mines and made occasional visits to Texas. When he happened to read Higgins' advertisement, he already suspected sulphur deposits at Spindletop, which he had visited in the past. Something clicked in his mind. Like Higgins, he became a prophet; unlike Higgins he was easily discouraged. Both men had the charm needed to persuade reluctant backers and they trusted each other. Luckily, important men trusted them.

After prospecting for gold in Colorado, Captain Lucas became a mining engineer at the Avery Island salt mine in southern Louisiana, in 1893. There and along the Texas-Louisiana border and the coast he had found traces of oil in salt wells he had drilled.

Lucas' reasoning, his persistence, his vision, filled De-Golyer with a lifetime admiration that found expression in a speech DeGolyer made on the occasion of the fiftieth anniversary of the "Lucas gusher." DeGolyer said he wanted to pay tribute at once to "an American dream and to a great American." The "dream" was really a powerful act of the imagination, an educated guess. At Spindletop Mound, "there were no oil seepages, only an escape of gas and slight incrustations of sulphur. There was the mound, so slight as to be hardly recognizable in any land less flat than this. Even it was likely to be misunderstood by the best experts of the time. Only the unwavering faith of Higgins and the Louisiana training and vision of Lucas could give it credit." But this vision and this training needed another factor, a favorable working environment. This De-Golyer found in our free economy. "Every man free to dream a dream and pursue it to the end! Every man free to be wrong! Every man free to be a potential manager!

"To me it is the fact under our system of free enterprise every man is a potential manager which makes it work so well. Our individual freedoms under the system are dear to us but it is the working of the system as a whole which is so overwhelmingly in the common good."

Both Lucas and DeGolyer suffered, or enjoyed, a salt dome syndrome.

Despite the example of Spindletop and Amerada's experiments, it took a long time for the salt dome theories to pay off in actual performance, primarily because they had to be constantly revamped as more scientific data accumulated. To simplify a complicated matter, one may say that the upthrusting of the salt stalk or plug fractured and faulted the overlying formations it pierced, the oil later seeping into some pockets on one side of a fault and blocked from the other side. The locater for a prospective well must know the location of the flanks of a dome and the location of its fractures and must judge whether they have allowed or blocked migration of the oil. It is possible to drill dry holes only ten feet from a paying one. It is also possible to "wildcat" a successful hole between dry holes for mighty production; it all depends on the fault structure.

The noted geologist Michel Halbouty, discussing the strange and varied patterns of wells at Spindletop dome, has written: "It is for such reasons that every well drilled on the side of a dome is a wildcat irrespective of its proximity to existing producers. Yet it can safely be stated that, regardless of the hazards and risks involved in the drilling and development of production on domes, the productive tracts on them, on a per-acre basis, are by far more prolific than from any other geologic feature in the world."

As early as 1914, DeGolyer became interested in the use of gravity surveys for mapping the structure of the earth below surface. His colleague in Tampico, P. C. A. Stewart, was the nephew of an emeritus professor of geodesy at Cambridge. On his first trip to London, DeGolyer got Professor Charteris to put him in touch with the great Hungarian scientist-educator, Baron Roland von Eötvös, who had invented the magnetic torsion balance in 1896, a device to detect variations, conditioned by the rock structure below, of the gravitational pull of the earth. Thanks to the intercession of Professor Charteris, Baron Eötvös agreed to sell DeGolyer a torsion balance, but the outbreak of World War I voided this plan. During the war, the enemy owned the only torsion balances in existence, using them to detect concealed rival artillery, as revealed by sound waves.

At the close of the war, however, DeGolyer went to Holland to consult Dr. Erb, who had remained with Royal Dutch Shell after its purchase of Mexican Eagle. Dr. Erb had no experience of the instrument in actual use, but encouraged DeGolyer's interest in it. Dr. Eötvös died in the spring of that year, but DeGolyer initiated arrangements to buy a torsion balance with Dr. D. Pekar of the Eötvös Institute.

Adequate testing would require enormous financial resources. This same year, 1919, was to resolve that problem. Lord Cowdray had invited DeGolyer in 1918 for necessary help in organizing the transfer of Mexican Eagle to Dutch Shell. He must have been pleased with his young assistant: he gave him a $5,000 bonus. More importantly, Lord Cowdray decided at last to extend his oil operations into North America, above the Mexican border.

What really interested DeGolyer now was not so much the smell of money, or the smell of oil, but the chance to practice science — learning it and applying it to action at the same time. His cosmopolitan experiences with distinguished men of many nationalities and vocations had made him into a multifaceted man whose inquiring, quizzical mind conducted mental expeditions into many fields of knowledge. He collected knowledge, remembering it, as other men collect guns or stamps or furniture. DeGolyer was not simply a consultant, appraising oil prospects for financing groups, and a half-time specialist for Mexican Eagle during the years from 1916 to 1919; he was also venturing out as an "independent." He had several informal partnerships with friends whom the revolution had also driven out of Mexico, partnerships for investigating well locations in Oklahoma and Texas. Besides oil, he still followed in his father's footsteps regarding zinc and lead mines, at least to the point of dreaming up projects.

He and Hopkins brought Earle Porter, kin by marriage to DeGolyer, into an informal partnership in 1917, Porter leaving his post as professor of chemistry at the University of Oklahoma. Porter was at first primarily interested in what he called a "zinc deal." He wrote DeGolyer at the New York office: "If you could find a group of men who would invest from one to five million, say, we would then proceed to get options." Instead, DeGolyer and Hopkins decided Porter should spend his time investigating oil activity in Louisiana and Texas at Hackberry and Sour Lake, adjacent to Spindletop. DeGolyer and Hopkins were to provide the money, Porter was to do the work — three or four months at first in Texas, and then probably in Wyoming. But it was nearly forty years later before DeGolyer's certainty of oil in Wyoming was proved.

DeGolyer knew as well as any man could the practical operating history of the Mexican oil fields; he now had to garner equal information about the fields at home. Total privacy would of course have been a blessing for any oil operation, on the same principle implied in the classic question, "Would Macy's tell Gimbel's?" But things operated to defeat the advantages of secrecy: 1) the normal human need to know and to share everybody else's affairs, becoming in business the obligation to know a competitor's mind and plans; and 2) the legitimate cooperation among geologists — whose profession is a collective enterprise for the accumulation and classification of knowledge — for the purpose of benefiting everyone by precise data. Thus, in Mexico, DeGolyer had shared fossil collections with rivals in the attempt to know thoroughly the geologic structure of the Tamasopo ridge, the locus of the great "Golden Lane."

Quite naturally, then, his instructions to Porter are cautionary: since Hopkins is known to have important connections useful in interesting outside capital, "it may not be necessary, nor desirable for the present, for the Hopkins connection to become known." If Porter can, he should map activity at Sour Lake, otherwise map Big Hill, southeast of Spindletop, and Davis Hill, eighteen miles northeast of Humble. More precisely: "As you no doubt know, by now there is no surface geology exposed in any of these coastal mounds and the whole trick is to get the total graphic picture-form and the exact location and elevation of all wells drilled in the past."

DeGolyer was collecting all the data possible on salt domes. He sent Porter also to map the North Texas salt dome at West Point, Freestone County, and then on to survey land around Eldorado, Kansas. He advises Porter: "As the fields mentioned and the domes are all salt deposits, you might read up on the subject. . . . The ideal thing would be for you to acquire as complete a knowledge as possible of every well and individual interested in it, because the whole thing is a gamble that some man will be found who has a partially developed proposition which can be sold to advantage here in New York." So, as "geological consultant," DeGolyer's role was double: to find and recommend promising prospects, and then offer them to big capital in New York for development. He had wanted Lord Cowdray, or his firm, to furnish the capital, but Cowdray was not then interested.

Scouting the operations of rival companies was standard; scouts were part of the payroll. Trading information could be mutually profitable. DeGolyer felt and always stated that failures, dry holes, offered as much useful guidance as the data on successes or gushers. When he set himself up as a "consulting geologist," he advised his kinsman-partner, Earle Porter, "to secure well logs by trading copies of your completed maps for the same." This Porter did at Hackberry Island in Louisiana, at Eldorado in Kansas, at extensions of the Spindletop Dome field in Texas.

DeGolyer, however, really held his own operations in suspension while waiting for Lord Cowdray to make up his mind about coming into the United States; but he had copious information ready when the cessation of war allowed Cowdray to think out his own plans.

His instructions to Porter became precise. The study of the Eldorado field, he wrote in late 1917, "will necessitate your getting acquainted with everyone possible and securing all the information possible in the way of well logs, depths, information regarding production, and that sort of thing, as preliminary to a plane-table survey of the field. I will send the plane table . . . or bring it myself, as I expect to get there in time to help out with that part of the work." The first thing to be done, of course, "will be to buy a map of the Eldorado field, including the Towanda extension . . . it is of particular importance for us to know the name of every well, so that the information collected in the way of logs and that sort of thing can be tied to its proper place on the map. . . . As I judge there are more than one thousand wells in the field, you can see that is quite a contract . . . I have absolutely nothing in mind with regard to Eldorado at the present time, but I think it very probable that we will be able to turn up something in connection with the study of the field. At any rate, I am going to risk the great cost of the operation in the sincere belief that it will result very profitably indeed." (And as it did, for Amerada.)

It was DeGolyer's confidence that swayed Porter into resigning his post at the university. DeGolyer agreed to meet Porter's annual salary the first year, plus full expenses for travel and investigations, plus a 50 percent share in fees and 33 percent in interests. It was a gamble but DeGolyer writes him, "I can hardly express my joy at the fact that you have resigned and decided to get into this thing sink or swim, survive or perish. I might add by way of consolation, that whatever happens, we will all do it together, so that if you starve you won't be by yourself." Meantime, he sent Lewis Chapman, another Mexican Eagle associate, to map the West Point salt dome in Freestone County, Texas, an assignment Porter added to his own when Chapman was conscripted into the army. The Freestone exploration was conducted by the Freestone Syndicate, which DeGolyer set up in 1916 with two other former Tampico associates, R. L. Mestres and Chapman.

DeGolyer's work for Mexican Eagle brought him to Mexico twice a year. Cowdray's lack of interest in possibilities in the States slackened once; DeGolyer returned in 1918 by way of California to survey developments there for Mexican Eagle. The situation in Mexico worsened from the foreign point of view. In his letter to Vaughan about education, DeGolyer stated that "the various forms of taxation which the government is able to devise are already almost too heavy to be borne and are being constantly increased. While I was in Tampico there was a row over who would be governor of Tamaulipas, and as a result that sterling patriot and lover of foreigners, General Navarette, was stabbed in the back and will trouble us no more. There is very strong belief up here that the United States is on the point of intervening in the whole affair, though I must say that past experience makes me such a decided pessimist on the subject that I shall not believe it until it is an accomplished fact."

But no matter. He still holds to his prediction that Texas and Oklahoma, and possibly Louisiana, Kentucky and Alabama, "are the great possibilities in the immediate future." The worse things got in Mexico, the better the chances of Cowdray's coming into the States. But Lord Cowdray was most reluctant to give up the hope of finding sizable quantities of oil on his Isthmus of Tehuantepec properties, which had never rivaled the Tampico strikes. One assignment given DeGolyer in 1916 was to study the salt domes of Texas and the Louisiana Gulf Coast for whatever light they could shine on the Tehuantepec problems. As a result of DeGolyer's work, flank production of importance was first found in the Isthmus. This success was to have a considerable later effect on encouraging Cowdray to subsidize the Amerada Corporation and its subsidiary for locating salt domes in the Gulf Region, the Rycade Corporation.

When he established himself as a young "consulting geologist" in New York in the spring of 1916, DeGolyer was nonetheless persuaded, despite moments of gloom about this prospect, that soon or late Lord Cowdray would have to expand his oil operations to include exploration in the United States. The Mexican political situation was too chaotic for security of production there; and even if that threat could be resolved, Mexican Eagle would have great strategic strength in owning neighboring refineries and shipping outlets in the Texas coastline of the Gulf of Mexico. DeGolyer felt certain the firm would try the States after the war.

But if Lord Cowdray was cautious at the moment, his example did not determine the belief of his number one Mexican expert, J. B. Body, or of Mexican Eagle's president, Thomas J. Ryder. Ryder, supported by British geologist L. Weston, felt certain that the political shambles in Mexico compelled Mexican Eagle to look to the great boom in oil occurring in Texas and Oklahoma, especially the latter. In 1916, Oklahoma oil production was supreme in the world, with a yield that year of 105 million barrels.

Soon Ryder and Weston informed the Chief that the United States with its "proven fields" would be superior to prospecting in unproven countries; moreover, Royal Dutch Shell was practicing this policy by coming into the States. And Standard Oil in its international interests confined itself to "proven ready production," as in the case of Russia and Rumania.

DeGolyer, J. B. Body, Thomas J. Ryder and Herbert Carr (head of the firm's New York office) decided in December of 1916 to anticipate the firm's predictable action. The four of them organized — largely at DeGolyer's persuasion — the Alabama Exploration Syndicate, into which the firm might come whenever it chose. Anticipating this alliance, the first proposed capitalization was $60,000. DeGolyer approved leasing 35,000 acres. Six months later, the price of the leases had gone up 1,000 percent. The company decided, then, to seek leases also in the Osage country of Oklahoma. Nonetheless, DeGolyer, still hoping and expecting that Lord Cowdray would add the firm to the new enterprise, wrote the Chief: "In my opinion, the possibilities for future development in the State of Texas are greater than those of any other state."

This 1917 memo to the Chief also reminds Lord Cowdray of a famous event of 1910. Writes DeGolyer, with pardonable partisanship: "It is my opinion that the most wonderful opportunity which exists in the United States today is that of buying partially developed properties on the basis of their developed production . . . profits resulting from this operation have been so great as to be comparable even with the profits resulting from Bonanza Wells such as Potrero #4."

At the same time, he was insisting to associates Body, Ryder and Carr that Alabama be decisive, go right ahead with exploration, let the firm come in later if it likes. His partners, waiting on the Chief's decision, wanted a four-month period of investigation before making any really crucial decision. DeGolyer thought this policy meant lost time, wasted expense money, opportunities missed.

Anyway, his strategy at the outset was to "play it safe." He characterized the enterprise quite candidly as "a mercantile rather than a mining operation." His memorandum is quite precise. "The controlling theory of operation would be the leasing of apparently desirable lands directly from the owner and the sale, as soon as possible, of a block of leases large enough to return the working capital to the treasury of the company and yield a cash profit on the transaction. Certain well-selected leases would be retained as a speculation to await the result of drilling operations by others. This method is sound and feasible. It is a mercantile rather than a mining operation though it retains certain highly attractive speculative features by allowing for speculation out of the profits in the holding of leases whose cost has already been recovered by the sale of other leases."

DeGolyer insisted that the soundness of the plan was guaranteed "by our ability to select lands on proper geological structure." And in the case of particularly promising lands which the company might want to drill, he proposed still another safeguard. The company "should confine itself to the leasing of land and get the oil wells drilled by either forming a drilling company in which it would receive stock in exchange for leases, or by ceding acreage to outside parties in exchange for their assuming an obligation." As for his own salary, since "operation and management would be directly in the hands of DeGolyer," he would receive a certain share of paid-up stock, otherwise supervising the operations only for actual expenses incurred in connection with the company's work.

It was clear that his return to a flourishing Oklahoma oil boom had caught him up in the fever to get in on the big money. In a letter to Body, Carr and Ryder of April 16, 1917, he cites the experience of a young geologist friend who had recently paid him a visit in Norman. This successful young friend had become geologist for a similar enterprise, the Fortuna Oil Company, formed in 1915 on a capital of about $50,000. This company, wrote DeGolyer, "has recently sold 640 acres in leases, undrilled, for $1,600,-000, and still holds the bulk of the property." He admits this example is unusual, but . . .

He was persuasive. And so Alabama Exploration Syndicate became the pilot company for the Amerada Petroleum Company which in turn became the Amerada Corporation. It took a year or so, no doubt because of the war, for Lord Cowdray to come in. His capital allowed DeGolyer again to turn his attention to pioneering in geological development, to emphasize mining operations over mercantile. In short, to return to his obsession with salt domes.

9   Formation of Amerada

C HRISTMAS of 1918 was memorable for DeGolyer. On
December 19, he got a cablegram from Lord Cowdray:
"COME LONDON EARLIEST POSSIBLE HIGHLY IMPORTANT BRING
LATEST GEOLOGICAL DATA INFORMATION PARTICULARLY OF
DISTRICTS YOU BOTH [DeGolyer and Ryder] RECOMMEND DE-
VELOPING NEXT FEW YEARS." The company was bouncing
back from wartime restrictions, and speedily. S. Pearson
and Son would, at long last, extend its operation into
North America above the Mexican border.

Royal Dutch and Shell were eager to buy up Lord Cowdray's Mexican Eagle, estimated then as worth more than
a hundred million dollars, in order to round out their enterprises. This purchase was in progress when Cowdray
decided to set up the Amerada Corporation in early 1919.
The new company, to search for oil in the United States
and Canada, was incorporated at $2,500,000. Thomas Ry-
der, who held the title of president of Mexican Eagle, was
named president of Amerada; Everette DeGolyer was
made vice-president and general manager. Other officers
included Cowdray's famed right-hand man in Mexico, Mr.
Body, and Herbert I. Carr, who had directed the New York
office of Cowdray's enterprises.

DeGolyer's salary was to be $25,000 a year ($10,000 of which would derive from Mexican Eagle until the company severed its connection with the Mexican business); plus of course, a considerable share of common stock and a percentage of "the new profits of the consolidated accounts of Amerada Corporation and its subsidiaries." The office address was 65 Broadway, New York.

After Lord Cowdray came into American oil finding in 1919 with the formation of the Amerada Corporation, DeGolyer's trips to London became as frequent as his trips to Mexico. Here is how he described himself in his British passport for 1919: Height — 5 ft. 5 inches; build — stout; hair: light brown; distinctive marks — nil. Either he measured wrong or grew some more, for on later passports and visas he lists his height as five feet six inches.

If the great business event of 1919 was the formation of Amerada, so far as the DeGolyers were concerned, there was also a private event to be celebrated. Their third child, another daughter, christened Cecilia Jeanne, was born on April 2. It was a good omen for the new corporation's birth. (In his first four years with Amerada, he noted, each year showed a consistent increase over that of the previous year by approximately one half million barrels, and reached in 1925, for crude oil alone, a total of nearly four million barrels annually. Mexican Eagle's annual total at the time was about thirty million.)

Actually it was not until March 6, 1919, that the Chief — meeting with his staff in London — wrote "Approved" on the six-page memorandum DeGolyer read aloud. Messrs. Body and Ryder were also present. DeGolyer's memorandum opens with the renewed and familiar assertion: "I have felt in the past and now feel that no country presents better opportunities for building up a new and successful oil enterprise than the United States." He lists

Lord Cowdray, 1920. On the back of this photograph, Cowdray inscribed a special message for his young protégé, E. DeGolyer.

eleven great advantages. First of all, the possibilities of buying proven production on reasonable terms are superior to those in older fields. And the taxation likewise will be reasonable rather than, as in Mexico, confiscatory. In the United States, there is freedom from "vexatious regulation of drilling operations." There is mobile and quick availability of drilling supplies and of trained workmen. Wildcat areas (that is, away from proven fields) can be explored in cooperation with other companies, "thus reducing the cost of unsuccessful ventures," and wildcat territory can be leased at low cost. There is the prospect of purchase possibilities in partially proven lands gradually being auctioned off in the Osage country, plus the prospect of ultimately leasing lands currently withdrawn by the United States government. There is a ready market in which to sell producing properties in cases where the company might prefer not to operate them.

In this memorandum, DeGolyer stressed an important geological competence — the ability to estimate and appraise well production and to forecast the future oil market, shaken inevitably by times of feast and of famine in supply. But DeGolyer is optimistic. Even though overproduction results in lower prices for proven lands, "the periods of depression from overproduction are always very short" so "the opportunity to buy advantageously is very great."

The first operations of the new company, he states, should center around Alabama, Texas, Louisiana, Oklahoma. "I proposed approximately three years ago that we carry on operations in Texas. Since that time, some three new fields have been brought in on the Gulf Coast at regions which were well known previously, and the very important Ranger Field, the sensation of North Texas, has been discovered. I am certain that if we had gone in then

we should have been a going producing concern in the
U.S. today and I am quite as certain there are still wonderful possibilities in the regions outlined." Characterizing
Alabama as "a very attractive wildcat area," he notes that
Alabama Exploration has 30,000 acres of leasehold there,
where "anticlines are only sixty miles distant from tide water at Mobile." As for Texas, "I have made a particular
study of this salt-dome region during the past several
years. Important extensions to known fields which we
thought to be almost exhausted have been opened up. As
an example, I will call attention to Goose Creek, which
was brought in as an important field during the latter part
of 1916, to Damon Mound brought in as a commercial producer in 1917, though not yet extremely important, to Big
Hill, Liberty County and West Columbia, brought in as
important fields in 1918." DeGolyer, of course, had urged
Mexican Eagle in 1916, unsuccessfully, to explore this now
proved producing Gulf Coast area.

He proposes leaving to attorneys the matter of whether
to organize as a general holding company with subsidiaries for separate states or whether to form one single company. A main office will be needed in New York and a
working office in Texas or Oklahoma. "I shall want to
spend most of my time in the field and in this latter office."
The company will need, at the start, "a good man in the
New York office, capable of taking care of details and negotiating"; "a good production man to supervise exploration"; "one or more good land men" and "possibly a confidential agent for the same type of work." Above all, much
preliminary work must be done in compiling maps and
records. "Approved," wrote Cowdray on his copy of the
memorandum.

The first audited balance sheet of the Amerada Corporation was dated December 31, 1920. It showed that the

company had absorbed the temporary Amerada Petroleum Company — under which momentary name organization took place in 1919 — and controlled two subsidiaries: Goodrich Oil Company (capitalized at $83,526), and the Cameron Oil Company (capitalized at $1,000). The net profit for the year was $384,351.52. Wells in Oklahoma, Kansas and Louisiana had produced slightly more than 250,000 barrels, the big producers being in the Blunt and Hominy fields in Oklahoma and the Urschel field in Kansas. The capital stock consisted of 20,000 shares at a par value of $100 each, all issued to the Amerada Corporation and fully paid. The deficit for the preceding 1919 year — spent on launching the company — amounted to $46,526.90. Three years later the net profit was just short of four million dollars. Lord Cowdray set that goal for 1924 operations. (In an article on the Amerada in 1952, *Time* magazine commented that by 1926 DeGolyer had already made Amerada a "small success.")

A significant item of the first balance sheet of the company is the figure paid out for "geological expenses" (salaries and travel expenses of geologists) in 1920: $124,-128.67. A bonus of $10,000 was provided for DeGolyer, plus his fixed salary. On August 20, the governing board authorized issuing 500,000 shares at $10 each; by year's end 224,660 shares had been issued.

The auditor's account reads: "The date of incorporation is June 4th, 1919. No accounts are submitted for the period June 4th 1919 to December 31st 1919. . . . The original capital of the Corporation was ten thousand shares of $100 each. Under date of October 22, 1919, the minutes of the Corporation authorized an increase in the capital stock to the extent of $2,000,000, divided into twenty thousand shares of $100 each."

There is a story about that second million. DeGolyer

crossed the ocean late that summer of 1919 to tell Lord
Cowdray a second million was needed. He also needed,
desperately he felt, news of a big strike. He had none. Just
before he walked into the conference he was handed a telegram. Beaming with delight, he passed it around. Lord
Cowdray read it, then said drily, "I trust this surprise was
not arranged beforehand." The telegram announced the
bringing in the day before of what promised to be a real
gusher. Then Cowdray beamed too — and signed the au-
thorization. DeGolyer was his lucky talisman, his rabbit's
foot. Some London book shops felt the effect.

Amerada's first southwestern well was begun in the
Oklahoma Osage country on February 12, 1920, and was
called No. 1 Signs. Of all the lore of the oil industry, the
legends of Osage country are among the most powerfully
imbedded in public memory.

The Osage tribe was moved in 1872 by the federal government into the northern tableland of Oklahoma to occupy some "leftover" land in former Cherokee country.
The tribe was pathetically poor, existing on government
subsidy and on money from leasing their land to cattlemen. But oil prospecting as early as 1904 began to hold out
promise of a brighter future. In 1912, the Indian Agency
held at Pawhuska the first auctions for oil and gas leases
on Osage lands. By 1918, nine auctions had been held, dis-
posing of oil and gas leases on nearly 200,000 acres of land
for $13,000,000.

Then in 1920 came the great Burbank strike. The Osages
in a decade went from bedrolls to bankrolls and became
per capita, after Burbank, among the richest people in the
world. The government had fixed their royalties at one-
sixth of the production of wells on their land, and in case
of wells producing over one hundred barrels, one-fifth. In
addition to royalties, the Indian owner got a well-location

fee of $35 for the drilling of every well, successful or not, and $100 in case the location were near his house, plus a fee for storage tanks erected on his property. There were 2,260 Osages listed on the tribal roll; the average bonus for each in 1919 (before Burbank) was about $7,000. The "take," for example, of one Osage family of eleven — father, mother, and nine children — was about $55,000. (The mineral lands of the Osages were held in common by the tribe; so each headright — as established by tribal roll prior to statehood in 1907 — shared equally in mineral income to the tribe.)

As the government opened more Osage lands to public auction, the competition in the bidding became staggering. The auction sale of February 3, 1920, drew more than five hundred prospective bidders to Pawhuska, including representatives of the seven-month-old Amerada, most of them coming from Tulsa by train. The train was late; the auctioneer did not start the bidding until ten-thirty in the morning. Because of rain and cold, the bidding was not held outdoors but moved into a theater building. At luncheon recess, Methodist and Presbyterian Ladies Aid groups vied for customers at chicken dinners, the Methodists charging fifty cents more than the Presbyterian one-dollar meal. In the evening the Christian Church served dinner. The auction ended just before ten. The returning Tulsa bidders got to bed long after midnight, to dream of the rewards from the three million dollars' worth of leases they had acquired that day. The *National Petroleum News* headlined its report of the auction: "Our Government's Biggest Gambling Center at Pawhuska."

Amerada did not really gamble very heavily. Compared with the $220,000 investment of the Phillips Petroleum Company and the $201,000 of the Marland Refining Company, Amerada's acquisition of Tract 31 at $55,000 looked prudent. But at that time, Phillips already had 415 producing wells, and owned properties of great promise. For fledgling Amerada to risk a quarter of what Phillips did was proof of DeGolyer's standard theory that "knowledge counts for nothing if you're not willing to take risks."

Amerada's first well, #1 Signs, proved the matter of risk. It turned out to be a dry hole. Five months later it was redeemed by #1 Hominy, from which Amerada sold its first oil on July 13, 1920. And it went on from there to operate successfully in the following Oklahoma fields: Seminole County, Cromwell, Tonkawa, Boggs, Duncan and Cushing.

DeGolyer had a special gift, about which all testimony is uniform, for picking out the right man for the right job. In a larger sense, he had an almost flawless intuition for recognizing talent and a man's competence. He knew how to choose. When his choice proved wrong, he usually discovered that the man wasn't wrong, but that the assigned job was. The man was transferred to some other activity. As a sample of his acumen, one may note that of the first eleven presidents of the American Association of Petroleum Geologists, nine received their training, or part of it, in the field under DeGolyer's direction. The choice of geologists for burgeoning Amerada was another proof. Sidney Powers, another University of Oklahoma product, became chief geologist of the company's Oklahoma division, with headquarters in Tulsa; John Lovejoy was in charge of the mid-continent division, with headquarters in Shreveport; and Donald Barton was engaged in 1919 as chief geologist of the Gulf Coast division, with offices in Houston. Barton would head the major wildcatting exploration (that is, drilling in areas where no oil had been found before). But at the outset, the company policy was to begin cautiously. Only ten percent of the budget for exploration was to be used for wildcatting.

As DeGolyer summarized the matter for his friend Ed Hopkins in a letter of August 30, 1920: "Our operations up to the present time have been quite successful, but it has been our policy to stick rather closely to proven production. Until quite recently, at any rate, the capital at our disposal has not been large enough to justify any very extended wildcat operations. As a result, however, of our success in establishing production and increase in capital, we are now in a position to go about it in a small way and I had planned to take up several blocks of acreage for the purpose of selling off part of them and building an exploratory well. I need not explain that this is a legitimate method of operation very widely indulged in even by the most important of the companies operating in the midcontinent field."

At this time, about a year after incorporation, Amerada had fifteen geologists on the payroll for Oklahoma and Kansas, three in coastal Texas. The geological expense for the first year had run to something over one hundred thousand dollars. Donald Barton, however, was early sidetracked from wildcatting to the development of geophysical methods and devices for locating oil. A Ph.D. from Harvard, Barton had done commercial surveying for oil in Texas and the South before joining Amerada in 1919. His instincts were scholarly and he was an inveterate preparer of papers or essays on his research. After returning from the purchase of the Eötvös torsion balance in Hungary, his assignment was "to make a thorough study of all the salt domes as a guide to investment and drilling operations by Amerada." Barton's urge to publish geological data was encouraged by his boss, who had steadily been doing the same thing since 1912. But this matter of pooling all scientific knowledge posed a problem. By 1923, De-Golyer felt that Amerada was doing far more than its share of this scientific contribution, and observed that the big companies were considerably more reluctant to do so than Amerada.

Not unexpectedly after the conclusion of World War I, the matter of national ownership of oil flared up again in the public mind. Amerada, British controlled, was a ready target, as was Royal Dutch Shell, which had started exploration in this country as early as 1916. DeGolyer, on his regular trips to London, urged Lord Cowdray to use his influence with the government to make Britain a "reciprocal nation" in regard to oil investments and exploration by non-British companies. On paper, there was a certain toleration, but for all practical purposes foreign companies were carefully shut out of the only two oil-producing areas in the Commonwealth, India and Trinidad. The natural retaliation in the United States would be "anti-alien" legislation, at least on a statewide level, forbidding the purchase of leaseholds to companies whose stock was more than fifty percent foreign owned.

The menace arose early, primarily against Royal Dutch because of its size and power. But DeGolyer found himself writing defensive notes at home, while urging action on the London office to ward off national reprisal. He wrote to Wallace Pratt in 1921 that obviously the matter of the nationality of the capital involved in Amerada's operation was a "touchy point at the present time." But he assured Pratt that despite the fact that the control of the company was British, "I might say that four or five Americans have practically their entire capital invested in it and that it is controlled and operated by Americans. There is no need of my saying that it is an ordinary mining operation and that the question of the *control* of oil is not involved."

That he felt on the defensive is clear from this assertion to Pratt: "So far as my own connections with English capital and foreign enterprise are concerned, I have no apology to make in respect of the benefits which have come to my country." The benefits, he observes, have been double. Obviously, one lies in the developed techniques of oil discovery, the other is the fact that "We have supplied millions of barrels of oil to the United States in the past from the Mexican operations. In fact our best American customers are the interests which I understand control your company."

He adds, emphasizing another area of service: "I have promised David White to work up a professional paper on salt domes in which I hope to make available most of the information gained by our surveys, and a very great amount of information which I now have in hand regarding the salt domes of the Isthmus of Tehuantepec."

After rumblings against foreign-controlled oil companies rose to a roar, DeGolyer sent a very long letter to Mr. Body on February 6, 1923, outlining the danger. "I do not think it safe," he observes, "for Amerada to take further leaseholds in Oklahoma. Messrs. Carr, Ryder and myself have organized a strictly American corporation known as the Rycade Corporation (first two letters of the last name of each) and we shall take all Indian leasehold in the future. Approval of such leasehold cannot be denied to us on the grounds of alien control, and we shall then be in position to offer the leasehold to the Amerada Corporation, and in the event of the transfer being disapproved, the Rycade will still have title to the leasehold."

He adds that he, Carr and Ryder consider the cause of the legislation to be "fundamental" and that "our positions will never be entirely safe until there is complete reciprocity between the British empire and the United States with

regard to land and lease holdings." Knowing the power of
the Chief, he urged on Mr. Body "the desirability of Lord
Cowdray's personal intervention."

The long letter was in explanation of a telegram sent a
few days before which stated that not only was British
control of Amerada jeopardized but also the possibility
that all British holdings "must be eliminated."

American newspapers and magazines were full of reports about the various state programs of anti-alien legislation. The *Literary Digest* called the furor a product of
"The World Race for Oil." Texas passed such legislation
in 1923. Oklahoma tried, but in May, Secretary of the Interior Hubert Work revoked the anti-alien laws in regard
to Indian Reservations. Nonetheless, DeGolyer wrote Lord
Cowdray on May 17, "I should like to suggest that it will
certainly be very much to the advantage of the Amerada,
as well as the Royal Dutch Shell group, for the British empire to become fully reciprocative, as I think that we shall
have to face anti-alien legislation in the future, and it may
be anti-alien legislation federal in scope."

Lord Cowdray answered promptly and calmly, though
with "great relief" at the action of Secretary of Interior
Hubert Work. Nevertheless he saw the handwriting on the
wall and had made his plans. His reply forecasts the future of Amerada, while revealing its success. Anticipating
that Oklahoma may in time pass laws "similar to those existing in Texas," he says, "let us hope that this will not occur until after the expiration of 1925, by which time we
hope, according to the programme we discussed and settled when I was with you, to be earning a net $4,000,000
a year. It may be that now that Amerada can handle the
Indian leases that we can justifiably look forward to even
bigger earnings by that date. But the goal is $4,000,000;

and anything better will be due to special luck or fore-thought."

He adds: "The possibility of adverse legislation (from our point of view) in Oklahoma must make us hurry forward and develop the Amerada property with every promptitude. You have now the resources to do so, and clearly if it be possible for us to put ourselves into the position of being an American-controlled concern before adverse legislation be enacted, it will be an immense relief to us all."

This position is, in fact, being prepared. "I assume that the scheme which we devised for handling the properties in Texas could be equally made applicable to handle the Amerada leases in Oklahoma (or any other state), should similar legislation to that of Texas be passed before we hand over the Amerada undertakings to the large American-controlled company that we have in contemplation."

The "handing over" was completed between 1924 and 1926. The Cowdray family split its 60 percent ownership in half. Wall Street's Dillon, Read and Company sold half the stock on the U.S. market at $26 a share. Still later, the Cowdray holdings were left at 17 percent. A share of Amerada stock bought in 1926 at $26 was worth, a quarter century later, $940. DeGolyer by then had pulled out to go into business on his own (1932), and had, alas, sold his Amerada stock.

Lord Cowdray died a year after the 1926 Dillon, Read sale of Amerada stock; his son, Viscount Cowdray, succeeded him as head of the family enterprises. Meantime, in 1923, the Rycade Corporation had been formed, with much legal counsel and procedure, to take over Amerada's Texas holdings of approximately six thousand leased acres. The sale was made at a price of $850,000. The president of the new corporation was Thomas Ryder; vice-president,

E. DeGolyer; secretary-treasurer, H. J. Carr. The technical development of these properties was to be immensely augmented in 1925, when DeGolyer organized the subsidiary Geophysical Research Corporation, which he served as president.

It was also in the year that Rycade was formed (1923) that DeGolyer was finally allowed, after what he called a "half-dozen" attempts, to resign from his long-time post as continuing consulting geologist for Mexican Eagle. He maintained, quite understandably, that he no longer had time to make two trips a year to Mexico. Dr. Erb, in charge of the geology department, accepted the resignation with greatest reluctance. He told Mr. Body that it was little short of a calamity for DeGolyer's geological knowledge of Mexico to go unused, and insisted on a final conference for drilling advice about the future.

But as Lord Cowdray had observed in 1923, "you now have the resources" — for Amerada had generously appropriated large sums for research. From the start, Lord Cowdray had affirmed the operating principle: "plow every possible penny of income back into the ground in exploration and new drillings; drill up the profits, thus pyramid them in the ground."

10   The Geophysical Revolution

THE DRAMA of the Amerada Corporation, during its first decade, lay in its association with geophysical progress. The amount of knowledge about oil exploration that had accumulated from Spindletop to the launching of the Amerada Corporation in 1919 was considerable and most of this had come in the preceding decade. As DeGolyer wrote K. C. Heald of the Gulf Oil Corporation in 1950, "As late as 1910, after the geologists of the Survey (USGS) had done a lot of work in Pennsylvania, the nature of oil occurrence was still in great confusion. About all that seemed to have come through clearly was a recognition of the gravitational stratification of gas, oil and water." And he observes that when he went to Mexico in 1909, "we were looking for anticlines but we stuck mighty close to oil seepages. With the crude methods then available to us, structure could not be mapped in Mexico with much degree of precision. I suspect that the companies would have done as well if they had drilled on oil seepages alone."

Even so, the field geologists were producing articles and classifying data as well as producing wells. His earliest contributions to the technical journals reveal his profound absorption in the problem of oil's relationship to salt domes. He writes: "I first became actively interested in the salt dome structures of the Isthmus of Tehuantepec during the early part of 1913, at which time I visited the Ixhuatlan field with the late Dr. Hayes and there met Paul Weaver. At that time Ixhuatlan and Tecuanapa were being exploited and were in their prime. The old San Cristóbal-Copoacán and Soledad fields had produced approximately one and one-half million barrels of oil and were on the decline. Various wells had been drilled on other salt domes but without favorable commercial results. Exploration had been confined almost entirely to the top of the domes and the production was coming from cap rock in all of the fields but Ixhuatlan, where production was from shallow sands arched over the salt core. The other fields had been drilled rather closely — somewhat overdrilled in fact — and though our company held thousands of acres of leasehold covering practically all known domes, and had built a refinery to handle the production, the whole venture was a disappointing one from the commercial viewpoint.

"My first real study of any of these fields was made in 1916, when Weaver and myself reviewed in detail the Concepción field of salt dome. . . . This first opportunity to study a dome in detail, however, aroused my interest in salt domes to a high degree. . . . It seemed probable that a study of one habit of oil occurrence in this peculiar and interesting type of structure in countries other than Mexico might indicate unexplored possibilities in our own problems of dome prospecting."

But he found the search of geological literature most unsatisfactory. "No real detailed study of even a single American dome was available and the more general descriptions ran high in theory and speculation but low in detailed description. Statistical reviews and trade journals indicated the rejuvenation of American domes, however, by the discovery of deep lateral sands, so I visited the various salt domes of Texas and Louisiana in order to obtain definite information on the relation of the lateral sands to the domes. This study was quite satisfactory, and through the kindness of the geologists and operators of that region, particularly Alexander Deussen and E. T. Dumble, I was able to get an exact idea of the significance of the new development."

He then decided, contrary to an earlier report he had made, that the deep lateral sands around the domes on the Isthmus of Tehuantepec were indeed promising. He gave thanks that the company, fortunately, had not rescinded a contract on a large hacienda which he and Weaver had earlier suggested. After further study of better exposed Texas domes, particularly West Point and Palestine, and concentrated reflection on the Humble field, he and Weaver recommended the drilling of twelve wells around known domes in the Isthmus and locations were successfully made.

But once geophysics came to the aid of geology, the increased knowledge led DeGolyer to prophesy. He wrote the second Lord Cowdray a memo on September 15, 1931, claiming that "a hundred thousand acres of geophysically selected leasehold should contain more barrels of oil than the average million acres selected under best previous practice."

The founding of the Amerada Corporation was perhaps the most influential single event in the application of scientific techniques to the finding of oil. Historically, the date 1919 is a major one in the industry. From it dates the universal respect oilmen hold for DeGolyer as the pioneer of geophysical exploration. For at least a decade he was to know more about it than any other living soul; for at least a decade he probably handled more geophysical development than any other single individual. As executive head of the corporation, he was able by 1920 to commission the construction of the two torsion balances which he had initiated soon after World War I with the Eötvös Institute in Hungary. He arranged for a joint field test by Amerada and Mexican Eagle, after contracting for the two instruments from Ferdinand Suss of Budapest. Construction of the instruments did not start till August 1921. While waiting, DeGolyer selected Donald C. Barton to handle the first surveys with the instruments, sending him to Budapest in May 1922 to receive the finished torsion balances, which had been standardized by Dr. Pekar of the Eötvös Institute.

Upon arrival in Budapest, Dr. Barton found that the instruments were still incomplete. DeGolyer directed him to go to Germany and to prepare a report upon geophysical research being undertaken there. As a result of this reconnaissance, Barton visited Ludger Mintrop and sent back a report on the seismic refraction method, which was regarded as sound but had not proved anything practically. Dr. Mintrop was a famous German scientist who directed the German use of the seismograph in World War I for locating — by the interpretation of recorded sound waves — hidden artillery batteries.

The Eötvös torsion balances built by Suss were delivered in New York on September 5, 1922. They were in Houston in early November. The first survey was conducted at the Spindletop Salt Dome, in early December. An electric-current atmosphere circulated in the watchful oil world. This was the first or at least one of the first surveys of an oil pool made by geophysical methods in the United States.

DeGolyer's notes on this survey run thus:

This survey, covering but a limited area, showed a brilliant and outstanding gravity maximum. It was regarded as a great success and as proving the utility of the method, though in the light of our more extensive knowledge of the gravity expression of salt domes, it must be regarded as in the nature of a lucky accident, since Spindletop is one of the very few definite gravity maxima in the entire coastal regions, and experience has taught us that it is the minima rather than the maxima which are important in salt dome prospecting.

Falsely reassured by the apparently brilliant success of the initial experiment, surveys were extended to other known domes, with vague and indifferent results. Various prospects were drilled and failed.

Just because the initial testing seemed at first such a major breakthrough, the meager results that followed when the technique was applied to other known domes doubled the discouragement and disappointment. Prospects were elatedly found, and then failed to have any economic importance. Actually, the first surveys were soon known to be faulty because of the limited small areas they covered. They were not regarded as adequate tests of the value of the torsion balance or of geophysical method.

DeGolyer was on the point of abandoning this experimental work when he got a report on a survey of the Nash area in southern Fort Bend County, Texas, which showed a gravity maximum as definite and as brilliant as that of Spindletop. He promptly ordered a well drilled in November of 1924. It encountered cap rock at 684 feet, salt at 943 feet. After a number of dry holes at first (causing the oil fraternity to call this "DeGolyer's Golf Course"), this became the first successful geophysical prospect to be proved in the United States, oil being discovered on the flank of this dome January 3, 1926. It was also probably the first oil pool to be discovered by geophysical methods in the entire world.

Meantime a German crew engaged by DeGolyer and under the direction of Dr. L. Mintrop of the Seismos Company had been working in Mexico for Mexican Eagle, trying in late 1923 to locate an extension of the buried Tamasopo ridge, the locus of the bonanza pools of the Golden Lane. The results were disappointing. At about the same time the Marland Company was using another Mintrop crew in various surveys in Oklahoma and northern Texas, likewise disappointing; indeed at one point DeGolyer and Marland's chief geologist had decided after comparing results that the method was not usable.

In 1924 DeGolyer had the same opinion of another experiment of the Marland Company, which had engaged a Mintrop "refraction" crew in March 1924 for work on the Gulf Coast. DeGolyer had to change his mind a little later. Though Marland's crew had no success, a second Mintrop refraction crew working for Gulf Production Company located by year's end the great Orchard Dome, also in Fort Bend County, Texas. This was promptly labeled "the first seismic discovery in the United States and possibly the first in the world."

DeGolyer saw he had misjudged the refraction method; he decided that "It was superior to the torsion balance in a highly competitive search for salt domes." So he and Barton started the search for an American to take up seismic work, and to become operating vice-president of the Geophysical Research Corporation, which DeGolyer organized in May 1925 as a subsidiary of the Amerada and Rycade Corporations.

The first problem in founding Geophysical Research Corporation was to persuade Lord Cowdray to grant, through Amerada, the necessary operating fund. The second was to find the right man to run it, in the position similar to DeGolyer's with Amerada. Both were easily solved. Although the promised Midas touch that the refraction seismograph at first suggested ended in near failure about 1924, the London management was willing to advance a hundred thousand dollars a month, on a provisional or temporary basis, for the development of the new "art" of finding oil.

Professor F. M. Bozell of the University of Oklahoma, an old friend of DeGolyer's, spoke with enthusiasm of John Clarence Karcher and his admittedly inconclusive seismographic experiments in Oklahoma. DeGolyer paid heed, looked Karcher up at an oil convention in Chicago in 1924, discussed the latter's reflection theories and their Oklahoma testing. DeGolyer was immediately impressed, asked Karcher to arrange to come to New York.

Karcher's background had close parallels with DeGolyer's. Though he was born in Indiana, his father had moved the family to a farm in Oklahoma in 1900, when Karcher was six years old. He got his early schooling at Hennessy, then entered the University of Oklahoma in 1912, the year after DeGolyer had taken leave of Tampico long enough to complete his degree requirements. DeGolyer knew him as a student there in 1916. Exceptionally brilliant, Karcher went on to the University of Pennsylvania for graduate work. While he was working for the Bureau of Standards in Washington during World War I, the United States government sent the young physicist to the front lines in France to help determine, by making studies of sound waves generated in the air by artillery fire, the location of enemy batteries. This, of course, was precisely what Dr. Ludger Mintrop was doing in Germany with his scientific instruments based on the seismograph. Already in 1919, Karcher had applied for patents in this country on the reflection seismic method, and was doing experimental work in the field by 1921.

An associate of Karcher's in the Bureau of Standards, Dr. W. P. Haseman, was working on a method to detect submarines by sound waves through sea water. After the war, the two men formed a company to conduct oil exploration by seismographic methods in Oklahoma. On their first experiment, Dr. Haseman tripped on a cable, unexpectedly escaped injury when he fell only a few yards away from the explosion. Undaunted, they persevered, but with indecisive results. The great Burbank field in Oklahoma roared in just at this time, deluging the oil market with a disastrous surplus. The bottom fell out of the price structure. The two scientists abandoned their venture for the time being.

A few weeks after his New York conference, DeGolyer discovered that their paths would cross on opposite cross-country trips. He wired Karcher to meet him at St. Louis for a talk between trains. There, in the vast and vaulted second-floor waiting room of the Union Station, they came to an agreement. For all practical purposes, the Geophysical Research Corporation was organized. DeGolyer would be president, Karcher vice-president and general manager. Amerada and Rycade would supply the capital, 50 percent each. In addition to his salary, Karcher was to get a 15 percent share of the stock, a proviso on which he was unyielding. Karcher was to recruit a staff of four or five young scientists, with special training in physics. He got a brilliant galaxy.

The first one he picked was Eugene McDermott, who had done his graduate work at Columbia University and was working with the New York laboratories of Bell Telephone. The first man in the field was Esme Eugene Rosaire, whom Karcher knew for his work with Western Electric in Chicago. From the University of Chicago, Karcher added the physicist, Dr. F. M. Kannenstine. Later came S. B. Weatherby, Ted Born and H. B. Peacock.

Rosaire reported to Houston in June 1925, "without," he said, "the slightest idea of what it was all about." DeGolyer commented: "We are at the beginnings of an art about which we know practically nothing." At any rate, extreme secrecy was being practiced by everybody then active in the new techniques.

Actually, although Geophysical Research Corporation gets credit for playing the major part in setting the pace for technical progress and for actual achievement in both refraction and reflection seismograph development, it got off to a later start than some others. When it was launched in 1925, there were already the three German Seismos crews working in the United States, two engaged by Marland, one by Gulf. The latter, to everybody's consternation, turned out to be the Mintrop crew that DeGolyer had recommended for Mexican Eagle in 1921 and which he had recommended abandoning in 1924 after poor results. Gulf snapped up the idle unit for use on the Texas-Louisiana coast. Marland claimed "exclusive rights" to Mintrop's method in the United States, but the quarrel was amiably resolved. Meantime, in 1924, Humble had decided to organize its own seismographic work from scratch — without use of foreign-made instruments — and under Wallace Pratt's direction was conducting "fan-shooting" of sites on the King Ranch.

Geophysical Research Corporation's first equipment was designed and built in New York by Karcher and McDermott; it arrived in Texas for use in the field in July 1925.

McDermott and Rosaire headed the two crews. Karcher and McDermott built their geophone or "pick-up" from a Baldwin ear-piece radio receiver. The oscillograph, or "camera," was made from a standard moving-picture camera and ran 36-mm. paper through the regular sprocket wheels.

The steady concern of these scientists was to perfect the apparatus; their steady problem was to solve difficulties that arose from use of the devices in the field. (It is interesting to note that the oil industry *currently* maintains approximately three hundred geophysical crews in the field, at an annual cost of about $36 million.)

Although DeGolyer's new company started its first work on the Nash Dome, its first really spectacular success came in 1927, with Amerada's prospecting of an area held by Louisiana Land and Exploration Company. The latter was a merger, arranged through Dillon, Read, of Colonel Simms' Border Research Corporation and a land-holding company of Mr. H. H. Timken (of Timken Roller Bearings) which had originally leased Louisiana land out of interest in the muskrat market. Amerada, through its subsidiary Geophysical Research, was to explore their leasehold by the refraction method. And DeGolyer was made a member of the Board of Louisiana Land.

DeGolyer and his new vice-president, who later became DeGolyer's administrative successor with Amerada, A. A. Jacobsen, felt so sure of their system, Amerada took the job for costs; instead of a fee they took stock and mortgage bonds in the new company as Amerada's profit. As a further sign of faith, they bought $95,000 worth of Louisiana Land's stock. So much oil was found as a result of this single exploration that Amerada's stock in the venture was worth $11 million a quarter century later, more than a thousand percent increase. In addition, by that time, this stock had paid more than four million dollars in dividends.

The two crews organized for this job had to work from boats. Since the German seismos methods were not usable for exploring water-covered areas, this Geophysical Research survey represented the first really extensive exploration of water-surfaced land.

E. E. Rosaire started the first crew to work in July 1927 on Sabine Lake, using boats he was able to secure locally. He saw a problem at once, and ordered the construction of a much more suitable "water equipment," a houseboat built on a barge. Sabine Lake exploration revealed no "anomaly," no salt dome. The crew moved on into Lake Calcasieu. The "shooting" took place in the water; the recording was made on land, thanks to watertight geophones and enormous lengths of waterproof cable. A dome was soon discovered under Calcasieu and its presence checked by cross-profiles.

There was a curious problem not present on dry land — the fish. The crew's catch was enormous — and illegal. Only the sneaky among sportsmen got their haul on a grand scale by resorting to dynamite. To prevent such unsportsmanlike catches, the state had passed laws, laws which the geophysical crews were unexpectedly violating. Crew leader Rosaire found himself served with an almost weekly warrant by irate game wardens. A special act of the legislature finally made things clear and kept him out of jail. A new law granted to "lessors of water-covered state fee lands" the right to permit oil prospecting. But the oil people cooperated. In order to protect the interests of fishermen, they accepted the assignment of a game warden to each water crew. His duty was to report to the Conservation Commission the extent of fish depopulation caused by explosions. To everyone's relief and surprise, the number of casualties turned out to be astonishingly slight and the number of domes found was surprisingly large. Late in 1927 Rosaire's crew was operating in Terrebonne Bay and located four domes in a matter of two days. They were able to explore 60,000 acres in one single day, from two shot points.

Still, operations were much easier on dry land. In those early days of seismic work, the dynamite charges usually averaged between eight hundred and a thousand pounds. They were placed in the bottom of a hole dug out to a depth of ten feet and about four feet square. The dynamite was covered with a little dirt, which in turn was covered with the broken-up, emptied boxes in which the dynamite was transported. This was a precaution to keep from leaving evidence around for scouts of rival companies. The "shooting master" had to calculate his fuse length to give him time to climb out of the hole and beat it to safety. Sometimes a car was kept running near the hole to provide a quick getaway. Adverse winds could interfere so unfavorably with the calculations that they often required field operations to be postponed. Since successive shots were usually fired in the same hole, thirty-feet wide craters were usually left. Again for secrecy, and primarily to relieve the unhappiness of the landowner at this result, locally hired workers filled them up by team and scraper.

The operator and the recording seismograph were usually housed in a lightproof tent which served as dark room, for the record was developed immediately after the shock impulse. Ice was required for this operation; a standard part of the crew equipment was a large icebox. A good day's performance was judged to be from six to eight shots, supplying one or two "profiles" of the structure.

The veil of secrecy spurred rivals to impressive spy tactics. Once Rosaire thought to sneak away under cover of dark with some very impressive recordings to show the Houston office. He found his and the crew's cars all chained together. The garageman explained this was done to insure safety and no theft. Actually, he was in the pay of a competitor's scout who wanted to be alerted about any nighttime travel away from the scene of the dynamiting.

The first impressive record for discovery was set by the Gulf Company, under chief geologist L. P. Garrett's instituting "fan shooting" * with the Mintrop Seismos crew. In rapid succession, Gulf made discoveries at Orchard (Fort Bend County, Texas), Hawkinsville (Matagorda County, Texas), Fannetta (Jefferson County), Starks (Louisiana) and Fausse Pointe (Louisiana).

But, high as it was, this discovery rate probably ranked second to the record set by Geophysical Research Corporation for Louisiana Land and Exploration in 1927–1928. Eugene McDermott piled up the championship record. Crews under his direction located ten domes in those two years.

These were the years when Karcher perfected the reflection seismograph method, reducing refraction methods to the same poor second that refraction had done to the torsion balance. Karcher introduced a number of innovations, including the electrical seismograph, the determination of the time of shot explosions by radio, the use of air sound waves for surveying position.

Geophysical Research Corporation's initial experimental work in 1925, done on the Nash salt dome, actually used a spare torsion balance hut as a darkroom — with an inferno-like temperature inside. All the apparatus was hauled out to the site by wagon; the crew rode out on

* A system of locating half a dozen or so explosive charges in an open-fan distribution, for better underground "mapping."

horseback. The field and laboratory men worked about fifteen hours a day, seven days a week.

No wonder that by the early thirties the whole Gulf Coast area regarded as salt dome territory had been thoroughly explored; no wonder that in a decade about sixty new salt domes were discovered. DeGolyer once wrote that "in 1903 and 1904, a prospect off a known dome was probably worse than a several hundred to one shot." Scientific exploration had yielded a rich harvest of new "known domes."

The accumulation of geological data and the increasing knowledge about how to interpret this classified information gave the geologist an acknowledged importance in locating favorable structures. But at most he could only recommend likely prospects; the finding of oil was not an exact science. But to be as nearly exact as possible was the ideal. Geophysics was simply an incorporation of certain principles of physics into geology for the purpose of making the mapping and locations of structures more complete, more accurate and faster. This could be done by fusing with geological science such theories of physics as the principles of magnetic attraction, the pull of gravity, the speed of sound waves, even the behavior of electrical currents.

Devices had to be invented in order to apply these means of detection of the earth's subsurface structure; and the inventions of course would require endless refinement and improvement. Nonetheless, only the drill itself could finally determine whether a geologically logical (or favorable) structure actually housed an oil pool. Geophysics emerged as a superior technique for reducing the guesswork, or rather the possibilities of error in interpretation of data, to a minimum.

Like the invention of the microscope, the geophysical

instruments to record the structure of the subsurface allowed a great enlargement of the geological eye, of what could be "seen" that remained invisible to the naked eye. Such an extension of scientific knowledge could obviously, in the matter of oil, be fortune making. In comparison with merely geological techniques, geophysics could — so to speak — sweep up the gold with a broom. The geophysicists were the conquistadors of the New World of oil.

The geologist was looking for beds of sedimentary rocks, laid down by ancient seas with their rich deposits of mineral and vegetable matter, which, under heat and pressure, turned into hydrocarbons, into oil. He was also looking for the two other kinds of rock classifications, igneous and metamorphic, so he could avoid them. They were his curse. By the nature of their formation in geological time, through volcanic action and other forms of intensified heat or pressure, they were very rarely likely to contain oil. But their location was important for another reason — they were the flooring for the marine-formed, or sedimentary, rocks in which oil had accumulated.

Since nearly all rocks contain at least minute portions of iron, a device to allow the measurement of varying magnetic attraction in underground strata would allow the prediction of upfolded sedimentary rocks, of anticlines and salt domes, prediction of their presence or absence, for they have a lesser magnetic intensity than igneous and metamorphic rocks.

To measure this intensity, geophysics developed the "magnetometer," which looks something like a photographer's box on a tripod. By a complicated and delicate system of charting the intensity of magnetic attraction as registered on the recordings of the magnetometer, immensely useful data could be added to the pool of geological knowledge about the nature of rock strata below the earth's crust.

Similarly, electrical methods attached to a drilling core could test the resistance to electric current of various rock strata through which the drill passed, contributing further facts which could be decoded into a picture of the substructure underground.

The torsion balance and the gravimeter permitted measurement of the gravitational pull of the earth, which varies slightly — a variation which Baron Roland von Eötvös's invention could detect — according to the nature of the rocks below. Again, information was gained in mapping invisible structure, and in discovering the presence of salt domes. The deciphering of the recordings of the torsion balance were of staggering mathematical complexity. In this DeGolyer had an edge. All who knew him agree that he was a mathematical wizard, gifted in this sort of brain work more than in any other. The gravimeter was in essence an improvement on the torsion balance. It required less mathematical calculation and it allowed swifter interpretation and mapping at far less cost. The torsion balance had to be transported on a truck and required the services of a crew ranging from eight to a dozen or more workers.

Most successful of the new inventions, however, were those that measured the inner space reactions to manmade earthquakes. Dr. Mintrop's seismograph method was the forerunner of this technique, recommended by DeGolyer for Mexican Eagle experimentation in 1921. As noted, the results of Dr. Mintrop's device and his German crews, both in Mexico and on the Gulf Coast, were at first largely disappointing until L. P. Garrett, chief geologist for Gulf Oil Company, refined the technique with his system of fantail shooting.

Just as observatories measure remote tremors in the

earth's surface from distances faraway, the seismograph instrument measured the tremors set up around it by explosions of carefully placed dynamite. By recording the speed at which the shocks pierced the strata of rocks, in already mapped structure, the instrument disclosed the variations in different formations by transmitting or reflecting back the sound waves of the explosion. Comparing these data with that of hitherto unmapped territory, the geophysicist had a guide to determine the rock structure of the new area. In brief, the seismographic method, and its later refinement known as "reflection" and "refraction" shooting, provided a photographically recorded indication of the substructure as the shock waves traveled through the rock and were reflected back to the recording instrument. Computation of the traveling speed of the waves could diagnose the various formations they traversed. Like the torsion balance, the seismographic instruments required a crew of a dozen or so men and truck or wagon transportation to the site to be tested.

The life of the crewmen was adventurous and arduous. They got to roadless locations with dangerous bouncing enroute. They tested swampland, infested with snakes, blew up thousands of bird nests and terrified the animal population — probably soured the milk of one generation of coastal cows. Their saga deserves to be written. Some of them have benefited in another way from the pull of gravitation, becoming ranking officers in the oil companies.

But all this work, save in a few cases of electrical logging, was not designed to discover the oil itself. The best the instruments could do was to add to the geological knowledge that determined the locations for drilling. All the methods had a variable dependability in different topographies. The only way to make sure oil was there, or not, was to drill for it. But such a revolution in locating skill, made possible by inventions and the scientific training that could crack the codes of the instruments, opened a new era in oil exploration. Whoever owned or patented the new devices could clearly command the field and pioneer the new age in petroleum.

DeGolyer had a grandiose scheme, apparently based on monopolizing the new techniques. He would find salt domes for Amerada and the company would sell or lease some of its discoveries to the other great companies for development and exploitation, exacting shares of stock in new discoveries. As we have seen, both Wallace Pratt and John R. Suman with Humble protested, even snorted, when approached about the plan. As Pratt wrote to his friend, "Old De thinks he's going to corner all the geophysical knowledge and then make us pay and pay." Suman wrote DeGolyer directly: "I say damn your advertisement." And he asked, in essence, if Amerada knows where all the salt domes are, why are you offering to let us buy up some of them? It doesn't make any sense.

It didn't, in fact, for another reason. Everybody got in on the act. But Amerada was there, in any significant major way, as chief pioneer. And the new techniques were by no means foolproof or even surefire. They now are indispensable and almost omnipresent or automatic in oil exploration; but it took a great deal of time to perfect their maximum usefulness and to counteract confusion.

The success of the refraction seismic explorations was of short duration, approximately 1924 to 1930, and was confined to a relatively small area, the shallow unit domes of the Texas and Louisiana coasts. Its performance is summarized as follows in the official biography of DeGolyer published in a pamphlet to accompany his receiving of the John Fritz Medal Award in 1941:

It resulted in a survey of the coast not once but many times, cost approximately twenty-five million dollars for geophysical work alone, and resulted in the discovery of some forty salt domes, thus doubling the previously known structures known to be favorable to oil accumulation in that area. Perhaps the most remarkable accomplishment of the whole Gulf Coast program was the exploration of some three million acres of water bottoms, swamps and marshes in southern Louisiana at a cost of less than four hundred thousand dollars and resulting in the discovery of some ten domes. Twenty-five per cent of the positive results of the entire refraction campaign were achieved here at less than two per cent of the total cost of the campaign. DeGolyer was one of the technical directors in the promotion of this enterprise and the work was done by the Geophysical Research Corporation of which he was president.

But if Amerada, as generally agreed by oil historians, not only pioneered but perfected the scientific methods now in general use for locating oil, and dominated the whole United States field of geophysics, credit must also go to DeGolyer's willingness "to take a chance." His mind was adventurous. And undoubtedly impatient. He did not tolerate fools gladly. When he set up Geophysical Research, one of his best friends and most discerning admirers, Wallace Pratt, commented that the move satisfied DeGolyer's need to run things and to dictate appropriations.

Perhaps it also registered London's growing concern at the amount Amerada's general manager was spending on experiment. A refraction seismographic crew (generally consisting of two to four scientists and a half-dozen or so helpers) "shot" about $18,000 worth of dynamite in a week. The average cost of discovering a dome was around

$400,000. But with the perfecting by Geophysical Research's J. C. Karcher of the reflection seismograph, from a patented device of Professor Reginald Fessenden which Amerada bought up, the cost was greatly diminished. Not only did its echo principle yield much greater accuracy in mapping underground structure, it required only a pound or two of dynamite for each shot where the refraction seismograph required from one to two tons.

Restlessly, DeGolyer sought refinements of techniques, other methods. He thought new inventions exhausted themselves shortly, revealing conditions that required still newer means of discovery. This belief he made the subject of one of the most agreeable experiences in his career, when he was invited by President Alverson to make the commencement address to the 1925 graduating class of the Colorado School of Mines, just about the time GRC was founded. From his New York office, he wired his acceptance of the invitation. He was immensely pleased and flattered. He insisted that Nell DeGolyer come with him, although she had resisted till then any opportunity of hearing him speak in public.

It was a highly successful occasion — terminated by a delightful surprise. After a luncheon for distinguished guests at the home of the president, ceremonies were held in the early afternoon. At the conclusion of his speech, DeGolyer was invested with an honorary doctorate. The student magazine, reporting the commencement exercises, praised DeGolyer both for his sterling speech and for his "boyish and genuine pleasure" in the surprise award. The magazine printed the entire speech, prophetically titled, "The New Frontiers." It is a surprising document.

With Governor Morley and other state dignitaries present, DeGolyer spoke on science as the "new frontier." There was no doubt, he assured the graduating class, that the "old" American frontier was gone. Nostalgia is permitted over this fact, he agrees, but not hopelessness. Indeed, it is the duty of those present to recall and remember the old frontier from whose life style most of them had sprung. "Many of you, I doubt not, are Westerners and sons of Westerners, as I am. Our fathers were of the adventurous vanguard of the great army of pioneers — they were the Pilgrims of the West. . . . They were traders, hunters, cattlemen, Indian fighters, steamboat men, miners, railroad builders, lumber-jacks, farmers and home-builders. . . . Their deeds were of Homeric greatness; too close to us, perhaps, to be seen in their true proportions, but material for epics to be written for their children's children. The perspective of time alone will develop their true greatness."

After summarizing their multiple achievements, he makes the important point that we must not mistakenly imagine that geography was the only fundamental shaping force in their lives. The influence of the land was matched by and "given character" by an accompanying change in civilization of the highest importance.

This collateral influence, this change, was of course the advance of the Industrial Revolution. "Our conquest of the wilderness was subject to and made use of machinery to an extent never previously experienced. It was more or less contemporaneous with the extension of the Industrial Revolution to the United States. If the West had been settled a thousand years ago, the changes which would have taken place from the eighteen fifties to the present would have been hardly less startling than those which have actually occurred."

The "epoch marker," he says, in the passing of the old frontier might well be the completion in 1869 of the first continental railroad. But, he challenges his hearers, do you take into account the meaning of the fact that "the first of all railroads had been built in England just less than two score years before that time"? The point is that the transcontinental railroad could hardly have been built much earlier, regardless of geography and even if "our country had been settled since the time of the Romans." In short, when we think of the "old frontier," we think of individual self-sufficiency, thus ignoring the role that scientific invention and the tools it provided played both in making the old frontier possible and in signaling its close.

But students who have chosen a branch of science as their life work will not be unaware of the importance of this switchover from individual self-determinism to the cooperative discoveries of science. For science is the new frontier. Its prospects are staggering. The enchantment of science, he claims, lies in its endless growth. "There is no such thing," he asserted, "as an exact science," for knowledge is always throwing bridges across the chasm that separates the known from the unknown. A heady and tonic doctrine, prophetic indeed for its time.

The speech revealed, unconsciously, much about the speaker — his pride in his pioneer ancestors and heritage, his faith in the future, his love of speculation and of the new, his intoxication with scientific knowledge. But it revealed two other traits. He advises the students to be imaginative. "Imagination is the key to discovery." (As Einstein was later to say so memorably.)

And DeGolyer invited the students to keep on reading. He singles out one book that he regards as indispensable for all Americans. "Read," he urged the mining engineers, "that most delightful and revealing of all American autobiographies of this century, *The Education of Henry Adams*." (Adams' masterpiece was first published in 1918, seven years earlier.)

Writing later to President Alverson in gratitude, above all for the honorary degree conferred of doctor of science, DeGolyer was still "boyishly touched." He wrote: "I suspect this may be the high-water mark in my professional career." He was thirty-eight years old, and no prophet about his career, however good a prophet about the future of science. Nineteen twenty-five won him another honor: he was named president of the American Association of Petroleum Geologists.

The elation of the Colorado experience was followed by a letdown, a real depression. In August and September he suffered what he called in letters to friends "a near nervous breakdown." Speaking of this casually to Max Ball in a letter in early October, he says that he has rallied completely and is now thankfully out of the dumps. He offered no explanation; perhaps there was none other than fatigue.

Both in action and in words, DeGolyer was an early advocate of shared geological data for the advancement of scientific knowledge. He was by no means merely idealistic or selfless; though he himself contributed articles to the professional journals and encouraged his staff to do so, he could and did draw a sharp line between what was, temporarily at least, the knowledge property developed by Amerada and what was documentation that could be added to the general sum of geological description.

This attitude was not contradictory; it was typical of DeGolyer's mind. He believed more in solving every problem in its relationship to the moment than in some abstract realm of absolute system. He had to a supreme degree the gift of lightning-swift intelligence and he enjoyed letting it function. His mind was not automatic and abstract; he always saw the concrete situation and tended to trust, like nearly all Americans of his generation, pragmatic rather than abstruse solutions. He was in business

and he recognized his obligations to the firm; but he was
not shortsighted and he recognized the firm's obligation to
corporate, pooled knowledge, systematized by science.
And so he steadily gave permission to his geologists Barton, Powers, Lovejoy, Ball and others to read papers and
publish them. But at times he said no, not yet, or counseled deletion of certain details about methods. He saw
that the oil business could subsidize geological progress
as a science. He tried to give both business and science a
fair relationship. He was not one-sided. Solutions that satisfied clear-sighted intelligence were the ones he chose.

There was a delicate line between public geological information and private data expensively gathered for the
company's use. With the coming of age of geophysical instruments, the problem was particularly acute. A scholarly
mind like Donald Barton's felt impelled to record publicly all new knowledge, with a legitimate vanity of wish-
ing to get credit for adding to the sum of geological data.

The correspondence between DeGolyer and Barton reveals an astonishing amount of time, not to mention psy-
chic energy, spent in mulling over the boundary lines of
scientific obligation and commercial advantage. It was a
high-wire performance obviously managed with impressive skill. At any rate, its importance can be noted in the
fact that the company required Barton to agree in writing
that if he should leave the company, he would not within
a time limit of one year "make use of physical methods of
exploration" or teach the methods to others or publish anything about them without permission.

The same sense of caution had to prevail about geological data on salt domes, for as DeGolyer wrote him, concerning general knowledge about such structures, "it is
upon the collection of data for such interpretation that we
are now spending our money."

With Powers as with Barton, DeGolyer steadily calls for more imagination. Although the company's early policy was to stick to proven fields, by 1923 DeGolyer was urging his geologists to reflect that Amerada had not done enough in the way of original discovery. One result was that exploration was more expensive, since leases in proven land cost much more than in unproven.

And so he writes Barton in the autumn of 1923: "As it stands, the economic geologist's work is wasted, no matter how excellent it may be from the geological viewpoint, if it is not timely enough from a commercial viewpoint. We have got to use imagination and concentrate when we are faced with competition."

In other words, don't allow the taste for scholarly reports to paralyze the active promptings of the competitive spirit. In DeGolyer, the competitive spirit was innate and remained throughout his life ungovernably strong. But it was only one side of a remarkably complete man. He was neither predatory nor uncommonly acquisitive. As a classic remark about him goes, generally attributed to Wallace Pratt, "he hated to lose three things: an argument, a dollar and a card game." But it would be a mistake not to see that the basis for this was not a "champion complex" but a phenomenal fund of energy, both physical and mental, and an exhilarating delight in living. This translated work into a form of play. As he often said, when praised for his copious activities, "If you enjoy something, you can't call it hard work, not even work. It's play."

Still, one does play sometimes for keeps. In 1925, a few days before he went to make the speech at the Colorado School of Mines, DeGolyer had to refuse Barton permission to publish a paper on the Eötvös torsion balance. His reason was straightforward: "It is a contribution to our competitors which I do not care to make at present." Barton replied that DeGolyer himself had recently published a paper on the Nash Dome, to which DeGolyer rejoined that his paper was merely scientific. He concluded the matter with a touch of humor: "There is an added advantage to my talking about this instrument instead of you: I do not know enough about it to be really enlightening."

This parting shaft did indeed contain a barb. When De-Golyer selected the Nash location for dome testing, most of the geological fraternity whooped and hollered. They gave it one chance out of a hundred to prove to be a salt structure. DeGolyer's own chief geologist in the area, that is to say Barton, reckoned the chances at one to twenty. Against such odds, DeGolyer had come in the winner. Why play, in such circumstances, if not for keeps?

He must have felt elated as well as vindicated. It was soon after that he replied to a request from the Norman chapter of Kappa Alpha, perpetually dunning their former "brother" for contributions, for a building fund by sending along a check for one thousand dollars. They had asked for one hundred.

In 1930, J. C. Karcher left the Geophysical Research Corporation to found — ostensibly — his own company, Geophysical Service, Inc. Eugene McDermott was his co-organizer of the new venture. H. B. Peacock, Roland Beers and Henry Salvatori also joined the new firm. Karcher added to the staff Erik Jonsson, Cecil Green, Herbert Purnell, John Gillen, Morris Spencer, Barney Fisher and Martin Kelsey. Actually, DeGolyer financed the entire project, secretly holding fifty percent ownership in the new firm.

DeGolyer's work was more and more concentrated in New York; he had become president of Amerada in 1929, then chairman of the board in 1930. As early as 1927, his letters speak of the lure of retiring. It never lured him enough. But by his early forties, he had made his fortune, and could reasonably count on remaining a multimillionaire. With the hush-hush founding of GSI, he was obviously preparing his departure from Amerada. A close friend estimates that at this time he was worth about four million.

Not that he didn't have his problems. The chief one was Amerada's subsidiary for Texas exploration, the Rycade Corporation. Geophysical methods paid off handsomely for Amerada in Oklahoma and in Louisiana. But Rycade was steadily unlucky in Texas. In 1930, Mr. Body wrote from London to congratulate DeGolyer on two new Amerada strikes in Oklahoma, each well yielding 14,000 barrels a day. He observes that Amerada's position is "wonderful" — and with a great deal more potential in sight. But in the same letter he tells DeGolyer "the Rycade reports recently have made quite depressing reading. . . . The new prospects, too, seem to be very slow in getting off the mark — we expected several wells to be on the way by now."

For two years, DeGolyer had been pressing the London office to review and revise the Rycade program. On February 15, 1929, he reported bluntly that "the main fact is apparent without much analysis — that is, that we have lost a great deal of money, most of it through the fortunes or misfortunes of war, and some of it through unwise expenditure. The policy which we have followed for several years and are still following, is to my mind an unwise one." He calls for an examination of whether to continue Rycade at all. And he notes that Rycade "had never earned a profit in any year during its existence." Part of this failure, DeGolyer felt, came from the London-fixed policy of releasing leases before sufficient testing. After experience, he

says, "I have about decided that the way to play a salt
dome is not to turn back." The new Chief believed in turning back early, a change from his father's Tampico policy.

The applied science that geology and geophysics
brought to the petroleum industry was a system whereby
the inevitable seven or eight dry holes out of nine drilled
could be absorbed into a planned and far-ranging exploitation. The one-try wildcatter had no such strength; he
abandoned after an unlucky location, a prospect that systematic investigation might prove right in the end, the
rewards compensating for the risk and the interim losses.

On such a cap rock salt dome as Spindletop, for example, in many cases wells had barely to be drilled into the
limestone to become enormous gushers, while others fifty
yards away struck nothing but salt water. And in most
cases, after discovery by geophysical methods of a new
salt dome, it took two or three years and often twenty to
thirty wells to discover the oil — or else to condemn finally
the unlucky location. And the cost of a well, in the twen-
ties, averaged out from $25,000 to $40,000.

The bright prospects often withered into bleak empti-
ness. Two years after the Eötvös torsion balance testing of
Spindletop Dome all Amerada's salt dome–based prospects
drilled had failed. DeGolyer was about to abandon the
method as too costly and too inexact. Then the "systematic" exploration was vindicated by the success of the
salt dome on the Nash Ranch in Fort Bend County, Texas.

The interim brought its many problems. Bigger companies than Amerada were trying to lure away his chief
geologists. Donald Barton wrote DeGolyer quite frankly
about this. DeGolyer was equally frank. He didn't want to
lose Barton but he admitted things looked dim for Rycade
(the Amerada subsidiary in Texas). He confessed that Rycade would probably be "wound up," abandoned, closed

out in 1925. But, he told Barton, the only ethical framework for any decision included both the company and Barton, namely to let Barton do what was best for Barton. The geologist loyally stuck with Amerada, a loyalty that paid off.

A. A. Jacobsen, a Danish-born, self-educated Cowdray man in Mexico, took over the presidency of Amerada in 1929 when DeGolyer stepped up to become the chairman of the board. Mr. Ryder, the original president, had died in 1927, after a long illness. Enclosing a certificate of a resolution passed by the board, expressing their sorrow in the death of Mr. Ryder, DeGolyer included a personal note for the widow. One sentence is indicative: his "cheerful disposition and humor were often the necessary tonic for dissipating a spell of depression." DeGolyer was not unfamiliar with black moods of despair, despite his own customary sunlit merriness. He and Ryder steadily made bets with each other on Amerada's success, Ryder being the optimist, DeGolyer the pessimist. Thus in 1924, for a stake of fifty cigars, a box of Corona Perfectos, the memo read: "Mr. Ryder wagers Mr. DeGolyer that before the end of 1924 the Amerada Company's production will reach a peak of 15,000 barrels net per day — for at least one day — and Mr. DeGolyer wagers that it will not." Ryder won.

Lord Cowdray also died in 1927. The passing of the "old guard" created problems for DeGolyer, always fiercely independent, always able to go directly to "the Chief." DeGolyer was considerably irked by the new drift toward "board" decisions on major policy, collective decisions nearly always requiring compromise of varied opinions and limitations of prudence, which put the brakes on boldness.

DeGolyer summarized his own thoughts about the techniques for discovering oil in an address delivered at Princeton University on December 12, 1939 for the Cyrus Fogg Brackett Lectureship in Applied Engineering and Technology, and published by the university later under the title "The Development of the Art of Prospecting."

He concludes that the history of oil prospecting shows it to be a "dynamic art" and that it consists "of a series of more or less individual techniques invented from time to time." And "not all of the prospective areas are amenable to investigation by the sum or any one of the techniques yet developed. . . . We are past the apex of our chief current technique — that of seismic reflections." Future developments that offer promise lie in soil-gas analysis, in new electrical methods, and improvements in the seismic reflection method. He concludes with a touch of irony: "Failing success in any of these, we may for a time be as we were in the beginning, dependent upon the adventurous wildcatter."

For inventions have their life cycle and are quickly exhausted or replaced, and are indeed relative — in the matter of oil techniques — to varying geography. He cites the refraction seismograph as an example of a technique particularly suited to one area and which exhausted its usefulness in six or seven years. As for its improvement, the reflection seismograph, he repeats that it has "peaked" by 1938 or 1939, although expenditures in its use are still running annually at $15 million. All told, he says, about one hundred million dollars have been spent for work by this method up until 1939. He gives credit to Karcher: "The reflection method of seismic surveying for underground structure was invented by Karcher as early as 1919, used experimentally in the field by him and Haseman in collaboration with McCollum and Eckhart in 1921, used successfully by him to map structure in 1927, and proved conclusively and with excellent and fortunate practical results in 1930." Karcher was, of course, vice-president of Geophysical Research when it was founded in 1925. Karcher took up the earlier refraction method in 1925, "improving it considerably by the introduction of the radio time-break, sound surveying and electrical recording." Approximately twenty million dollars, for the geophysical work alone, had been spent on this method before it exhausted its usefulness by 1930. DeGolyer calls it "one of the most brilliant successes of applied geopyhysics in oil prospecting."

In this lecture, he made a point which he frequently noted: "In truth, prospecting for oil in the United States has always been a highly competitive cooperative effort." This ambivalence between competition and cooperation, and their needed merger for progress, was a keystone idea in his thinking about everything. It defined his notion of a just relationship between pure science and applied technology, each feeding and supporting the other. For all his interest in knowledge as an end in itself, DeGolyer lived in a concrete, tangible, material world by choice. In him, action and thought were not divorced. Like his mentor at the University of Oklahoma, Vernon Louis Parrington, he was ultimately a pragmatic man, which is to say an American of his time and place.

And to a meeting of the American Petroleum Institute, DeGolyer explained that the success of the seismographic method depended upon this: "the recognition of different formations by the speed of transmission of artificially induced sound waves." The speed of sound through salt is about three times as fast as its speed through the ordinary sands, shales and clays which compose the rock of the Gulf Coastal area. The dynamite being exploded at the shot point, the time of firing was transmitted by radio to the observing instruments placed at a known distance (usually from two to five miles away). If the arrival of the sound of explosion through the earth was recorded in less than normal time, the existence of a salt dome was indicated.

And the classic short history of salt dome exploration was written by DeGolyer himself, in a brief essay much admired for its skill in making a scientific subject clear and understandable to nonspecialist readers. When it appeared in *Fortune* magazine, it prompted hundreds of letters for its incisive clarity.

It was largely an accident that DeGolyer wrote it. He was having lunch in Dallas one day in 1949 with two friends, Holland McCombs and William Weber Johnson, both with the Southwest bureau of Time-Life, Inc. DeGolyer enjoyed their company; both men had been in charge of Time offices in Mexico and South America; both were devotees of the history of the Southwest. They frequently used books in the DeGolyer collection. McCombs mentioned that the editors of *Fortune* magazine were conducting an informal poll among business leaders about the usefulness and the policy of the magazine. He asked DeGolyer if he had any comments to make. "You ought to use more articles about how specific business enterprises operate, what they actually face in the way of concrete problems," said DeGolyer. He amplified his belief in the power of techniques in shaping business operations. The talk turned to other matters. Johnson recalls that DeGolyer, in response to a question, traced the history of the unsuccessful attempt to use camels imported from Egypt as a means of transportation in the arid West.

Naturally, when McCombs was back in New York and reported DeGolyer's suggestion about *Fortune*, editor

Ralph B. Paine at once told his Dallas bureau chief to get DeGolyer to write an article on the techniques of finding oil.

He did. It was a sensational success. Both the magazine and DeGolyer were deluged with letters. Many of DeGolyer's came from crackpots, wanting an immediate approval of their own notions of likely places to drill wells. Some were pathetic: one gentleman, after long search, had found some shares of stock his father had bought in 1914 in a Tampico wildcatting enterprise, and wanted DeGolyer to help him establish claims; others who had bought into the frantic Spindletop schemes expected late windfalls. Some were rewarding and informative: for example, Emil Lengyel, the famous scholar then at Columbia University, had known the two daughters of Budapest's Baron Eötvös and gave DeGolyer some interesting background material on the baron.

DeGolyer begins the article with a story he relished and often told:

"How did you discover the Panuco field?" I teased Professor Cummins one sultry summer day as we sat in his Tampico office. The patriarch stroked his long white beard and looked thoughtful. That was forty years ago. Both of us were geologists and knew that the field lay in the broad alluvial plain of the Panuco River in northeastern Mexico, miles from the nearest significant rock outcrop. There hadn't been a single damned reason, that I could see, to think that it was a good location. The professor looked up at the ceiling and shook his head. Then he looked at me, seriously, as though he were trying to determine whether or not I could be worthy of a great secret:

"Been asked that question many times. Never made any

answer — too technical!" His best eye gleamed. "Goin' to
tell you, though — you c'n understand." A long pause. With
a triumphant snap of the end of his beard, he leaned for-
ward and whispered, "Little bird told me."

Panuco, of course, developed into a great oil field, but
DeGolyer agreed that the professor was pretty lucky. Even
so, Cummins was overly modest. DeGolyer shows that the
professor used his experience and knowledge of mountain
folding to bring off "a beautiful piece of constructive geological reasoning."

After rehearsing what is known about the occurrence of
oil, he adds: "Oil and gas bubbling upward through water
can be trapped into bubbles of larger volume by holding
one's cupped hand immersed and palm downward over
the stream of bubbles. An oil and gas pool in the earth is
essentially a great bubble floating on a sea of salt water,
its shape and extent modified by the form, thickness and
extent of the porous rock in which it is contained. In our
experiment the cupped hand has served two functions essential to accumulation: 1) It has blocked oil and gas from
traveling farther, the cap rock function; 2) by its cupped
shape a trap was formed into which oil and gas bubbles
carried by circulating waters could be accumulated into a
pool."

The thing, he writes, is the trap. "Almost the sole business of the modern oil prospector is a search for underground traps." But even a trap in a prolific region may be
dry. In the long run, oil prospecting is "still a matter of
chance." Although it's no longer a matter of all luck, or
messages from little birds, about seven out of eight wildcat wells are dry — despite all the increased scientific
knowledge. He traces the extension of this knowledge and
shows why the oil industry had to "put science on its pay-

roll," as better methods of discovering traps slowly evolved, as better understanding of the various kinds of traps emerged, as "geophysics came to the rescue of the industry and of geology with the introduction into the Gulf Coast region of the torsion balance." He says: "This was in late 1922 and, although I was partly responsible for its introduction, I may as well admit that I have never understood the functioning of that delicate instrument well enough to explain it clearly." With the help of illustrations, he does a good job of it, but points out that in 1924 the refraction seismograph method gave better diagnosis at a much more rapid rate, and it in turn after six or seven years gave way to the perfected reflection or echo method, whereby the measurement of sound waves, set off by the explosion of dynamite at or near the surface, can be achieved with an error rate of one-half percent or less. This seismic method, by correlation, allows the geological structure of an area thus surveyed to be mapped, to be "diagnosed." And yet in the end, only the drilling will tell. "The drill is the final arbiter."

What about you, he concludes, as a landowner? His advice is to sit still; if your property is part of an attractive prospect, you have already heard or will hear from the geologists or their oil companies. It is their business to scour every part of these United States in a search for oil.

DeGolyer's book-buying sprees continued unabated. His long relationship with famous book dealer Edward Eberstadt, a specialist in Western Americana, is representative of the friendship with many bookmen. He made his first purchase from Eberstadt, then located on West 42nd Street in New York, in October of 1928.

Eberstadt sent him a bill on November 1, listing thirty-six items for a total of $1,242.50. All the books were about the West, including Zenas Leonard's *Narrative* at a cost of $350 and Nathanial Wyeth's *Oregon, 1833* at $275. He also sent a personal letter, excusing his loquacity on the occasion of DeGolyer's visit. "I must say that I enjoyed your visit immensely and had a lovely time talking about myself to an entirely new pair of ears." He promises, in case of a second visit, "to put a clothespin on my mouth and devote part of the time at least to showing you a few books. It occurred to me after you left that perhaps you came up to look at books rather than to listen to one of my monologues."

DeGolyer had gone out to California; he did not send a check for the bill until November 16. Typically, in one of his characteristic moods, he met effusiveness with silence. To Mr. Eberstadt's genial letter of two pages, he merely replied: "Dear Sir, Herewith is check in payment of your invoice." This brusqueness prompted Eberstadt to apologize again, with humor. The day he got the check, he wrote DeGolyer: "They say brevity is the soul of wit, and I must say yours of the 16th is a pippin. I got twelve hundred and forty-two and a half separate and distinct chuckles out of your two lines. Hoping to be tickled some more, I remain . . ." But he couldn't resist a four-word postscript: "Please write real often." DeGolyer was won over. A long friendship began. DeGolyer became a favored customer, given first chance on rare items that turned up, and he in turn advised Eberstadt on his investments and got stock for him in the Amerada. He also helped Eberstadt out in times of crisis.

DeGolyer's next bill came two months later, on January 5, 1929, for only four books. He bought Spalding's *Annals of the City of Kansas* for $450, paid $75 for Morgan's *A Glance at Texas* (1844), $75 for Almonte's *Texas* and $45 for a copy of Stephen F. Austin's Map of Texas. He was a steady customer after that. By September of 1929 he was accorded special treatment. Eberstadt mailed his new catalogue to DeGolyer a month before the regular mailing and wrote him: "I thought you might like to look it over at your leisure so that you will get any of the items which you may wish. . . . Drop a line advising the numbers you want, they will all be set aside for you." From this preview, DeGolyer ordered a total of $944 worth of books, billed on September 30. He must also have had afterthoughts. Another bill for $120 was dated October 1, another on October 18 for $295, another on October 24 at $15 and two on November 4 for a total of $223.50.

Somehow, DeGolyer overpaid his account; Eberstadt sent him a rebate of $384.50. He might have kept it on account, for the next bill, dated April 19, 1930, is for $1,570.50.

The Depression had set in and Eberstadt was most grateful for DeGolyer's continued buying. He wrote a personal letter to accompany his bill of April 19, saying, "Thank you very much indeed for your order from catalogue 94. Its publication is a silent testimony to my at least temporary divorce from Wall Street, and now if you will only do as well for me in the oil situation as you have consistently done in connection with books, all will be well, for I have held on to my oil stocks, and if these ever come back, I will be able once again to put on my spats and strut forth with my cane, as in the boom days of 1929." Two days later, DeGolyer ordered another $660 worth of books from Eberstadt, again Western Americana.

The economic weather of course made very rough sailing for men in Eberstadt's kind of business, always among the first casualties in a "bust" period of the economic cycle. But DeGolyer kept the orders coming. On May 23, he paid $425 for a copy of Reid's *Tramp* (Eberstadt had been trying to locate one for six months); his bill for June 5 came to $252.50. In a note attached to this bill, Eberstadt wrote plaintively: "Why didn't you tell me Amerada was going to hop upwards? Do you want me to keep starving?"

Nevertheless, he had a lifelong gratitude for DeGolyer's support. Much later, he reminded DeGolyer of it. Writing to him on October 28, 1937, Eberstadt asks, "Do you remember way back in '29 when the old stock market went fluey and ruin and disaster stared us all in the face? I expect you do, but perhaps you don't remember that in that fatal time, and with the ship apparently sinking, you ascended the bridge, kicked the captain overboard, and for some perfectly insane reason gave thought to one poor guy way down 'tween decks a-hiding under a bunk, a-trembling with fright, and praying to God for the storm to pass over. The gent who had so suddenly got religion was me. I refer to your hefty order which came to me on that calamitous day. I need not tell you that I shall never forget it."

In fact, Eberstadt had a new reason for remembering it. He had wired DeGolyer, then in Houston, four months earlier (June 22, 1937): "RECENT MARKET DROP CAUGHT ME   KINDLY WIRE ME SEVEN HUNDRED FIFTY ON ACCOUNT STOP URGENTLY NEEDED." DeGolyer complied at once.

Then, later, he sent in another big order. This brought another wire from Eberstadt: "THANKS IMMENSELY FOR ORDER STOP COMES AT PSYCHOLOGICAL MOMENT STOP WAS ABOUT READY TO JUMP OFF ROOF STOP." This was followed by the letter of gratitude of October 28, in which Eberstadt enlarged on his telegram: "Well, Mr. DeGolyer, your letter of October 19th came at just another of those psychological moments when all hell — and a peculiarly personal hell — broke loose and began to singe and burn me like nobody's business. I expect neither of us gets a kick out of a moaner, but disaster in retrospect is always amusing. When some months ago I sent you that telegraphic SOS I had been riding the market short for damned near a year. Them $750 bucks of yours enabled me to keep my position for almost another week. Then I was forced out and two days later the damned market started down . . . as I say, your letter of October 19th brought me all the way back to 1929. It was a pat on the shoulder and it seemed to say, 'buck up, what the hell's the difference?' . . . I sure have missed your old-time visits as also your letters. Do please let me know the next time you come to New York for I would love to have an old-time chat and visit with you. Failing that, call in your secretary and dictate one of them old-time letters of yours."

And so it went, a friendly relationship mingled with business. DeGolyer could protest mightily over some charges but he rewarded fair-and-square dealing. And he was a good customer. At the height of the Depression, in 1931, his purchases from Eberstadt ran to about $4,000.

With glee, Eberstadt offered him — and sent confidently on approval — a copy of Stephen F. Austin's famous 1836 address at Lexington, Kentucky, on the Texas Revolution. DeGolyer returned it. "I happen to have two examples of it," he explained, "one fairly good and the other rather poor." But he added, "I enclose herewith, to soften the blow, a check for $1,000 which please credit to my account." This from a man whose legendary "toughness" is still current in oil field lore.

Eberstadt matched this generous dealing with some of his own brand. He secured for DeGolyer in 1931, with considerable triumph, a book that "Mr. De" had long wanted, Riley Root's *Overland Journal.* He charged DeGolyer $600 for it. But less than a year later, several other copies turned up and were sold at $250 per copy. Eberstadt wrote De-

Golyer to inform him of this, adding that he was prepared to meet this price and was therefore crediting DeGolyer's account with $350.

"You precious burglar," DeGolyer called him at intervals, adopting with him the tone of fond raillery he usually took with valued friends. Sometimes, he was genuinely sharp. And blunt. For instance, he wrote irascibly on March 28, 1938: "Before I break down and pay your last bill, I want to complain with some degree of bitterness over the prices charged. The book listed as Pino on the bill is really the second revision of Pino done by Escudero from the original Pino and the Ojeado of Barreiro in 1832. Either the Barreiro, of which I have a copy, or the original Pino, of which I do not have a copy, should be more valuable than this book, yet I note a copy of Barreiro in a recent catalogue at one hundred pesos Mex., which is something less than $30. Please go into a trance and see if you can do something about this." And he adds a stern P.S.: "I suppose you have charged too much for the other two items, too." To this display of knowledge and anger, Eberstadt replied calmly. He admitted that the $75 charge for Pino's early history of New Mexico was a bit excessive. But he has been sick and his sons have been handling the business. Writes Eberstadt: "The boys have to learn and it's better for them to get a 'call' once in a while than for me to try to teach them from my own profound knowledge. Youngsters listen to someone else much more avidly than they do to their pa. The present lot were priced in my absence. Pino should be $50, the *San Xavier del Bac* I should guess as fair at $30 and the *Why We Celebrate* at $17.50." DeGolyer was mollified, but no doubt he was even more pleased at this bland and adroit maneuver, something he could admire. The orders kept on pouring in. DeGolyer kept on coining facetious names for his friend, calling him the "Pope" of books, Edwardo Primero and some things less quotable.

As a final sample of this bookman's friendship, one may note an exchange in 1940. DeGolyer wanted two volumes related to the adventures of the Spanish revolutionary in Mexico, Francisco Javier Mina, 1789–1817. He thought Eberstadt was asking too much for them, so he offered to trade some of his duplicates for the Mina volumes. Eberstadt accepted, with only a minimum of bargaining. In agreeing to the transaction, he wrote DeGolyer: "Well, old friend, I have always found you to be more than fair and in the present instance I am perfectly willing to agree to whatever you think fair for both of us. I would like to have both copies of the Johnson, for one at the current market would not cover the cost of the Mina. If you can send the two and let me know how much cash, or credit against future purchases, would please you, we think we can call the deal a *fait accompli*."

Three weeks later DeGolyer bought fourteen volumes from Eberstadt's catalogue 115, still building up his trans-Mississippi and Spanish colonial history collection. There was another order in September for $900, and a year after the trade, DeGolyer turned in an order for $1,825. Now living in Texas, when he was in New York he would invite Eberstadt to have lunch with him. But from the forties on, his collecting interest was primarily channeled into books about science and its history. Other less specialized rare-book men, such as Jacob Zeitlin, got the bulk of the purchases.

DeGolyer displayed the same decisiveness in book buying that he did in everything else. His friend Bill Wrather put a Dallas dealer, H. W. Caldwell, in touch with DeGolyer about 1925. Wrather, examining Caldwell's rare Texas items, told him exactly which books DeGolyer would want.

Off went the list to New York, where it was readdressed to Tampico and there caught up with the ever-mobile dynamo. DeGolyer wasted no time. He wired Caldwell in Dallas to bring his books to the Texas Hotel in Fort Worth on such and such a date.

Forty years later, Caldwell still remembered this first meeting with DeGolyer in precise detail. "I packed," he recalled in 1965, "a couple or so suitcases full of books and drove over to Fort Worth [thirty miles from Dallas]. Mr. DeGolyer knew precisely what he wanted and what each book was worth. As I remember, he bought everything I took over, and paid me with a check. I think the costliest item I had amounted to $65, an 1859 edition of the Texas Almanac. At any rate, he alerted me to what I should be on the lookout for him, and for the next thirty years I got many a book for him. I never dealt with a book purchaser who was as positive as DeGolyer about what he wanted and what he ought to pay. He was a great gentleman. When I think of him, I still feel a little bit of awe. I wasn't accustomed to customers who made up their minds with such lightning-like speed. Not all book collectors are great readers, but I knew at once that DeGolyer was a man who loved to read. And I also remember that I thought when I first met him there in Fort Worth that he was the best-dressed man I had ever seen."

III

Back to the Southwest: an Independent at Last

11 Geophysical Service, Inc.

T HE PERIOD between 1928 and 1932 was as crucial and epoch-making for the oil industry as the landmark date of Spindletop in 1901. The reasons were at least three: 1) the discovery of the great Oklahoma City field in 1928 again flooded the market with excess crude oil and drove the industry into a "poverty of riches"; 2) the discovery of the unparalleled East Texas field in 1930 — forty-six miles long and from three to twelve miles wide — in Kilgore and its environs completed the financial mess caused by the Oklahoma City discovery, reducing the price of crude within six months from $1.10 a barrel to ten cents a barrel; 3) the Great Depression of 1929–1933 grievously damaged the national economy in every sphere of activity.

It was during this unstable period of money crisis that Everette DeGolyer again made a typically independent decision. Just as he had left — momentarily — Mexico and Lord Cowdray's Mexican Eagle enterprises in 1910 in order to return to Norman, just as after World War I he decided to leave Mexican Eagle and devote himself to detecting oil deposits in much larger areas than the Tampico Golden Lane, so in the early 1930's he decided to resign as chairman of Amerada — which he had made in twelve years into the largest independent oil company in the nation — and to venture out on his own as an independent oil operator. He had gone in a dozen years from vice-president and general manager to president and on to the chairmanship of the board. But, as he stated in letters to several friends, "I am tired of working for bankers, and I want to work for myself."

Such a major wrench is never a simple decision, and DeGolyer's explanation was no doubt a great oversimplification. Although the departure from Amerada, when it became official in 1932, was friendly and with no hint of internal dissension, there are signs that DeGolyer himself felt that his great program of research and experimental techniques in geophysics had strained the "practical" sense of the company's backers who, quite legitimately, were more interested in dollar profits than in enlarging the domain of geophysical knowledge. And certainly the bad financial times dictated a policy of frugal retrenchment.

DeGolyer seems to have weathered the Wall Street "panic" of 1929 better than most, primarily because of heavy and lucky holdings in Samuel Insull's utility stocks. And, at any rate, by 1930 he knew he had something else going which made the mere notion of being frugal on technical experiment distasteful to him. He was in these troubled times about to be loyal again to his famous credo, so often repeated and republished in oil histories, which went as follows:

Prospecting for oil is a dynamic art — a series of individual techniques — sometimes overlapping, sometimes separated by a time gap — but techniques which lose their usefulness and which leave us without guide to our prospecting until we devise some new method. The greatest single element in all prospecting, past, present, and future — is the man willing to take a chance.

Actually, he was getting ready to take several chances. First, by branching out as a truly independent oil operator on his own; second, on the continuing supremacy of Texas and Oklahoma as the great oil reservoirs of the country; third, on the superiority of a new geophysical method which he and Karcher were refining and perfecting over any previous detection devices. Indeed, the only element of doubt lay in the first of these chance-takings, since by 1930 the other two items had been assured.

The Oklahoma City field, eleven miles long and ultimately producing 770 million barrels of oil, was a triumph for Cities Service geologists and for the company's faith in them. When Cushing was discovered in 1913, wells, — all dry holes — had been drilled hopefully near Oklahoma City. The first one was even drilled to a depth of 3,000 feet before hope gave out. Nonetheless, Cities Service geologists, who had located three of the five "giants" of the Greater Seminole field, insisted that they had found "structure" near Oklahoma City. They had. Their first well in the new venture there was started in June of 1928 and blew in six months later with a wild 5,000 barrels a day, prelude to what became the greatest of all Oklahoma fields and the ninth most productive field in the nation. This well had been drilled to a depth of 6,335 feet.

Six miles south of the city, this discovery well lay only a dozen miles north of the University of Oklahoma and the town Everette and Nell DeGolyer still regarded as their second home, Norman. DeGolyer must have recalled ruefully — as he had occasion to do many times — the counsel given him by one of his professors when he left the university to go into the oil business. "Don't," had been the advice in 1910. "All the great fields have already been discovered."

But Oklahoma held an even deeper lure for DeGolyer the scientist. It was a steady belief of his that "geological tools and techniques exhaust themselves by virtue of their very usefulness." By 1929 or so, he felt that the refraction seismograph had served its purpose; it had to be refined, developed, or replaced. He and Karcher were already at work on a project of their own. In 1930, they organized their own geophysical research company, with DeGolyer posting most of the capital, and called it Geophysical Service, Inc. No doubt, DeGolyer was already planning the break with Amerada and its subsidiaries, including Geophysical Research Corporation.

The new company was established to exploit Karcher's development of the "reflection" seismograph. Unlike the refraction seismograph (ideally suited to the Gulf Coast but to nowhere else), the reflection seismograph could find clues to subsurface structures in which the different rocks were of uniform hardness or of the same "speed." The earlier refraction method had been indispensable in locating salt domes; the later reflection method could pinpoint the location — at least provide clues — of a potential pool itself. It was a refinement and an extension of the earlier technique.

Amerada had first crack at it. Its use was a gamble. Amerada was finding oil without it, and most physicists insisted that the new method was scientifically unsound. Amerada's board endured three years of failure, as one dry well after another was drilled on structures "located" by the reflection technique. After three years, in 1930, the board told DeGolyer he had enough evidence by then to justify renouncing the experiment. He realized perfectly well that from their point of view they were right. Often enough in the past ten years he had been stubborn with the board, had been overriding, but he had gotten results. For example, Alfred Jacobsen — who moved up to president when DeGolyer became chairman of the board — had opposed the immensely successful Louisiana Land and Exploration project. With the failure of his new technique, DeGolyer's renown was eclipsed. In the oil fraternity, he was now described as "crazy with dynamite." It was bound to happen to a man who made a career out of being unorthodox.

Still, he was unshaken. Early in 1930 he received in Amerada's New York office three maps from Karcher, field reports on reflection seismograph testing in Oklahoma's Seminole plateau. He later told Ruth Knowles, longtime Petroleum Specialist for the United States Government and author of the excellent *The Greatest Gamblers*, that as he sat chewing the stub of his cigar he suddenly said out loud, "Well, this one's it, it's really diagnostic." Amerada was in for another round, at least one more, before throwing in the sponge. It was one of the three or four major decisions in DeGolyer's life.

The "diagnosis" showed a hole in the center of the plateau, with surface formations dipping *into* it from every direction, always a bad sign. By geological practice and evidence, they should have dipped *away*, not into, the crater. In actual proof, the spot that tempted DeGolyer and Karcher was surrounded by dry wells. And yet the three Karcher maps indicated a dome far underground where the rock beds arched into a possible structure. DeGolyer decided that Amerada should drill it. At 4,214 feet the drilling bit pierced a dome, and the great Edwards field was opened. Whereas the Oklahoma field discovery well came in at 5,000 barrels a day on December 4, 1928, the

DeGolyer Edwards discovery well blew in at 8,000 barrels daily.

Its importance is vividly and succinctly stated by Ruth Knowles:

> *This was the most important well drilled in America since Spindletop: reflection seismograph revolutionized prospecting for oil as completely as Spindletop had done. Half of all the oil that would be discovered from that date on would be discovered by reflection seismograph in structures which would not have been found otherwise.*
>
> *When DeGolyer's other two prospects found oil, all possibility of doubt was dispelled. Now it was the whole oil industry that went "crazy with dynamite."*

These are large claims, but Mrs. Knowles supports them to the hilt. Out of 361 "structures" located by the reflection seismograph in Oklahoma alone in the seven years following the opening of the Edwards field, 146 produced oil. This represents a formidable reducing of the odds against discovery. According to the statistics of Mrs. Knowles, the success record of wells drilled on geophysical recommendation is one producer out of every six, on merely geological recommendation one out of ten, and on nontechnical guess one out of twenty-four.

And yet Amerada had to pay a penalty for its insistence upon scientific knowledge in detecting oil plays. The incredible East Texas field, producing over the astonishing area of 211 square miles (the Oklahoma City field of twenty square miles had been one of the nation's largest), was discovered by Columbus Marion ("Dad") Joiner without any benefit of geology whatsoever, in fact against all sorts of geological certitude that oil could not possibly exist in those sands. There were a few geologists who dissented from this nearly one hundred percent negativism, including one geologist working for Amerada. Young Albert E. Oldham, on Amerada's payroll, was sure that oil had been trapped in the area, even though Shell's subsidiary Roxana had failed to find any there as early as 1915, primarily, as it turned out, because Roxana's geologist-president drilled more than a mile east of the recommended location, which was right in the heart of later success.

Young Oldham recommended to Amerada the purchase of leases that would amount to $150,000 dollars, in 1929, when Dad Joiner was drilling his first two dry holes and before his third initiated the unbelievable bonanza. Oldham's recommended leases were scattered over an area twenty miles long and eight miles wide. The board voted no. A year later they had the shock of realizing that this immense tract was totally enclosed by the vast East Texas field. As Goethe observed, in a different context, there is always more to be learned about nature and her secrets than human beings suspect.

The East Texas experience chastened geologists, as it did governmental agencies. DeGolyer later commented about it in a report emphasizing the risks of prophecy: "As an example of the hazards . . . may we cite the discovery of the East Texas field. The discovery well in this field was drilled in 1930, by a near-bankrupt wildcatter on the basis of a casual and random location. There was no surface indication of the existence of an old field of any type and the odds against the discovery of a mammoth pool of the type actually found would have been conservative at a thousand to one. The result, however, was the discovery of some five billion barrels of new reserves, or almost 10 percent of the oil discovered in the United States up to the present time. It is entirely possible that other East Texas fields remain to be discovered. . . . No other field yet found even approaches it in ultimate production." (Report of DeGolyer and MacNaughton to Commodore W. C. Greenman, Director Naval Petroleum Reserves, Navy Department, Washington, D.C.)

And of the economic upheaval caused by this field and the 1928 Oklahoma City discovery, DeGolyer stated in 1945 (in a speech commemorating Wallace Everett Pratt as first winner of the Sidney Powers Memorial Medal): "One might say that the period beginning roughly with the discovery of the Oklahoma City field at the end of 1928 and ending with the Code for Fair Practice in the Petroleum Industry promulgated under the National Recovery Act in the early autumn of 1933 was a period of uttermost demoralization in the petroleum industry. It was a period of overproduction, low prices, attempts at voluntary proration, hot oil, military law in the Oklahoma City and East Texas fields, court action to establish proration by State regulation, attempted federal regulation, and of many other evils consequent upon these events. The period ended when it did because the various State conservation laws had finally been established judicially and, with the backing of the Connally Hot Oil Act, State regulation had finally become reasonably effective. The price of crude oil reached a living stage speculatively in anticipation of benefits which were to accrue from the administration of the Petroleum Code but which during the short life of that ill-fated instrument, were never realized."

Nonetheless, the reflection seismograph method performed brilliantly for Amerada in Oklahoma between 1928 and 1932. But the financial panic afflicted all business. Writing to J. B. Body just before Christmas of 1931, DeGolyer observed: "The oil industry continues to be in trouble, but the Amerada is working into a magnificent position and should be extraordinarily profitable on any real turn for the better. As it is, we estimate a profit of some $100,000 without any non-recurring type of profit for November."

J. Elmer Thomas congratulated DeGolyer on Amerada's success November 28, 1931: "I think that, considering all factors, Amerada Petroleum Corporation made the best showing in 1930 and 1931 of any stock on the board, and you and Jake [Alfred Jacobsen] deserve the greatest credit for this, I am sure." Mr. Thomas was petroleum analyst at the time for Fenner and Beane, forerunner of the firm later known as Merrill Lynch, Pierce, Fenner and Smith, Inc. With such confirmation, DeGolyer felt he could honorably quit Amerada and devote himself to his own enterprises. Curiously, as his book buying shows, his primary intellectual curiosity was about the Southwest. He was preparing to move back "home."

If DeGolyer's own fortunes rose and fell with the shifting tides of oil in these times, his book purchases do not reveal it. In addition to Eberstadt's, another of his favorite rare-book dealers was James F. Drake, then at 24 West 40th, New York. During this troublesome period DeGolyer paid on June 2, 1930, $1,200 for Galsworthy's *Man of Devon;* he kept on collecting Kipling, Sheila Kaye-Smith (for whose works he had a special fondness), Walter de la Mare, Edwin Arlington Robinson; but his interest in the Southwest was just as strong, although books about the latter cost him far less than the "literary" items. For example, in 1928, he paid $1,750 for three volumes of Kipling to bookman Drake, a sum that might add a hundred or more useful Southwestern titles to his collection of trans-Mississippi history and lore. The point is that while collecting Kipling, DeGolyer was also adding such representative titles as these to his library: E. Smith's *Account of a Journey Through Northern East Texas*, Lindsley's *His-*

tory of Greater Dallas, Point Isabel on the Rio Grande,
Robinson's *Mexico and Her Military Chieftains.* The latter was truly a rare book; it had been published in Philadelphia in 1847 — and DeGolyer's copy has been used for
source material by at least four authors of now standard
books on the history of the Southwest.

DeGolyer's December purchases in 1930 from Drake
alone (a year and three months after the Depression had
hit) totaled $5,055.75. And he was, of course, steadily buy-
ing from other favorite stores all over the country, for he
was an avid devourer of catalogues: book, coin, art, auction or what not.

12   Altogether on His Own

DEGOLYER'S RESIGNATION from Amerada became effective October 1, 1932. He wrote to Clive Pearson, son
of the late Lord Cowdray, to explain that he was resigning
in order to engage in "general oil prospecting." Clive Pearson answered with an immediate cable, urging him to retain association at least as "consulting geologist," or any
other satisfactory post that DeGolyer could dream up for
himself. DeGolyer replied that he really did "want to go

Clean-shaven most of his life, DeGolyer grew a moustache as a young
executive of Mexican Eagle Oil at Tampico.

into business for himself." He added: "Messrs. Mathey and Jacobsen are advised and agreed — conditions of friendliness all around."

Nonetheless, DeGolyer felt an obligation to make his decision sound inevitable to the Pearson family. Expressing the wrench the change would make, he observed that there were "compensations in opportunity." Why? Well, "leasehold is cheap and the use of geophysics is just beginning. As a pioneer in that work, I feel that I understand its application as well as anyone in the world today — a condition which will not long hold."

He was leaving a mighty good thing. His earnings there in one year, take 1927 as example, amounted to the following: 1) director's compensation for the preceding year, 1926 — $123,327.09 (ten percent of the net earnings were shared annually among the four directors: DeGolyer, Ryder, Carr and Body); 2) shares of stock — $28,000; 3) combined Amerada and Rycade salary, $30,000; 4) dividends on stock held during the year — $49,874.00. All in all, $231,201.09. By the time he left Amerada, he had made his "first million" at least twice over; in the next quarter century of his life he would average out about the same sum, or two million, per year, plus starting the fortunes of a dozen brilliant younger men. In time, he got bored with making money and gave much of it away.

After leaving Amerada in 1932, he wrote to Mr. Body two years later to apologize for his long silence. He says: "I have had a very interesting time for the past two years. Except for an interlude of about four months during which I worked with General Johnson on the oil code and afterwards with Messrs. Farish and Teagle in a battle against price fixing, I have been engaged in geophysical prospecting and trading on my own account. I have not had any great success but on the whole have not been unsuccessful.

It is work that I enjoy. I have a number of interesting prospects and I have recently made an arrangement with a group of New York bankers — Case, Pomeroy — to cover an exploration program for the next two years. I still live in Montclair and have a small office at Room 1725, 120 Broadway, but I spend most of my time in Texas."

Ralph Arnold wrote to DeGolyer in October 1932: "I have just learned from Sidney Powers that you have resigned from Amerada. I assume that this is to give you time to devote to your scientific work." And Max Ball had written a week earlier: "You should be much flattered by the comment your resignation has provoked and by its results on Amerada quotations." In reply, on November 18, DeGolyer wrote Ball: "I went down to Princeton yesterday afternoon and spent a pleasant afternoon with Thom. . . . I have been trying to promote the science of geophysics in that university for the past year or two, which was the reason for my visit yesterday. At the present time I seem to be running around, frankly without getting anything particular done."

In at least a part-time way DeGolyer had been an oil consultant and an independent operator ever since he returned from Tampico for good. Although Geophysical Research Corporation was a subsidiary of Amerada, its program required it to make investigations for other oil companies that might want to use its specialized services. This involved DeGolyer in the delicate task of loyalty to two employers; GRC conducted researches for Amerada simultaneously with commissions from rival companies. DeGolyer was proud of his ability to be scientifically objective and to keep his own sense of fidelity to various obligations. He was proud that this scruple was recognized.

He mentions this matter toward the end of his career in a letter to Leonard McCollum, president of the Continental Oil Corporation. McCollum had sent DeGolyer a clipping from the Mexico City newspaper, *Excelsior,* which praised DeGolyer oratorically for his services to the oil history of Mexico. On August 14, 1950, DeGolyer wrote McCollum: "There has not been a minute of the last twenty-five years and more when I have not been the repository of confidential information which, presumably, I could have used to further the interest of myself or some organization other than the one from which the information was obtained. During all or part of that period I have been a director in various oil companies: Louisiana Land, Transwestern, Republic Gas, etc., and during the period of existence of DeGolyer and MacNaughton, I have been continuously an independent operator. I did a good deal of consulting work even when I was the head of Amerada. During the early period of geophysical surveys, Amerada was leasing competitively in areas where we were surveying for others, such as Gulf, Texas, etc., and I often knew of the finding of a new dome before the clients themselves knew about it. With all of these opportunities, no questionable use of confidential information was ever made and it has been a matter of great pride to me that not even a suspicion of such use has ever come to my knowledge."

When he left Amerada and New York in 1932, DeGolyer was forty-six years old. He could have retired and lived comfortably, even sumptuously, the rest of his life. He was carrying life insurance amounting to $175,000. He applied for another $50,000 with Aetna, and an additional $50,000 with Prudential. But he was in excellent health. Filling out the questionnaires of the life insurance companies, he noted that he took exercise daily, for one hour, at eleven o'clock in the morning in a New York gymnasium. He confessed to drinking wine and beer with his meals ("never water"), but added that "I have rarely used liquor immod-

erately." Asked to mention his hobbies, he filled in the
blank with the phrase "book collecting." He estimated he
smoked a dozen cigars a day. He indicated he ate meat
three times a day and was rather indifferent to vegetables.
In a curious question about his bath habits, he stated that
he took a shower daily, a hot one followed by very cold
water. The additional $100,000 of insurance was granted.

In 1932, his daughters were nearing college age and son
Everett was nearly ten. The oldest daughter, Virginia
Nell, elected to go to Smith, but her primary interest was
in music. She gave promise of becoming a concert pianist
and studied with that brilliant virtuoso, Brazilian pianist
Guiomar Novaes. Dorothy, who was interested in painting,
and Cecilia, a reader, were in private "finishing" schools.
The youngster, Ev, was already making dinner-table conversation an ordeal with his steel-trap mind which never
forgot a fact and never hesitated to produce it when anyone carelessly betrayed it. He was obviously destined to
become a scholar, most likely in history.

The Montclair home on Watchung Road was deliber-
ately meant to imitate English homes the DeGolyers had
admired on their trips to London and as weekend guests
of Lord Cowdray and other Pearson associates. But with
the Depression, it was impossible to furnish the house with
the English furniture required. The DeGolyers had no
stock whatsoever "on margin" and were not personally affected by the financial crisis as so many were. But they
were of course affected by the general business lag as was
everyone else. In May 1929, before the "bust," they had
decided to move to a mountainside home on Lloyd Road
in Montclair. So they did, and remained there until the
move to Dallas in 1936. A feature of the Lloyd Road home,
later to be copied in their Dallas residence, was an "Indian
room" which housed the Indian blankets and Mexican

paintings and pre-Columbian artifacts which the DeGolyers had been collecting for twenty years, a collection to
which they steadily added.

Although Mrs. DeGolyer was reared as a Methodist, and
their wedding was performed by the Methodist preacher in
Norman, in Montclair the entire family followed the patriarch's choice and attended, for twenty years, the Congre-
gational church. Later in Dallas, the Methodist connection
was reestablished.

It took DeGolyer several years to decide where to transfer his individualistic family to in the Southwest. His major holdings or properties were in Texas. He may have
been persuaded by a sensational news story of the time, in
which the heirs to the Campbell Soups estate were reported to have suffered a great loss in fortune because several states were able to impose taxes on it. Perhaps De-
Golyer decided to concentrate on Texas because of that
example, among other reasons. The family moved to Dallas in 1936, buying a house in burgeoning University Park,
but Nell DeGolyer did not like it. The DeGolyers started
planning their final home, certain now that they would
end their lives in Texas. After the Tudor residence in
Montclair, the brilliant Texas sunshine demanded a stone,
Spanish-style structure in souvenir of their early and formative days in Mexico. They began the search for a large
property that could accommodate a Mexican-style hacienda.

After leaving Amerada but before coming to Texas to
stay, DeGolyer for the third time went on the payroll of
the United States government. He had served as a college
student on the U.S. Geological Survey; and in 1918, he undertook a study for the government of oil-well resources
and depletion along the Gulf Coast. His job in 1933 was
infinitely more difficult. He agreed to serve under the

direction of General Hugh Johnson, a fellow Oklahoman and also an oilman, on a commission established by President Franklin D. Roosevelt to restore order and stability to the chaotic oil business, paralyzed by the Great Depression and by the fantastic abundance of oil occasioned by the Oklahoma City and East Texas oil fields. It was a time of near chaos for the industry. Roosevelt's National Recovery Act obviously included some regulation of the oil troubles, in the interest of the national economy.

DeGolyer's assignment was a thankless task. This is perhaps the least documented part of his career. But at any rate he discovered in the Texas "regulation" of what the whole industry called "the mess" one of his heroes of the oil industry. This was Colonel Ernest O. Thompson, the Texas Railroad Commissioner under whose jurisdiction fell the duty of preventing the enormous waste current, at first, in the oil and gas of the East Texas fields.

Because of the standstill occasioned in the nation's industries by the Depression, the country simply could not consume any adequate amount of the vast quantities of oil being produced. As one oil operator protested after paying fifteen cents for a bowl of chili in an East Texas café, "I have to pay more for a small bowl of chili than I make out of a whole barrel of oil." It was an amazing situation in a country where in the decade from 1919 to 1929, the car and truck and bus population, all dependent on oil as fuel, had increased four hundred percent — four times as many vehicles on the road in 1929 as in 1919. In addition, oil had found a tremendous market in the fuel needs of airplanes, ships, factories, agricultural equipment and homes. Oil was selling for more than three dollars a barrel when DeGolyer located his first great well near Tampico in 1910; in 1931, it was selling for ten cents a barrel. You could fill your tank, say, for a nickel, or less than the cost of a hamburger.

This might have been wonderful except for the fact that World War I had demonstrated the priceless value of oil to a nation — and by the 1920's the United States, incorrectly, was suffering from a staggering fear that its oil resources were already nearly depleted. It was known, as Admiral Nimitz stated in World War II, that success in war depends on "men — and oil, bullets and beans." The chaotic exploitation of the nation's oil reserves in the 1930's demanded a national program of conservation.

First to act was Governor "Alfalfa Bill" Murray of Oklahoma, who, when he could not persuade oilmen to adopt a program of proration, decisively shut down by governmental fiat twenty-nine Oklahoma fields by martial law "until we get dollar oil." In Texas, Colonel Thompson discovered to his shock that the East Texas field alone could produce 100 million barrels a day — or twenty-six times as much as the whole world was then consuming daily. In the mad rush to drill wells into this gold mine, unimaginable quantities of natural gas and of oil were being sacrificed beyond any chance of possible recovery. Luckily, concerted action by the states concerned effected a program of sensible scientific control and conservation. It is estimated, for example, that the East Texas field alone — under sound principles of conservation — will yield six times as much oil as it would have done without such control, or six billion rather than one billion barrels.

General Johnson's commission working under the National Recovery Act chose to defend conservation and production on a pro rata basis over an oil-industry favored program of price-fixing. DeGolyer strongly championed the former, vigorously opposed the latter; with a small segment of the oil fraternity he remained under a cloud for

the rest of his life, unfairly, as a "radical." It never bothered him much. He was, in fact, a Republican and on the
whole a politically conservative man, actively supporting
the unsuccessful campaign of Wendell Willkie and the
successful campaigns of Dwight D. Eisenhower.

When he took time out for government service in 1933,
the code DeGolyer sanctioned was chiefly grounded in
control of crude production; this control, he felt, would allow other problems to fall into line. But this code was
soon scrapped and another, entirely opposite, substituted.
The latter, DeGolyer later regretted, was based too arbi-
trarily upon price-fixing. On the whole, DeGolyer took a
dim view of the Roosevelt New Deal. He thought it might
lead the country into "either revolution or dictatorship."

Although DeGolyer felt that his time and energy spent
on General Hugh S. Johnson's NRA Petroleum Code in
1933 had been a thankless and generally futile task, there
were two compensations at least. He won the close friendship of his associate in preparing the code, Joseph Pogue,
a friendship that lasted the rest of his life; and he won the
gratitude of General Johnson who, in one of his newspaper
columns, referred to Joe Pogue and DeGolyer as "gen-
iuses."

Although DeGolyer's Felmont and Atlatl Corporations
were housed in Houston's Esperson Building, and Transwestern Oil in San Antonio, Dallas was a logical choice for
the DeGolyers as residence in 1936. It was the nearest
metropolis to the heart of the East Texas field; it was about
equidistant from such other southwestern oil centers as
Tulsa and Oklahoma City and Houston. And the resident
office of Geophysical Service, Inc. was in Dallas. It had
the additional attraction of being the home choice of the
DeGolyers' closest friends from the Tampico days, Mr. and

Mrs. Edwin B. Hopkins. Mr. and Mrs. Leon Russ and the W. E. Wrathers were also living in Dallas; they too were a bond with DeGolyer's start in Mexico and with Mexican Eagle. And, of course, such close friends as the two chief associates in Geophysical Service, J. C. Karcher and Eugene McDermott, were living in Dallas.

DeGolyer nearly decided to settle his family in Houston, later claiming with mock seriousness that the piece of property he had picked out for a homesite was suddenly washed away in a torrential Gulf Coast rainstorm before he could close the deal. At any rate, the three daughters and son Everett liked Dallas at once. They were close to grandparents in Norman and close to uncles and aunts both in Norman and in nearby Fort Worth. Fort Worth, a mere thirty miles west of Dallas, was also the home of such early associates and valued friends of DeGolyer as geologist J. Elmer Thomas and David Donoghue (also a famous book collector) and the gifted Scot, John Muir.

From a purely practical standpoint, Dallas was at the time the largest and liveliest city in Texas, the fastest growing, and above all was regionally and nationally regarded — perhaps less by virtue of fact than by virtue of the "promotional" skill of its citizens — as the unrivaled cultural oasis of the Southwest. Its Little Theater was the most famous in the nation, three times winner of the Belasco Cup in national competitions; its musical life, its symphony, opera seasons, book stores and Neiman-Marcus were nationally admired.

The junior DeGolyers were delighted with the move. Since the daughter of Tampico associate Leon Russ was making her debut that autumn, both Virginia and her sister Dorothy Margaret decided to join the 1936 Dallas debutantes. Following the tradition, the DeGolyers presented their daughters at the customary family ball, on December 21, a date chosen to allow the presence of younger sister Cecilia, then a freshman at Smith. The following summer Virginia married John Sherman Maxson, son of a distinguished family and college football star. Later he joined his father-in-law in operating a ranch southwest of Fort Worth. Another son-in-law, George Crews McGhee — who married Cecilia in the autumn of 1938 — made his own fortune in oil by age thirty and has ever since dedicated his life to public service, having been United States ambassador to Turkey and to West Germany, after serving as undersecretary of state in various departments.

The DeGolyers quickly became active in the cultural life of their new community. Inevitably, with his magnificent collection of pre-Columbian and Mexican art objects, DeGolyer was invited to become a member of the board of the Dallas Museum of Fine Arts, later serving a four-year term as president. Equally inevitable, he would become president of the Dallas Arboretum Society and member of the board of the Dallas Public Library, and vice-president of the Margo Jones Theater-in-the-Round. Mrs. DeGolyer became a patron of the Dallas Symphony Orchestra and of the spring season of the Metropolitan Opera in Dallas, member of various garden clubs, and president of Planned Parenthood, Dallas chapter.

Edwin B. Hopkins, whose "gift of fatherhood" DeGolyer claimed to envy, had a special project. He wanted Dallas to have a great preparatory school for boys comparable to those in the East. With the considerable financial backing of DeGolyer and others, this project became the Texas Country Day School, now evolved into the St. Mark's School of Texas and enjoying a deserved prestige based on the later academic success of its students. Another project of Hopkins', to which DeGolyer seems to have turned a deaf ear, was his insistence that DeGolyer examine oil prospects in Venezuela. ("A killing," predicted Hopkins, correctly.) The remarkable success of the St. Mark's School is, in a way, a silent tribute to DeGolyer's intellectual influence on the community, for this extraordinary enterprise has benefited handsomely from the gifts of not only millions of dollars but also of dedicated time in planning its future from such men as these trained by DeGolyer: Eugene McDermott, Cecil Green, Erik Jonsson, Ralph Rogers, J. C. Karcher, Lewis MacNaughton.

In Dallas, DeGolyer got his exercise not in a gymnasium workout, as in New York, but by playing golf at the Dallas and the Brook Hollow country clubs, but he was never good at it. According to his realistic and truth-respecting wife, he was probably "the world's poorest athlete." Nonetheless, he respected athletic prowess in others. When his early Amerada associate, John M. Lovejoy (later president of Seaboard Oil Corporation of Delaware) managed at last to "break 100" in his golf score, DeGolyer took proper note. Vacationing in Bermuda in 1935, Lovejoy promptly wired DeGolyer of his feat. DeGolyer paid a visit to Tiffany's and a day later sent in an order, as follows: "Please engrave a silver vase of Type No. 17040, as shown me by your Mr. J. L. McCauley on June 10th, charge to my account and deliver to my office. . . . I wish the following Latin quotation engraved between the two bands of machined lines around the top of the vase:

Nunc Hodie Perfecte Incipiamus
Quia Nihil Est Quod Hactemus
Fecimus

On the upper side of the base of the vase please engrave: 'J. M. L. — 91' and opposite it 'Bermuda 1935.' "

13

To Meet a New Need: DeGolyer and MacNaughton

FROM 1932 ON, or until his work for the government in World War II, DeGolyer's career became increasingly allied with the Southwest. Leaving Amerada, he quickly established himself as an independent producer with his Felmont Corporation in Houston, and a little later with Atlatl (meaning spear thrower or target aimer). This company was sold in 1955 for in excess of nine million dollars. Concentrating on Texas, he brought in highly successful fields at Old Ocean (the great discovery here in 1934 launching him and Karcher into really big money), La Rosa, Van Vleck, Placido, Cold Springs, and a considerable number of additional minor Texas fields. One of his most spectacular feats in the thirties occurred in Illinois. Here he proved once again the importance of reflection seismograph techniques.

After a very successful "boom" in 1905, initiated by Mike Benedum in one of Standard Oil's first ventures into actual oil production, Illinois production was supposedly over by 1930, judged by many in the industry as finished, as far as new fields were concerned. DeGolyer thought otherwise. In January of 1937, at a location based on seismograph detail, he drilled a well near Patoka which promptly flowed 1,500 barrels a day. In the early days it would have been a gusher. But here, too, DeGolyer was different. He had the well brought in slowly, through flow lines into steel tanks, without wasting oil spouting over the derrick's crown block.

Reflection seismograph parties continued their explorations and, as a result of this work, some four thousand wells were drilled during the next two-year period. This activity proved successful far beyond normal expectations and converted the "finished" Illinois area into, at that time, the fourth largest producing state in the nation. Once again, "the little man," said to be "crazy with dynamite and new ideas," became the "premier prince of geologists" and the "know-how" man of the industry.

He was now operating the Felmont Oil Corporation and the Atlatl Oil Royalty Corporation, and was backing Green, McDermott, Jonsson and others whom he had advised in one way or another. He formed an informal association in 1936 in Dallas with Lewis MacNaughton in what was to be his last major enterprise, the DeGolyer and Mac-Naughton Corporation, a geological and engineering consulting service which, formalized in 1939, became the most renowned petroleum consultation service in the world. Since then the customers of the firm have included many governments; government-controlled entities; companies and corporations, large, medium, and small; and many individuals as well. It is said, and is more than true, that De-Golyer and MacNaughton and their men have sweltered in practically all the deserts of the world, and shivered at the North and South poles. They have pursued petroleum investigations from the Arctic Islands to Patagonia and around the world, from west to east and vice versa.

DeGolyer's new junior partner shared the nomad boyhood with pioneering parents typical of DeGolyer and

Karcher, except that he never touched base in Oklahoma. MacNaughton was born on Cuba's Isle of Pines, to which his father, a Spanish-American War veteran, had returned with his bride from the States. But the family never stayed long in one place. The boy entered school first in California, but soon was enrolled in New Jersey, then Connecticut, then New York. In fact, MacNaughton remembers that he attended sixteen different schools before the father finally settled in Saugerties, New York. There an intelligent minister had formed a club for youths to study his hobby, geology, with him. MacNaughton liked to study rocks, too, and when he had saved up enough money — after working in a paper mill for a year — he chose to major in geology at Cornell. He worked his way through college, as DeGolyer and Karcher worked their ways through the University of Oklahoma, and got a job in 1922 with Standard Oil of Venezuela, for summer work in mapping the Orinoco delta country. After graduation in 1924, he accepted a cataloguing job for over a year with the American Museum of Natural History in New York, then took off for the Texas oil fields with the hundred dollars he had saved. (He preferred to try California but didn't have enough money saved to pay the way.) The boat from New York — cheapest way — landed in Galveston. In Houston, MacNaughton got a job with Wallace Pratt, "the geologist's geologist," who assigned him to do field geology for Humble in East Texas (three years before Dad Joiner made his great strike). In July 1928 DeGolyer, who had heard of MacNaughton and his geological work for Pratt, engaged him as geologist for Amerada's subsidiary, Rycade, and in 1930 transferred him to Amerada's staff, first based in San Antonio and then Houston.

So MacNaughton formed the new company with DeGolyer in Dallas in 1936. After the incorporation of the company in 1939, it was known for a year or two as DeGolyer, MacNaughton and McGhee (DeGolyer's son-in-law), but George McGhee decided he wanted to go into diplomatic service and, having made a sufficient competence for civilized living by the time he was thirty, withdrew to devote his time to public service. He was later succeeded by the dynamic John H. Murrell (whom DeGolyer chaffingly referred to as his *pistolero intelectual*), a graduate of the United States Military Academy at West Point where he distinguished himself in football as a sterling back, and he proved to be a pistol. He had the dash, the willingness to take chances, the contempt for men who shy away from challenges that characterized both DeGolyer and MacNaughton. Murrell had an inherent knowledge of the petroleum business.

The establishing of the firm of DeGolyer and MacNaughton anticipated a new need for the oil business. In the early thirties the term "consultant" was jibingly construed in the oil fraternity to mean most often "a geologist temporarily without a job with one of the big companies." This was not the case in the firm of DeGolyer and MacNaughton. The long and necessary fight in the thirties for conservation and production control, usually called proration, radically changed the conditions of wildcatting. Until the proration system or formula became effective, oil production was at the mercy of the boom-or-bust cycle, that is to say, of enormous periodic waste in this natural resource. The oil company out to make its "killing" benefited from practices that allowed wells to be too closely spaced and to flow wide open — nearly nine-tenths of the oil ultimately to be extracted from a well was hurried on in the first year or so of its life. But this, alas, meant a great loss in the potential reserves of the well for this reason: crude oil is inert and is moved to the surface by the energy present in it in the form of gas. Unrestricted flow quickly exhausted this built-in pressure source. Thus, gas escaped from its solution within the oil as the open flow liberated the underground pressure; oil shot into the air, but so did the gas, a total waste. And with the gas liberated aboveground, much of the oil was still left in place, "dead" for all practical purposes. Scientific developments made possible the recovery of this "dead" oil. But this required a considerable outlay of capital, beyond the reach of many operators who, in the days of flush production, had got back their investments and made their profits in the first year or so.

And still another consideration reinforced the need for long-time financing in the discovery of oil. This was the result, of course, of the proration, or conservation, system. As later partner John Murrell puts it: "They [DeGolyer and MacNaughton] foresaw that curbing production would drastically reduce the sudden large incomes that had hitherto rewarded one who made a discovery. Such reductions, they surmised, would bring about a need for long-term financing for many entities in the industry." This was the price of stabilizing the industry.

But such financing required more than blind faith that there was oil in the ground. The need arose from *independent*, detached evaluations of reservoir prospects. Financing had to rely on the integrity and the knowledge of those men upon whom the bankers relied for the appraisal of properties. It was at this time of change that DeGolyer and MacNaughton formed their association as "consultants" to the industry. The existence of such a firm, as Murrell observes pointedly, was both essential and inevitable. And with the evolving scientific aids to finding oil, and their costliness, such appraisal work became indispensable to the industry. With his uncanny gift, or genius, of forecasting future developments, DeGolyer had once again hit upon exactly the right idea.

Murrell recalled, in a speech to the Newcomen Society which honored the firm, that he was often glad to be only the junior partner — most of all on a trip to Saudi Arabia, when at the conclusion of a successful three-week assignment, the hosts invited the American team to a banquet. "In the manner of the country," Murrell said, "we all squatted on the ground around a tablecloth laden with the roasted carcass of a sheep surrounded by bowls of rice, dates and other sweetmeats. Before we began eating, the two senior partners were introduced to a fine old Arab custom. As guests of honor, they were presented the *pièce de résistance* of the banquet — the two eyes of the sheep. My admiration for Messrs. DeGolyer and MacNaughton was never greater than it was then, as I watched them manfully uphold the dignity of the firm. They later told me the sheep's eyes went down something like oysters. But I thank my lucky stars that I was only the third and junior partner — and that sheep have only two eyes."

DeGolyer's scientific curiosity inspired him to form still another company in 1936, Core Laboratories, Inc. One of his geologist friends happened to use in his presence the word "millidarcy." DeGolyer asked what it meant; the friend confessed he didn't really know. Perplexed and intrigued, DeGolyer ran down the definition in a Pennsylvania laboratory which analyzed cross sections of cores of sands shipped in from wells. "Millidarcy" was the measure of how permeable the sand was in regard to the movement of oil through it. DeGolyer observed that the analyzed cores lost many of their original characteristics in the process of being shipped. He decided to experiment with mobile laboratories which could analyze on the spot fresh cores as they were lifted from the wells. This was the ori-

Lewis MacNaughton and E. DeGolyer in their Dallas office.

gin of Core Laboratories; since then, core analysis has added several billion barrels of oil to the nation's recoverable reserves. The core analysis method provides a technique to determine the proper spacing of wells and, above all, how fast to flow them so as to get out the greatest possible amount of oil with maximum economy. The man who didn't know what "millidarcy" meant — but who felt a compulsion to find out — attributed this contribution to "sheer luck."

When DeGolyer was packing to leave for the Middle East again, after the war, a friend asked him: "Why, with all your money, do you keep traipsing around to these out-of-the-way places?"

DeGolyer seemed surprised at the question. "I want to know more," he said.

Upon reaching age fifty in 1936, DeGolyer told many that what he wanted to do was to retire and devote himself to his writing projects. "We are going to build an estate," he announced, "where I can lead a quiet and country life." When this word was passed around in the geological fraternity, everyone had a proposal for using De's leisure time. One of the first to mature plans was the geology department of the University of Texas, with an appeal to DeGolyer's lifelong obsession with the academic world. Aided and abetted by Major J. R. Parten, a former Humble executive and member of the university's board of regents, the department wanted DeGolyer not only to teach geology on the Austin campus but also to structure a department commensurate with its position in the greatest oil state in the nation. DeGolyer, meditating as usual a history of oil exploration in the country, was more than tempted. He agreed in principle. Perhaps he could start in the academic year beginning in the autumn of 1938. But the "estate" was still in a formative stage at that time (it had become a major preoccupation in which he and Nell filled dozens of scrapbooks with pictures and plans of the mission style house they wanted), and he postponed definite acceptance. Maybe next year. And indeed, with the estate finally ready for a housewarming in the late spring of 1939, he accepted for the autumn. He would commute from Austin to Dallas, for the weekends were reserved for family and enjoyment of the new estate. It was not to be. World War II had erupted in Europe. Nonetheless, DeGolyer compromised by offering to teach two courses, one for graduate students only and one for undergraduates, in the spring semester.

He installed himself in Austin for the spring term of 1940, and unexpectedly found himself living in baronial splendor. He had written his good friend Edgar Tobin of San Antonio (whose Aerial Surveys had contributed immensely to oil discovery) of his plans and Tobin had suggested that he live in his wife's ancestral home on Windsor Road, a showplace of Austin. DeGolyer was the sole occupant of this immense castle. He loved it and it was some compensation for abandoning the Dallas country estate.

DeGolyer was no stranger to teaching. He had been sporadically a lecturer in geology at the University of Oklahoma after he came back from Mexico. He had read many papers to various meetings of geological groups, had written copious articles about his profession. In 1929, he had been invited to present a series of lectures both at the Massachusetts Institute of Technology and at Princeton. He was a seasoned public speaker about his specialty. And yet he discovered he had little time to pursue his own projects. He assigned, as he soon realized, too much work to his students — and found himself, in reviewing the material, barely keeping ahead. He took seriously his implied moral obligation to help revamp the university's geology course, and spent much time with his colleagues. Diligently he attended faculty meetings. As a successful organizer of personnel, of large staffs himself, he was very curious to see the internal discipline of a large university. Before long, he decided, as he later observed, that inefficiency was inseparable from the tradition of academic freedom. He didn't propose to alter what often looked to him like chaos, he was simply making an observation.

The University of Texas, hamstrung in rewarding excellence by the tradition of paying all professors of the same rank about the same salary, had just innovated a way out of the dilemma by awarding special Distinguished Professorships. There were six of these when DeGolyer joined the staff; he made the seventh. At any rate, the salary could not have mattered much to him. As Distinguished Professor of Geology, his yearly base pay was $6,500. At that, he was getting a thousand dollars more a year than the chairman of the department, Professor H. P. Bybee. He taught Geology 387s for graduates, which included ten hours of laboratory work per week, and Geology 373s for seniors. His grade book, punctiliously kept, shows he was a fairly lenient teacher.

Inevitably, he was invited to make the address at the annual membership banquet of the honorary geological fraternity, Sigma Gamma Epsilon, at the Driskill Hotel in March 1940. He complied gladly. He titled his talk, "Severinus Brought Up to Date." His point was that the "knowledge explosion" in geology, and in science in general, had outdated the ancient tradition that the way of the geologist was to don his boots and get out into the field. There is now so much accumulated data, DeGolyer said, and such an urgent need for trained scientific analysis of the data that the real textbook of the geologist in the future would be literally the book and not the rocks. Gently rebuking his students for what he suspected was their casualness about the long reading assignments he had given, he said that the important geological decisions of the future would be made by sedentary men, poring over and collating reports — and correctly interpreting them. The field experience of no one man would be adequate in the future; scientific progress and the development of scientific techniques had insured the necessity of mastering vast compilations of pooled knowledge.

"Severinus, one of the fathers of mineralogy," DeGolyer told the students, "dismissed his students during the latter part of the eighteenth century with this patriarchal injunction:

Go, my sons, buy stout shoes, climb the mountains, search the valleys, the desert, the sea shores, and the deep recesses of the earth. Look for the various kinds of minerals, note their character and mark their origins. Lastly, buy coal, build furnaces, observe and experiment without ceasing, for in this way and no other will you arrive at a knowledge of the nature and the properties of things.

"This is good doctrine and orthodox. Doubtless the geological elders of every generation have addressed their juniors thuswise. Whether they are moved by just a little dash of the old Indian tradition to 'make the boy's meat hard,' I will not say."

DeGolyer continued, reminiscing: "My experiences as a youngster, and it is of respectable enough antiquity to be valid in a science so young as geology, have been about as follows. I did my first geology in the horse-and-buggy or, more precisely perhaps, the horse-and-saddle age. Equipment consisted, beside the conventional geologist's pick and collecting bag, of a clinometer hand compass for measuring dips and strikes and taking the bearings of traverses, an aneroid barometer for elevations, a tally counter for counting the horse's paces, with a notebook and protractor, and the usual complement of black and colored pencils. For the sake of completeness, let us not forget the eraser."

"I doubt," he commented, "that any older generation of geologists of that day ever watched my work without lamenting to the effect that geology could not be done from a horse's back. 'He moved too fast. There were places that were inaccessible to a man on horseback. The only sound way to do geology was on foot, walking the beds out.'"

But, added the speaker, by the early 1920's geologists were furnished with cars — "long-legged Fords or Dodges" — for transportation purposes. "I had become of the older generation myself," said DeGolyer (he was then nearing forty), "and repeated the plaints with the necessary amendments to the effect that geology could not be done from a car. Those were the days of open cars. I distinctly remember visiting several of my men in the field in western Kansas shortly after the discovery of the Russell pool, the discovery pool for that area. It was exceedingly cold. Much of the time the temperature was around zero, and it was with a distinct shock that I found our ace geologist in a closed car. The lamentations of a geological Jeremiah were gone through with again, with some added bitter remarks arising out of increased cost, for I had by this time become a manager as well as a geologist. I have no doubt but what young men as young as you may in the future repeat this age-old complaint about the decline of your science because of the increasing softness of its practitioners."

His major point was to emphasize the usefulness of a

new kind of equipment: the library. "The library is not the least of your equipment. . . . A single example: Oil fields were being developed on the salt domes of the Gulf Coast in this state for at least eight years before anyone was bold enough to and lucky enough to find the prolific flank sand deposits; yet a geologist who was bookish and inquiring enough to have read the descriptions already in print of the Rumanian oil fields should have realized the opportunity which the flank sands presented. In truth, I feel one cannot say too much for the library and the inquiring mind for second-hand information."

He concluded that Severinus' amended advice would be about as follows: Stay home, my sons. Grow soft physically if you must but keep mentally alert, especially when the sound of dynamite is heard abroad in the land. . . .

It was tonic and heady stuff but although DeGolyer was "bookish" he could not entirely practice what he preached. He remained incessantly on the move, traveling by car, train, plane, ship — all over the globe. Some years he logged as much as a hundred thousand miles of travel in one year, a figure which was almost standard for his partner Lewis MacNaughton. Still, in the abstract and divorced from personal temperament, it was as memorable a speech as any student of geology was apt to hear in 1940. (And indeed DeGolyer's next major assignment — the one in which he would make his most direct contribution to the welfare of his country — with the Petroleum Administration for War, in 1941, was to immobilize him in a desk job which made the most formidable demands on his gifts for synthesizing scientific data.)

One reason he accepted the professorship at the University of Texas was the opportunity it allowed him for gathering still more material on his long-projected history of the oil industry. He discovered shortly that the university's library resources, however, did not match those of his own private collection. Nonetheless, he very much enjoyed the experience of teaching. He wrote to his friend Walter W. Stewart, of the School of Economics and Politics at Princeton's Institute for Advanced Study: "I am no longer professor. Nell absolutely refused any favorable consideration to my spending another year at Texas and, therefore, I have had to resign. I did this with great regret, as teaching caused me to review and study propositions that I had been accustomed to take for granted, and it was a wonderful opportunity to do a lot of professional reading."

He added modestly, speaking of five Vanuxem lectures he was scheduled to give in one week at Princeton in the autumn of 1940: "Of course I can tell everything I know about oil in the first period, but even the slight experience I have had at being a professor has enabled me to string it out to the five necessary lectures. In fact, I might be able to talk a whole year about it if that were necessary. It seemed to me that I got to be a good deal like a fire horse during the Texas experience. I ran to the classroom when the bell rang and talked until it rang again. I am sure all professors are not like that, but many of them must be." And he confessed to Stewart that a monklike existence fostered scholarship. In principle, he was supposed to do as much research at home as he had done in Austin. "But it doesn't quite work out that way," wrote DeGolyer.

Teaching only two classes, DeGolyer had a rather free schedule at Texas — contrary to Severinus, he didn't stay home. That spring he went to New York twice, once to receive the Anthony Lucas Medal Award, and then to be honored by election to the Alumni Associates of Phi Beta Kappa. He gave the dedicatory address for the new Geology and Geography Building at the Colorado School of Mines, flew to Chicago to speak to the American Association of Petroleum Geologists, made a speech in Houston at a meeting of the American Petroleum Institute, gave a talk in Dallas and later presided over the annual meeting, in Austin, of the Texas State Historical Association. Conveniently for him, the annual commencement convocation at Princeton came in June after the University of Texas semester was over — he journeyed to Princeton on June 14 to receive his second honorary doctorate.

DeGolyer had originally planned to try the teaching experiment for two full years. But World War II had broken out; he had to change his plans. President Painter and the department, and members of the board, urged him to stay. Again, as he wrote one friend, Nell DeGolyer put her foot down and "wouldn't hear to his being away from home another year." Perhaps in compensation, he was presently to give the University of Texas most of his "literary" first editions. It was an experience he enjoyed, as he wrote many friends. But contrary to his own advice in his speech to the geological students, he wasn't yet ready to become the "sedentary" master. But the appeal of the academic career remained constant. A year later he was giving the Vanuxem lectures at Princeton, five in a series, on "Oil: Introduction, Composition and Occurrences," "Prospecting and Theory of Production," "Conservation," "Position of the American Petroleum Industry" and, finally, "World Position of the Oil Industry." The lecture bug had bitten him. He even agreed in 1947 to a sort of road-show tour of addresses across the nation, at universities and before petroleum clubs, for the American Association of Petroleum Geologists.

An additional profit for the University of Texas from DeGolyer's semester stay on the campus came in the form of his ultimate gift to the library of more than 1,200 volumes and manuscripts, whose value amounted to well over

$50,000. In 1941 and 1942 he gave important specialized works to the Petroleum Reference Library of the university's department of geology. Later, over the next five years, during a period when many of his "literary" first editions were on loan at the main library, he transferred title to the university of books in a field which he had ceased to collect. At first, he gave his rare volumes of Whitman, and finally a collection rich in first editions of Melville, Dickens, Kipling, Walter de la Mare, George Bernard Shaw, Sheila Kaye-Smith — even a first edition of *Alice in Wonderland*. In addition to Whitman and Melville, the American writers represented ranged from Ernest Hemingway to Sherwood Anderson, from Booth Tarkington to Christopher Morley.

He gave the university the expensive copy he had of Galsworthy's *Man of Devon*, so costly because this was the presentation copy which Galsworthy had inscribed to his close friend Joseph Conrad, mailing it the day before publication; DeGolyer gave his valuable "copyright editions" of Kipling's *Just So Stories*, of which no more than ten copies had been printed. The ultimate transfer of these 1,200 titles was delayed until war's end, since DeGolyer's governmental duties kept him in Washington and part of the time out of the country on secret missions to Saudi Arabia and Mexico and elsewhere. And he insisted on personally supervising the cataloguing of the items himself before the gift was made final.

Most of these transactions were handled by Miss Fannie Ratchford, the university's esteemed librarian, who was also the foremost Brontë scholar in the world. The exchange of letters involved two minor matters of considerable human interest. One of the boxes shipped down to the university from Dallas turned out, by mistake of course, to be a Neiman-Marcus box of rare china, still unopened. Miss Ratchford returned this box — and the De-Golyers were able, tardily, to thank a friend for a handsome gift. Another item Miss Ratchford returned she found enclosed in the Galsworthy novel; it was an unsigned Valentine but inscribed to "Daddy DeGolyer" in childish handwriting.

President T. S. Painter wanted to organize a reception for the DeGolyers in honor of the gift. This DeGolyer tried to avoid. "I do not really care much for receptions," he wrote Painter. But he was prevailed on to attend. One thing led to another. DeGolyer agreed to serve as chairman of a newly organized group to be known as "The Friends of the University of Texas Library." Its first meeting, on May 30, 1947, was attended by such notable Texas citizens as H. H. Dewar, Palmer Bradley, Dudley Woodward, J. A. R. Moseley, George P. Hill. Then Professor Harry Huntt Ransom wrote an article about the DeGolyer gift for the university's alumni magazine; since then, as president and later as chancellor of the university, Dr. Ransom has made the University of Texas Library one of the admirations and envies of the academic world. His spectacular acquisitions have been subsidized in part by the university's ownership of oil-rich lands (making it the second richest university in the world), some of whose wells were drilled on DeGolyer's advice.

In one of his letters to Miss Ratchford, DeGolyer confesses to a consuming interest in Samuel Butler. "For some reason," he wrote her, "Butler has fascinated me and I have read a great deal of his work and have collected him more or less assiduously." But he assures her that he does not want his gift to be maintained intact, "as I feel this would make it less useful." And later, he repeats that "any method of handling the books which makes them most useful and most available to the library is satisfactory to me." He adds that any type of bookplate will do. He wanted the books to be read by inquiring minds.

Finally, he noted with some pride that reading was not neglected in his hometown. One of his favorite books was Cornell president Andrew D. White's *History of the Warfare of Science with Theology in Christendom*. He wrote Miss Ratchford that he had recently checked on the book's circulation in the Dallas Public Library. The return dates for the book showed it had been checked out more than one hundred times. "To my mind," he wrote, "this almost entitles us to the championship belt for intellect in the entire South."

When he became chairman of the committee of trustees to select a new librarian for the revivified Dallas Public Library, he gave the duty concentrated and detailed attention, as though it were another geophysical investigation for DeGolyer and MacNaughton. A parade of summoned applicants passed through the town; the committee took seriously its obligation to a community that knew about and read Dr. White's *History of the Warfare of Science with Theology in Christendom*. As a trustee of the library, DeGolyer encouraged ambitious projects. When a proposed budget one year shocked the other trustees, DeGolyer said the budget shocked him too — not because of the amount, which was only $800,000 — but because of the meager allocation for book purchases. He thought the board ought to try to get the extra-large budget from the city fathers, but he also thought the funds marked for book purchases ought to be tripled. "I cannot understand," he said, "why a library does not concentrate on books instead of on other services. If I had made out this budget, I would have allocated $500,000 of it for buying needed books."

He did not have his way in this. But he was successful

in helping resist the wave of censorship, both political and
moral, that swept the country in the fifties and often concentrated on harassing library distribution or circulation
of controversial books. DeGolyer put his foot down. "We
are not going to block," he said, "free access to ideas and
to thought." This support was crucial in a city, and a state,
overwhelmingly conservative in habit and in temperament. Of course, he was having to make the same defense
nationally, against some of the "big rich" who were target-
ing the *Saturday Review* for its stand against McCarthy-
ism.

"By the standards of the oil fraternity," he sometimes
observed, both with ironic amusement and with disappointment, "I suppose I am regarded as a dangerous liberal." The "liberals" would not have agreed. DeGolyer was
his own man, always suspicious of the doctrinaire and the
programmatic. He solved problems by what he judged to
be common sense. There seems to have been in his makeup
only a slight streak of idealism. He was a thoroughly pragmatic, realistic American, as the temper of the times
trained most Americans to be. His respect was for brains,
understood as the triumph of rational thought. But he
knew perfectly the limitations this kind of excellence imposed. Even he, tough and searching in mind, respected
the presence in experience, as we shall see later, of a fundamental and rationally inaccessible sense of mystery.

By the terms of the DeGolyer will, his estate will become a public benefaction for the city of Dallas. A long,
one-story structure of stone and stucco, the house sits, or
seems to grow out of the ground, in the midst of forty-
four densely wooded acres overlooking and bordering the
east shore of Dallas's White Rock Lake. With his sardonic
streak of humor, most often turned on himself, DeGolyer

Front (lower) and profile (top) views of the DeGolyer house in Dallas, called because of its numerous oak trees Rancho Encinal. White Rock Lake lies about a hundred yards from the arcade gallery in the upper photograph.

liked to refer to it as "a California architect's notion of what a Texas oilman would want in attempting to duplicate a Mexican hacienda on the outskirts of a big modern American city."

The house was largely designed to provide a library big enough to handle DeGolyer's collection. The library, with ceilings a bit less high than the rest of the house to facilitate easy access to top shelves, dominates the western end of the long house (it is two hundred feet from the DeGolyer bedroom suite to the kitchen) and opens in a large bay onto a view of the lake. A massive stone fireplace, capable of handling six-foot logs, in the middle of the south wall, is the only area not lined with book shelves. The books are often two rows thick, carefully catalogued and arranged; DeGolyer could always at once pull out any requested item. The walls are paneled in Texas oak; an immense Oriental rug carpets most of the floor, comfortable sofas and chairs invite both talk and reading. In the bay stands a very large mounted globe, gift of Lewis MacNaughton to his partner. Over the fireplace there now hangs a portrait of DeGolyer, posed wearing the gown and insignia of his honorary degree awarded him by Princeton University in 1940. The portrait is by Douglas Chandor, a gift of DeGolyer's friends. This portrait displaced an earlier one, that of President-General Santa Anna, whose handsomely ferocious countenance now confronts guests in the dining room.

Mementos of DeGolyer's career abound in the room but are so inconspicuously displayed they are rarely recognized. A guest may move a polished rock from a table to make room for putting down his highball, not realizing the stone is a Tamasopo limestone relic from the site of Potrero del Llano #4. He may flick his cigarette ash into a tray without knowing that it was shaped from a core drilling at the discovery well at Nash Dome. But the whole room is testimony to DeGolyer's attachment to concrete things, to the tangible, to the natural. Off the library is a patio court, surrounded by bedrooms, where fountain and bougainvillea and caged birds and banana plants evoke a perfect image of a quiet Mexican interior garden.

The east wing of the house, the "Indian room," is an informal counterpart of the library at the opposite westward stretch. Dominated by a curved corner fireplace, massive as a limestone creek bank, the clay-colored plastered walls are hung with Mexican blankets and rise to a ceiling composed of rough-hewn enormous beams and vigas laid in herringbone pattern. The slate-paved floor is also covered with Indian rugs and blankets; niches in the wall, painted in cobalt blue, house images of saints. In this room are pre-Columbian statues and artifacts, paintings by Diego Rivera and others, a matchless collection of Mexican crafts of all sorts. It, too, opens onto its own private veranda with a walled court with fountain. It is this house with its library and gardens which will give Dallas something of a parallel to the Huntington Foundation.

Into this house for sixteen years there was a steady stream of distinguished guests — statesmen, business tycoons, scholars and intellectuals, artists and writers, college presidents and European dignitaries. It is not fiction, as some people believe, but fact that as the guests at the traditional house-warming party drove their cars down the road to the exit gates onto Garland Road, they were confronted by a huge sign, erected after their arrival. It read: "We didn't like your house either!" The sign was wrong. People of the most diverse sorts like the DeGolyer house. It has the three qualities typical of Everette DeGolyer himself. It is, despite its unobtrusive splendor, informal, independent and individual.

In March of 1940, just about the time DeGolyer was lecturing the Texas students on updating the advice of Severinus, the *Saturday Review* made an important decision. Though much respected as the country's only "literary weekly," the *Review* had floundered along, on subsidy and always with yearly deficit, ever since its founding in 1924 by the *New York Post* literary foursome: Henry Seidel Canby, Amy Loveman, William Rose Benét, and Christopher Morley. (Largely because of his admiration for Morley, DeGolyer had been a constant reader of the magazine since its first number.) Harrison Smith, early publisher with Richard Haas of William Faulkner, Sinclair Lewis and other mighty names, bought the controlling interest in the *Review* in 1938 and tried to make the magazine pay its own way. So, in 1940 a young man who had made a brilliant career as managing editor of *Current History* was engaged to take over the editorship of the *Saturday Review*. He was twenty-five years old; his name was Norman Cousins.

Cousins at once initiated an editorial program to broaden the interests and the circulation base of the magazine, then surviving on a distribution of about twenty thousand copies weekly. His primary aim was to make the magazine a "review" in the British sense of the word, with as much attention to ideas and to current events as to literature. One aspect of this broadening was to canvas life in the rest of the nation and to provide coverage of the intellectual and cultural stir both west and east of Manhattan. He was aiming at a global magazine, rather than a specialized literary journal.

One of the first projects in this particular part of the program was to schedule a series of "regional" issues of the *Review*, to offer its readership an "inventory and sampling" of the cultural climate in various sections of the country.

More or less by accident, the first choice was the Southwest. Cousins may have been influenced by the remarkably lively and impressive performance of the University of Oklahoma Press which, under the successive leadership of Joseph Brandt and Savoie Lottinville, was making publishing history with vital and exciting books on the Indian, the cowboy, the oil industry, the Old West's history and other material indigenous to the area. Cousins and Lottinville were friends, the latter was a friend of DeGolyer.

Such an issue required a regional editor; Cousins invited John H. McGinnis, nationally known Shakespearean scholar at Southern Methodist University and editor of the well-established book page of what was then Texas' only statewide newspaper, the *Dallas Morning News,* to supervise the special Southwest number. McGinnis was also the editor of the region's leading literary magazine, *The Southwest Review* (founded in 1915 by Stark Young, then a young professor at the University of Texas), and knew personally the leading writers of the area. He accepted the assignment with delight. Cousins flew to Dallas in the autumn of 1941 for a conference, his pocket filled with data and suggestions. McGinnis transferred this outline to his own pocket and said, "Let's talk about the idea first." He arranged for the Dallas writer and editor, John William Rogers, to entertain Cousins in his home, along with DeGolyer and others who might contribute articles to the issue. Thus fortuitously were Cousins and DeGolyer brought into an association that made the *Saturday Review,* and greatly enlivened the career of each. They owed their friendship and publishing partnership partially to chance, and partially to Savoie Lottinville, who had spoken to Cousins about DeGolyer's love of books and interest in publishing.

The two men found each other *simpatico* at once. Cousins, a born crusader by temperament and in pursuit of nobility of action as a national or even supranational ideal, was determined to make the *Saturday Review* an influence that counted, a shaper of the national life style and values. His task was twofold: 1) to get the magazine out of its ivory-tower context, and 2) to increase measurably its dwindling circulation. His own intense interest in politics and history dictated a more catholic editorial policy; and it was obvious to any clear-sighted mind that the magazine needed a realistic and businesslike program of newsstand distribution and subscription-seeking. Cousins' problems with his new assignment were exactly the sort to enlist the attentive interest of a mind like DeGolyer's, long habituated to making alliances between knowledge and business work.

When Cousins came to Dallas to confer with McGinnis on the regional issue to be called "The Southwest: Inventory and Sampling," the magazine's board was already in the middle of reorganization plans, and was looking for additional financing. Cousins broached the matter to DeGolyer who had no difficulty in comprehending the problems of magazine publishing and who promised to consider outright purchase of the magazine himself. But Pearl Harbor and World War II intervened. All DeGolyer's energies were absorbed in his duties as Deputy Petroleum Administrator; in 1942, in fact, the DeGolyers were obliged to live in Washington. But Cousins saw DeGolyer in Washington and by June of 1942 the new publishing setup was ready for announcement. For only a modest initial investment of $25,000, DeGolyer became the chief stockholder in the new corporation, with 250 shares of stock; Harrison Smith came next with 150 shares, valued at $15,000; Cousins, Professor Canby, and Amy Loveman held 50 shares apiece. The *Review* got, despite wartime shortages, an adjustment allowing enough paper to insure an increased circulation of 25,000, but its major development had to await the end of the war.

DeGolyer's association with the *Saturday Review* may have sprung from still another reason. His son, Everett Lee, aged seventeen, had entered Princeton in the fall of 1941. Although he was already six feet tall at age sixteen, towering over his mother and father when he was graduated from the Texas Country Day School in Dallas, the family thought he was too young for college. He spent a year at the Lawrenceville School before enrolling at Princeton. He wanted to major in history. After history, he most liked music. Geology held little interest for him. It seemed clear he would not train to go into his father's business. He claimed that the necessary talent, or "fluke" of a gift, for mathematics had passed him by. It was clear that his life would be, should be, connected with the world of books. Perhaps DeGolyer thought of the *Saturday Review* as a potential career for his son.

The special issue assessing the Southwest was published in May 1942, after long but exciting and good-natured wranglings between the New York office and the individualistic McGinnis, who treated deadlines with contempt — as he did the matter of expenses — and who, like Balzac and Churchill, figured that you put copy into type only as a more convenient way to start your editing and rewriting. But at last McGinnis (whose extraordinary feeling for place derived in part from the example of Goethe's revolt against French neoclassical models with the assertion that "initially, all art is local") was satisfied. That special issue remains memorable. Represented were all the leading living southwestern writers at the time, with the single exception of Katherine Anne Porter, who did not, correctly, consider herself a "regionalist." (McGinnis felt, accordingly, that she should not be mentioned anywhere in the issue, an omission hard to justify, in a number calling itself an "inventory" — as various persons pointed out.) There were present, however, the greatest of American folklorists: John A. Lomax; Oliver LaFarge, whose *Laughing Boy* had won the Pulitzer Prize in fiction in 1929; the historian so esteemed abroad but not at home, Walter Prescott Webb; Paul Horgan, later to win the Pulitzer Prize in history for his *Great River: The Rio Grande in North American History;* J. Frank Dobie, dean of Texas letters; Stanley Vestal, Indian-reared, Oxford-trained author of sterling biographies of Kit Carson and Sitting Bull; George Sessions Perry (whom Harrison Smith was championing as a future John Steinbeck); Witter Bynner, the finest poet ever to choose the Southwest for residence; and still others. DeGolyer contributed an article on "New Mexicana."

Cousins' bloodbath with southwestern individualism, integrity and stubbornness won him two things: a remarkable special issue of the magazine and the lifelong and admiring friendship of DeGolyer. DeGolyer thoroughly enjoyed the whole affair: he took a devilish delight in watching Cousins, inescapably the man of action, come to grips with unrealistic perfectionists. In its small but symbolic way, it was a drama of life's central existential predicament.

After only two years, Cousins had run the circulation up by fifty percent, to 37,000. When the announcement was made in September 1942, of the formation of the Saturday Review Associates, Inc. — which bought the magazine from Harrison Smith, sole owner since 1938 — there were three new names added to the masthead. In addition to Smith, Cousins, Canby, Loveman, and Benét (all of whom remained as editorial mainstays as well as stockholders), were the poet Leonard Bacon, E. L. DeGolyer and J. R.

Cominsky. Jack Cominsky resigned a business and advertising post on the *New York Times* to become the *Saturday Review*'s vice-president in charge of business affairs and advertising. Of this group, DeGolyer became the particular friend of Cousins and of Cominsky, both of whom he admired profoundly.

Nine months after this reorganization, Cousins was able to write his new patron on June 9, 1943: "Incidentally, I think you will be pleased to learn that the *Saturday Review* has shown the first black-ink report in its history. The accountant's statement for the last nine months shows that we are approximately $10,000 to the good on our operations. All the old obligations of and claims upon the old company have been completely liquidated, so that we are entirely in the clear." Despite being thus ahead of budget, Cousins of course made it clear that this favorable situation was not to be regarded as a guarantee against further deficit, especially if the magazine were to be further improved and broadened in its interest base.

In its climb to really big circulation, the *Saturday Review* achieved a polarity between realized objective and unrealized ideal. By this stairstep succession upward, each landing stage might be notched up as a success; at the same time, it represented a point to be surpassed. If you looked backward, by this agreed-upon plan of expansion, you saw a profit, a goal reached. If you looked ahead, you saw a new budget which would be a deficit until the new sights were achieved. For ten years, the balance-sheet interpretation would show this pattern; profits were plowed into the successive expansion programs. So, at any point almost, you could take a double reading: prideful if you looked back, challenging and deficit risking if you looked ahead. It was a system that paid off, even if it meant living in a constant state of "pull from the future," and no chance to rest on laurels. It is, of course, a fairly standard pattern in most business enterprises.

Cousins' jubilation in his letter of June 9 was easy to understand. Before Harrison Smith took over in 1938, the *Review* had operated as an "endowed institution" at an annual loss of $50,000 or more. From 1938 to 1942, Smith had invested $18,000 in the magazine, plus making use of a $20,000 "loan" from Harry Scherman, president and founder of the Book-of-the-Month Club. And Smith had cut the annual loss by more than half. Then Norman Cousins in his first year cut that half by half, the deficit down to about $10,000. Thinking of what had been achieved, then, by midsummer of 1943, in nine months since the reorganization, Cousins and the Saturday Review Associates could reasonably toast the future — a future without the limiting wartime restriction on paper.

IV

Oil General
in World War II

14

Oil and War: PAW and PRC

I N HIS PROFESSIONAL CAREER, DeGolyer had meantime accepted another post with the government, one of transcending importance. The spectacular success of Hitler's Stuka dive-bombers in turning the Maginot Line, in effecting the fall of France in June of 1940, had simply dramatized what everybody knew: that World War II would magnify the supreme importance of oil in modern warfare.

Acting before Pearl Harbor, President Roosevelt in March of 1941 instructed Secretary of the Interior Harold L. Ickes to establish a technically expert body to study the nation's oil reserves. As his deputy, Ickes appointed Ralph K. Davies, vice-president of Standard Oil of California. Taking the title of defense oil coordinator, Secretary Ickes announced in July 1941 the appointment of a staff of specialists "to administer the coordinating program for the oil industry." The staff comprised DeGolyer as director of conservation; E. B. Swanson as director of research; Robert E. Allen as director of production; Wright W. Gary as director of refining; H. A. Gilbert as director of transportation; John W. Frey as director of marketing. Chief counsel for the board would be J. Howard Marshall, former assistant dean of the Yale Law School; special assistants were George W. Holland and William S. Arnold; and the executive officer was Stanley Crosthwait. At first DeGolyer was able to commute by plane, but wartime travel was an ordeal; in 1942 he and Nell DeGolyer took up residence in Washington.

As director of conservation, DeGolyer's job, of course, was to save oil, not to find it. As chairman of the Interstate Oil Compact Commission's engineering committee since its inception, he had sparked the industry's own conservation program — a program whose necessity the wild waste in East Texas had dramatized. Under Ickes, he brought about recovery of 600 million extra badly needed barrels from one field alone. But once he had organized the program, he rebelled, as usual, against a desk job. He always preferred to devise the grand strategy and to leave the details to others. Like many another successful man, he knew the art of delegating routine work to others. By the end of two years, he felt he had done his duty. But he found it hard to resign since friends in the industry sought to dissuade him. Instead he got another assignment from Ickes, with the very secretive new Petroleum Reserves Corporation of which Ickes was also director.

As the possibility of direct American involvement in World War II became increasingly a foreseeable probability in early 1941, President Roosevelt accepted the necessity of forming a governmental agency to coordinate oil supply and transportation and distribution in the interest of "national defense." Hitler had invaded Russia in March of that year; Russia was clamoring for U.S. lend-lease aid and oil provisions on a scale to match our aid to the British. It was perfectly clear that in modern "mechanized warfare," oil was *the* essential, indispensable resource. It had to power tanks, ships (most navigation was now oil fueled), trains, other means of transport, dive-bombers, ammunition and weapons plants — plus its now irreplaceable role in the technological civilian society.

Oil had not been anywhere near so crucial in World War I. But by 1918, the role it would play in any future war was obvious to some military experts, including General Charles de Gaulle. Despite this evidence, however, the majority of the military remained skeptical about the value of air warfare as compared with traditional land maneuvers. But they freely admitted that motorized equipment, for quick transport of troops, had provided the margin for victory in World War I for the Allies. France, for example, was saved in 1914 when a fleet of frantically assembled taxicabs and motorized trucks allowed delivery of French troops to strategic points to block German possession of Paris. After the war's end, the French High Commissioner for Petroleum Products in World War I categorically stated that the decisive battles of Verdun and of the Somme in 1916, and the battle of the Aisne in 1917, were won by the Allied use of motor transport of troops.

Still, the Allied air force between 1914–1918 numbered only 1,500 planes; their primary use was for scouting. The war was nearly over before formation flying and minor night bombing suggested to the wary the future potential of air warfare. And in fact the use of oil in World War I was a mere dribble compared with the incredible and staggering amounts consumed in World War II. A statistic is revelatory: on a typical day in 1918 the United States (which supplied 90 percent of Allied oil for the war) shipped about 23,000 barrels abroad, and the Allied air forces required less than 3,700 barrels of aviation gasoline per day; whereas in World War II one single mission over Germany, involving one thousand planes, alone required twelve times that total daily World War I consumption! The peak daily production in 1944 of 100-octane gasoline alone was 450,000 barrels.

A similar staggering increase in oil use had likewise developed, of course, in the peacetime civilian economy. For instance, by 1940 there were more than 27 million cars on the roads in the United States as compared with fewer than six million in 1918. In 1940 there were nearly five million trucks in use, but in 1918 there were fewer than half a million. In 1914, the farm tractor "population" was a mere 17,000; by 1940 it had "exploded" to the figure of 1,567,000. And of course oil was powering all sorts of labor-saving devices: mechanical pumps, shovels, cranes, bulldozers, drills, etc. For the national life, civilian or military, oil had become about as indispensable as bread or breath for individual life.

Nonetheless, when President Roosevelt set out tentatively to organize the oil industry for "national defense" in the prewar (for America) spring of 1941, the newly created agency, headed by Secretary of the Interior Harold L. Ickes, was faced with three special difficulties.

The central role that oil would play in the war was still unrecognized by many military leaders; this meant that the agency — finally christened the Petroleum Administration for War — would have to fight many battles to secure priority on materials indispensable for meeting the colossal demands, as it turned out, for oil and for that essential element that provided the "margin for victory," 100-octane gasoline. The second difficulty was that this unawareness on the part of leadership of the problems involved in fantastically hiking the supply of oil products was matched by the public's optimistic view that the nation's reserves of oil could never be exhausted. The great, flush production years of 1928 (the Oklahoma City field); of 1931 (the seemingly boundless East Texas supply), and of 1933 and 1934 naturally led people to believe that oil would be in forever renewable supply underground like the harvest crops above it.

The third problem concerned the personality and career of Harold L. Ickes.

By 1940 the oil industry for some years had been seriously concerned about making scientific estimates of the nation's probable reserves and was troubled by the prospect of ultimate exhaustion. Perhaps the two men in the industry who gave this matter closest attention and serious study were Wallace Everett Pratt (optimistic) and Everette Lee DeGolyer (pessimistic). But the mood of the public in the wartime crisis was that all you had to do to increase oil supply was merely to twist a valve, and consequently the agency's program of augmented exploration and the increased drilling of "wildcat" wells, to discover new fields, was hampered both by military and public misconception. And when the public rebelled against gasoline rationing, considering the shortage of oil "phony," the oil industry itself — not the government — paid for the advertising campaign to persuade the public to recognize reality.

The third difficulty of the new government agency was two-sided. The oil industry, in general, simply did not like the appointment of Ickes as Coordinator of the Petroleum Administration for War. The highly articulate, colorful, cantankerous "curmudgeon" (as Ickes styled himself) had been a thorn in the industry's side ever since 1933, when Roosevelt named him administrator of the oil section and the oil code of the National Industrial Recovery Administration. Ickes had first annoyed the industry by proposing a moratorium on oil production in 1933; production was flush and prices were plummeting, down to ten cents a barrel. Many oil company bankruptcies threatened. But

Ickes' proposal was intensely opposed. In the bitter tensions of the Depression days it sounded to the oilmen like a crafty path to far-reaching governmental control of the industry.

Ickes continued to fight for a conservative bill passed by the Congress but was unsuccessful. One oil group even demanded his ouster. A man of bulldog tenacity, Ickes persisted; when the Connally Act (the "Hot Oil" act) was passed in 1935, Ickes was named its administrator, an inevitable but still unpopular choice.*

In the same year, the oil companies sponsored a creation of their own to provide an industry-wide conservation program, the Interstate Oil Compact Commission. DeGolyer became chairman of the engineering section of this commission in 1935. The special field of petroleum engineering is to secure maximum production from a well for the longest time, by choice of derrick, drilling equipment and management of the oil flow. Secretary Ickes did not hesitate to characterize this commission as "innocuous." In 1939 Roosevelt tried again to unite Ickes and the industry in a Petroleum Conservation bill. Congress failed to pass it.

When the war storm began to brew, the oil industry fully expected, and largely deplored, the nomination of their "enemy" to the post of Petroleum Coordinator. Only diplomacy could save the day, and the day was saved. Ickes quelled fears of coercion, summoned a thousand or so representatives of the petroleum industry to Washington in early June 1941, and offered the peace pipe of cooperation. Unexpectedly but admirably, one aspect of the historical record of achievement of the PAW was the superb union of government and industry skills and strength

---

* "Hot oil" was an excess over proration allowance, shipped by unscrupulous producers over state lines to elude confiscation. The Connally Act forbade, under severe penalty, such outlaw practices.

working in cooperation to meet, and resolve, a nearly disastrous crisis. This success impelled President Harry S. Truman to comment in 1946: "I have been impressed with the great contribution of Government-industry cooperation in the success of the war petroleum program, and feel that the values of such close and harmonious relations between Government and industry should be continued."

In his book *Fightin' Oil* (1943) Ickes is quite forthright about his initial problem. He knew the petroleum industry had been shocked at the creation of the "office of Petroleum Coordinator" by President Roosevelt when the country was not yet at war. He knew this would be interpreted as an additional step toward governmental control of free enterprise. He knew the suspicion with which he was regarded. He writes, about his first meeting with industry representatives in June 1941:

The atmosphere that prevailed as we foregathered on that summer day back in '41 was pretty much the same that one might find just before a mutineer was to be strung up to the mizzenmast. I was held to be a very bad character indeed; an unhealthy influence on our national life; one who went about looking for industries that he could clamp chains on.

It may have been my imagination, but I thought, as I entered the room, that someone quickly but deftly frisked me for concealed weapons. I thought that I saw one of the oil men looking out of the window to determine, I suspected, his chances for making a quick get-away. It was a pretty tense moment.

After all it was not to be wondered at that the oil men had their fingers crossed when our meeting was called to order. Wasn't I one of the more toxic of the New Dealers? Didn't I look with suspicion on anyone who made a profit?

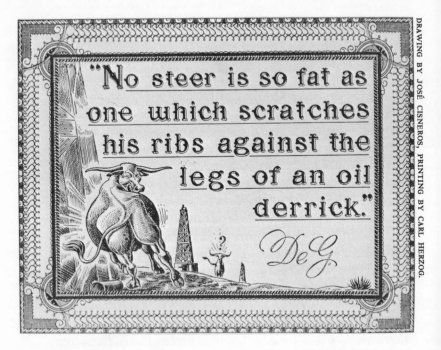

Outside cover-fold of a Season's Greetings card sent by E. DeGolyer to baffled friends in the oil fraternity. DeGolyer was a pessimist in regard to the nation's oil reserves; new exploration in Texas meant persuading old-family famous ranches to allow oil drilling.

Didn't I believe that Government should rule business with a blacksnake? Wasn't I the "so-and-so" who had tried to take over the oil industry back in 1934? And, finally, hadn't I aspired to be an "Oil Czar"?

The solution — the only one available — was to make of the new Central Oil Agency a team, a partnership of government and industry with all the key posts, save that of the coordinator, staffed by the only personnel capable of making the project work: the technical experts in exploration, production, refining, transporting and distribution of oil, who were the leaders in the industry. Accordingly, on June 4, 1941, with the approval of the President, Ickes named as his deputy petroleum coordinator — to whom he could delegate authority equivalent to his own — Ralph Kenneth Davies, director and senior vice-president of the Standard Oil Company of California. In addition to this deputy, the organization provided for three assistant deputy cordinators (of whom Everette DeGolyer became one in 1942). These four posts were not to be filled by "dollar-a-year" men or part-time consultants; they were to be regular full-time governmental jobs.

Under these five posts (the assistant deputy posts were not necessarily all operative at the same time), there were about twenty-five key committee chairmen and staff members who completed the echelon of directorship. These included many of the most famous names in the petroleum industry, such as J. W. Frey, J. T. Duce, C. S. Snodgrass, W. B. Heroy, J. H. Marshall, E. Holley Poe, Paul Raigarodsky, J. E. Pew, R. E. Allen, E. B. Swanson, H. A. Gilbert, J. R. Parten, among others.

DeGolyer began his duties on July 25, 1941 as director of the conservation division. The functions of this division were defined as follows: "To promote cooperation with

the States and the industry in the conservation of oil and
gas. To study existing standards of production practice,
management and control, and to promote wider acceptance of best practices." The assistant director of this division was W. B. Heroy, DeGolyer's specific choice. When
DeGolyer was appointed to the post of assistant deputy
coordinator in June 8, 1942, the conservation division was
absorbed into the production division. Heroy became then
director of the petroleum reserves division, later the foreign production division.

Wartime Washington called for maximum efficiency,
maximum use of time, maximum use of tact. The latter was
no more DeGolyer's strong suit than it was Ickes', though
DeGolyer was anything but a "curmudgeon" in temperament. Nonetheless he was an impatient man, especially of
trivia and of excessive protocol. If protocol had an artistic
meaning, he liked it, liked to watch it. If the meaning were
purely vain and personal, DeGolyer delighted in meeting
it with casualness. This trait nearly cost him success in one
of his most important PAW projects.

The country's main source of petroleum reserves was, of
course, the East Texas field. While DeGolyer was still
director of conservation, the vast field was threatened by
excessive salt water. No risk could be run of such engulfing;
time was of the essence. The project to dispose of it required priority materials whose use had to be approved by
the War Department. Seeking approval, DeGolyer stated
the case tersely to the colonel in charge of priority assignments. The colonel was inclined to put a great many questions. DeGolyer knew the matter was essential, thought
anyone else would know the same, and was not inclined
to draw diagrams. And he was not inclined to entertain
the colonel's assertions that the project was "merely a plan
to help the big oil companies." The colonel got so enraged,

he abruptly broke off the conference, refusing to talk further with DeGolyer then or ever.

A conference was called to consider the matter, but the colonel succeeded in barring DeGolyer. DeGolyer did, however, manage an invitation for Brig. Gen. Walter B. Pyron, Gulf Oil official and Texas National Guardsman of Houston, then on duty in Washington. At intervals Pyron would leave the meeting, returning each time with fresh arguments. Finally, Pyron won, perhaps by outshouting the colonel. The loser, exiled to an army siberia, learned later that Pyron's many exits were to telephone DeGolyer a running battle report and to get fresh verbal ammunition.

DeGolyer's comments which enraged the colonel may have been lacking in tact, but for three decades he had been known as a geologist devoted to scientific methods in both conserving and producing oil and as to the problem of salt water, he was the acknowledged expert. On this subject here is what Nubar Gulbenkian, in his autobiography *Portrait in Oil*, says about him — in discussing the purchase of Mexican Eagle by Royal Dutch Shell:

Unhappily, before the whole Mexican Eagle transaction had been completed, news came that salt water instead of oil had appeared in the "Golden Lane" of Mexico. At that time, wells were produced at full blast and no one was sufficiently advanced, technically, to know that the flow of a well should be so regulated that the salt water which lies under the oil should not be sucked up with the oil. There was just one man, de Golyer [sic], who predicted that the appearance of salt water presaged the beginning of the end. At first, his forecast met only with scepticism, but he was right and thenceforward his reputation as a consultant geologist in the United States was made; for the next twenty years no oil company would venture to go to the public for capital without a certificate from de Golyer.

The war project to save East Texas oil was completed in time, pumping the salt water back underground to build up producing pressures — and thus adding about 600 million barrels of oil to the recoverable reserves of the East Texas field. Not selective in regard to enemies, DeGolyer would later have to take a drubbing from the big oil companies, as a result of his wartime mission to the Middle East. DeGolyer was steadily caught in the crossfire between government and industry.

Aside from the spectacular success in providing oil where it was needed when it was needed, perhaps the most dramatic achievements of the PAW lay in the chemical miracle of developing 100-octane gasoline — which allowed planes faster speed, wider range, greater maneuverability, swifter ascent — in the laying of the Big Inch and Little Inch pipelines, and in the foreign technical oil missions, of which DeGolyer headed two — to Mexico in 1942 and to the Middle East in 1943. Both missions were secret and were designed to discover additional sources of oil for the Allies. In the case of the Middle East mission, one specific intention, or hope, was to find an oil supply more readily available to the Allied troops fighting Rommel in North Africa, and on the point of invading Europe from the Mediterranean.

To an extent that could not be divulged to the public — without handing Hitler a chart of his submarines' successes — the dwindling of oil stocks available to the armies went through periodic and alarming scares. Oil stocks constituted more than half the tonnage of all supplies shipped overseas. The first problem had been that of transportation. For this country, that problem was largely solved by the summer of 1943 when the amazing feats of laying the world's biggest pipeline (Big Inch) and the world's longest (Little Inch) were completed, allowing Gulf Coast oil to travel to the eastern seaboard by pipe rather than over the treacherous sea lanes vulnerable to the enemy submarines.

But the next problem was the shortage in oil supply itself. At one point early in 1943 New York was down to two days' supply of fuel oil, Boston to two and a half, Providence to three. In a mid February *Supply Bulletin,* Deputy Administrator Davies reported, "We are barely and with difficulty making both ends meet." Endless shuffling of supplies had to be made to meet needs, both domestic and military. Little Inch, fortunately, started delivering fuel oil to the East in the first week of March.

Where was all the oil going? A few statistics are revelatory. Every B–17 bombing Germany required for the flight a tank car of gasoline of 10,000 gallons, enough to run an average American car for a dozen years. In less than two months the United States Fifth Fleet consumed 630 million gallons of fuel oil; to move an armored battalion one hundred miles required 17,000 gallons of gasoline; the Far Eastern Air Forces used nearly 150 million gallons of aviation gasoline in a single month of attacks on Japanese shipping.

By dint of formidable planning and study, backbreaking work and the unique cooperation between government and industry, this staggering thirst for oil was met. Little wonder that Senator Joseph C. O'Mahoney, chairman of the special Senate Committee to Investigate Petroleum Resources, was able to state: "I have no hesitation in saying that no achievement in all the history of wartime and of industry ever exceeded the wartime oil job."

So, the peculiar difficulties that confronted this particular governmental agency were successfully, even triumphantly, resolved. One reason why the original friction between Secretary Ickes and the industry was overcome is to be found in the intelligent organization of the PAW which allowed key staffing by seasoned oilmen rather than career functionaries. To make certain that the oil industry felt fully represented in the great decisions, such as the construction of the Big Inch pipelines, and to insure their requisite cooperation, Ickes called top officials of the major companies to Washington for conferences. And he created a kind of forum for debate on the PAW policies by the creation on November 28, 1941, of the Petroleum Industry War Council, designed to supplement on a nationl scale the five regional district committees of the industry which from the start represented an industry implementation of the PAW program.

15

Secret Missions

IT WAS, curiously, the mission that DeGolyer headed to the Middle East that touched off the greatest explosion of the Petroleum Industry War Council in its not always calm relationship with the Petroleum Administration for

War. A direct result of this mission was to insure and speed up the supply of technical facilities which enabled the area to yield indispensable help in meeting the peak requirements in the Pacific. But the report, made available to the industry by the DeGolyer mission, contained some upsetting and unwelcome truths. The crucial section of this report runs as follows:

The center of gravity of world oil production is shifting from the Gulf-Caribbean area to the Middle East area — to the Persian Gulf area — and is likely to continue to shift until it is firmly established in that area.

When one considers the great oil discoveries which have resulted from the meager exploration thus far accomplished in the Middle East, the substantial number of known prospects not yet drilled, and the great areas still practically unexplored, the conclusion is inescapable that reserves of great magnitude remain to be discovered.

The proved and indicated reserves in this area are comparable with those of the United States, yet all of the Middle East reserves have been discovered by the drilling of less than a total of 150 wildcat wells. In the United States we drill more than twenty times this number of wildcat wells each year.

It is the opinion of this mission that, given time and a very moderate amount of oil field material, any single one of these four groups [companies operating in the Middle East] can develop and maintain within its own properties sufficient production to supply world requirements from the Middle East area for many years to come. For the next 10 to 15 years at least, the Middle East area is likely to develop and maintain productive capacity of as much as four times its probable market outlet.

The report made clear not only the immensity of Persian Gulf oil but also the international context of foreign relations which would influence the American oil industry after the war. And this report, unlike that of the DeGolyer mission to Mexico, had not been made directly for the PAW but for a new agency, of which Secretary Ickes had the title of president, and which the industry regarded with much suspicion. This was the Petroleum Reserves Corporation created in June 1943, upon instructions from President Roosevelt. The charter for this new agency granted it the power to conduct oil activity abroad. This charter and the plans for the agency were surrounded with secrecy.

The steps that led to its formation are many and complicated, for it was only one thread in the evolution of a new national oil policy in regard to foreign lands, primarily the product of the wartime experience. A much larger design in this pattern was the ultimate formulation of an oil agreement between the United States and the United Kingdom, first proposed by the American State Department, which was very slow in materializing. The Petroleum Reserves Corporation was the immediate result, however, of our government's attempts to establish some system of protecting American interests abroad. When certain American oil interests protested to Ickes that certain foreign interests were conniving against American holdings in the Middle East, he took the matter to the State Department, the navy, the War Department and the Foreign Economic Administration. The outcome of the discussions was the creation of the PRC.

The secrecy surrounding PRC, however, did not impress the industry or its body, the PIWC, as a wartime necessity. As rumors spread, the industry doubted indeed that it was organized as a wartime agency; suspicion grew that it was a device to get government into the oil business. Strong statements were made about such an evil. In this climate of concern, the PRC announced in February 1944, that it had "agreed in principle with two American oil companies to build and operate a government-owned pipeline from a point in Saudi Arabia (with a connection to Kuwait) to a point on the Mediterranean Sea." The two companies were the Gulf Exploration Company and the Arabian American Oil Company, owned by Standard Oil of California and by the Texas Company. The companies were to repay the government for the costs of the line over a period of years, but the government would retain ownership. In addition, the companies would set aside one billion barrels of oil reserves for the government to use when required in the future.

The PIWC inferred from this project that the Petroleum Reserves Corporation was not instituted to help prosecute the war but to make plans for a future in which the government would be involved in the oil business. At its February meeting, the PIWC passed a resolution that "steps should immediately be taken to dissolve the Petroleum Reserves Corporation to the end that a considered and sound national oil policy may be formulated." At its March meeting the PIWC took the position that the pipeline proposed for Middle East oil was not defensible as "security" in the event of another war.

Secretary Ickes gave assurances that the project was in no way an entering wedge for the government to enter the oil business; that its purpose was to further the interests of the American people and to provide supplies for future needs of the army and navy; and that "there was no need to fear the future importation of cheap oil." But his arguments did not persuade the opposition. George A.

Hill Jr. prepared a statement of rebuttal endorsed by the PIWC.

However, the DeGolyer mission report did not go without public acclaim. In its issue of April 3, 1944, *Time* magazine came to the defense. The story began:

Everette Lee DeGolyer, 57, of Dallas, is perhaps the world's greatest oil geologist. . . . The man whom the industry reverently calls "the father of geophysical exploration in the United States." This man was the one whom Harold Ickes recently sent to survey U.S. oil properties in the Middle East, and who now attempted to explain to Americans why the United States is dabbling in Middle East oil.

Time comments that the industry's "almost-unanimous" opposition to the Ickes' plan to build an Arabian pipeline "reached a new high" when the President of Sun Oil Company, J. Edgar Pew of Philadelphia and Dallas, called the pipeline "an invitation to the next world war." It adds "at this point . . . DeGolyer spoke up."

"I hold no brief," DeGolyer is quoted as saying frankly, "for the Government's Arabian pipeline [but] until some satisfactory substitute is found . . . I am for the line. The oil fields of the Middle East are practically certain to be of paramount importance as a source of the world's oil supplies for a generation to come. . . . The fact that the Iraq Petroleum Company [jointly owned by the British, the United States — Standard Oil of California and Socony-Vacuum — the French and the Dutch] is even now asking for steel with which to build a line of substantially the same size . . . is sufficient answer as to whether additional petroleum is needed in the Eastern Mediterranean."

Now, DeGolyer observed, the only country that could

supply steel for increased pipeline delivery was the United
States. But, should our government provide these facilities
for the international oil group and thus maintain their
monopoly of delivery to the eastern Mediterranean? And
delivery really, through this monopoly, to Europe? De-
Golyer, to the contrary, thought the problem of oil in the
Middle East was simply one of "seeing that the oil produced in each political unit gets its fair share of the total
market" — a situation not then prevailing. He ridiculed the
assertion that the construction of the Arabian pipeline
was but the first step toward government's taking over the
oil industry. "No one," he said, "cried 'entering wedge'
when the government built the Big Inch and Little Inch
pipelines . . . nor when the Government spent hundreds
of millions of dollars on the 100-octane program."

From his apprenticeship to Mexican Eagle, with its
benefactions from Lord Cowdray's close friendship with
President Porfirio Díaz, and from his long observation of
the international cartels in the world of oil, DeGolyer
stressed authoritatively a significant point: "It is difficult
for our people to realize the degree to which the chancel-
leries of the Great European nations are willing to interfere politically in support of the business interests of their
nationals, or the degree of economic vassalage accepted
by the smaller states in the Persian Gulf in the treaties by
which they are allied to Britain. Able as American business
may be, it can not support itself against such unequal
competition.

"Building the Arabian pipeline is to the advantage of
one group and they are for it. It threatens the markets of
another group and they are against it. Actually, the problem is not one to be settled by the oil industry.

"I submit that whether or not objections to the present
enterprise, its initiation or method of handling, are valid,

it was conceived, as one editor put it, in the interest of national security and for no other purpose."

But when all the testimony was in, Congress was cool to the venture. American oilmen still feared the risk of government involvement was too great to accept. They were impressed that both the secretary of the army and secretary of the navy championed the project, and they admitted the Arabian pipeline might be useful to insure an emergency or reserve supply of oil for both army and navy — but even so, they preferred not to risk the chance that the government, as partner, might soon or late use control of the oil reserve as an international political or diplomatic weapon. Although the pipeline project was abandoned, the Arabian-American Oil Company did get materials and began producing oil for the war effort six months before peace was finally won in the Pacific.

The controversy, however, was soon assimilated into a much grander concern, the matter of an Anglo-American oil agreement. And the debate had the effect, at least, of arousing England finally to make an answer to the earlier proposal of our State Department that the two nations discuss a mutual undertaking in the field of international oil. Again the pipeline battle was renewed in larger terms and controversy raged. But the initial struggle had revealed that the United States did not have, although it sorely needed, a national oil policy, as industry and government alike agreed. Finally the air cleared and industry strongly supported the final agreement to set up an International Petroleum Council to establish "the machinery for effective and equitable solution of petroleum problems encountered in the progress of international petroleum trade."

Ralph Davies stated that the agreement was "the first

step — and an all-important step — along the road of international cooperation."

The "team" of wartime government and industry was united again, not simply in the war effort but in mutual recognition of the need to define a national oil policy. The "team" at least asked the right questions; the right answers are, as in so many other matters, still being sought.

What was DeGolyer's own final judgment on Ickes? He wrote only one. In reviewing Ickes' *Autobiography of a Curmudgeon* for the *Dallas Morning News* in May 1943, DeGolyer ribbed his PAW boss a bit but doubted that he qualified as an authentic curmudgeon. A curmudgeon, the review observed, is not simply spikey and grouchy, he is avaricious, like Ebenezer Scrooge. "Who, oh who, would ever accuse the Public Works Administrator of avariciousness? Clearly, this patron saint of the shovel-propped is not what he claims to be."

DeGolyer is unimpressed with Ickes' "sixteen points" for winning the peace once the war is over. They remind the reviewer of Clemenceau's waspish comment after World War I about Woodrow Wilson's "fourteen points": "Le bon Dieu had only ten." But DeGolyer concludes that "Horrendous Harold" — for all his wish to be remembered as a holy terror — will be disappointed by time. He will be recalled "as that able and fearless public servant, 'Honest Harold.'"

16

Wartime Aftermath

DEGOLYER might have been justified in retiring from public life to devote his time and energies to his own private interests; but he could not cease being a public figure — with his expert and unique knowledge — after the several technical oil missions to the Middle East and to Mexico. He was continually having to make public statements and to give testimony before congressional committees in the aftermath of the war's disturbing new alignments.

The discovery, or at least revelation, of the vastness of Middle East oil deposits by the reports of the Middle East oil mission was explosive in several ways: such reserves available to rival nations posed diplomatic and military problems, intensified by the dramatic role that oil supply played in World War II; such reserves threatened, of course, ultimate overwhelming competition with American interests; and they made imperative an American stocking of oil reserves against potential enemy attack. In a related way, the oil mission testimony gave proof of new military, diplomatic and economic horizons.

It was not the delivery of speeches and the appearances before Armed Services committees of the Congress that alone absorbed DeGolyer's attention to the new complexity of the future of the oil industry. As usual, when plagued with accumulation of unshaped new information, he planned to reduce it to order by writing a book about it. The secrecy that surrounded the wartime missions was at least now partially or mostly void. Inevitably, however, any public discussion of the problems meant that De-Golyer would be steadily skating over thin ice or oppositely getting into hot water, as he did. For a man whose business was consultation services provided for the oil industry, his outspokenness was an act of considerable courage, aside from the spur of civic, social duty.

The first of the two PAW "secret" missions to Mexico was made in August 1942. After this country's own reserves, those of Mexico were the most potentially accessible. In the war crisis, no stone could be left unturned. But Mexico's fields stood in desperate need of modernizing and rehabilitating. As Señor Buenrostro, general manager of Mexico's nationalized oil company Petroleos Mexicanos, admitted, Mexican equipment was already obsolete in 1938. After expropriation, the government had conducted practically no exploration. The problem was to extract maximum oil from the Golden Lane without wasteful, destructive excesses. The mission's major recommendation was for the United States to make Mexico a secured loan of $24 million to build a "high-octane aviation gasoline plant" at Mexico City. Such a loan would require the joint approval of State Department (policy), PAW (technical sanction) and the Reconstruction Finance Corporation (financing and priority of required materials).

Ickes protested to the President on February 16, 1943, that State was "dragging its feet." He added: "We have had before our office for some time one proposal from a group of independent oil men looking to the negotiation of such an arrangement with the Mexican government, but in the absence of State Department clearance, we have been unable to give these people an answer or to make progress in any way."

Obviously, after the expropriation and Mexico's growing recognition of its monumental difficulties without a sufficient supply of trained personnel, the State Department recognized the need for delicate maneuvering. It was no easy decision for Mexico to make. Should it allow U.S. petroleum interests "to assist in the development of its petroleum resources"? If so, under what terms should such assistance be arranged?

The problem was of course two-edged. Technical advisers and technical plant builders would never succeed in time for wartime benefit to the U.S. aviation forces without the know-how of management, in short, of business. There was the rub. The State Department, with long-range relationships in view, was afraid of shortsighted solutions, even though the visit of PAW's technical mission was originally solicited — at least for purposes of the record — by the Mexican government in the spring of 1942, under the regime of President Avila Camacho. As Ickes wrote President Roosevelt at the start, this country could hardly view with indifference the "appalling waste of Mexico's precious resource" when United States petroleum reserves were rapidly declining, consumption at that time "being at the rate of one billion barrels per year in excess of new discoveries." According to Ickes, unless measures were taken, "as much as 50 percent of the oil in the Poza Rica field may become fixed in place and remain forever unrecoverable."

The State Department insisted that it be made clear to the Mexican government that the technical mission represented no one department or division but the government as a whole. State itself apparently requested that

DeGolyer be named chief of the mission in view of his "high attainments" and "his fine professional and personal reputation."

Even a second mission in the autumn of 1943 could not solve the problem. The 100-octane plant did not get built, but in the course of the negotiations, undoubtedly Mexico got some superlative technical reports, analyses and advice, and the long path toward some possible future accommodation of the mutual oil interests of the two countries was opened. DeGolyer informed F. E. Wellings of Iraq Petroleum Corporation in June 1946 that "it appears that the Mexicans may be on the point of opening up the country to outside exploration again. They have not been too successful in their own efforts due, I suspect, to the small amount of effort."

Incidentally, the Mexican oil missions caused DeGolyer to make a special gift to the University of Texas which allowed him a diplomatic solution to a possible embarrassment. As a show of gratitude for DeGolyer's review of the material needs of the Mexican oil industry on the government mission of 1943, Petroleos Mexicanos insisted on giving him a remembrance of his trip. The choice of present was entrusted to the general manager, Efrain Buenrostro, who tried to locate some rare old Spanish work for DeGolyer's library. Each time Buenrostro suggested a "find," it turned out to be a book DeGolyer already owned. Buenrostro thought of something else, a plaster cast of one or more of the *cabezonos* or great stone heads which Mexican archaeologists had recently unearthed at La Venta in the easternmost part of the state of Tabasco. Buenrostro had personally escorted DeGolyer on a tour of the new discoveries at the end of the mission's investigations. DeGolyer, he recalled, had shown to the experts of the National Museum of Mexico present on the

trip a particular interest in a stone head about eight feet
high and six feet wide. Its weight was estimated at sixteen
to twenty tons; naturally, any cast would be much lighter.
DeGolyer's interest sprang in part from an article he had
read about La Venta in the *National Geographic* three
years earlier, especially since a dated object from the area
gave these Olmec heads an antiquity at least contemporaneous with the time of Christ.

This gift idea appealed to DeGolyer and he at once set
about persuading President Homer P. Rainey to accept it
in the name of the University of Texas. For understandable
reasons, he wanted in fact to direct Buenrostro to ship it
there. Without waiting for Rainey's consent, he gave such
directions in advance. The university was, of course, delighted. Relieved, DeGolyer wrote Rainey: "If charges
are not prepaid, please advise me so that I can make
repayment to you." When other casts were later shown
in American museums, DeGolyer took delight in needling
director Jerry Bywaters of the Dallas Museum of Fine
Arts for claiming a Texas "first," when the Dallas Museum exhibited them seventeen years after the Mexican
government's gift.

In August 1945, DeGolyer wrote Leonard McCollum
that "I am writing a book on the foreign oil policy of the
United States, if there is one. I doubt whether you will
speak to me after you see a copy but at any rate it will
be an honest effort.

"As you know, I went into the oil business in Mexico.
. . . Among my tentative conclusions are: First, that any
foreign operation is in constant danger in a small country
where it represents the most important and the dominant
factor in the economic life of the country. I would suggest
that under such conditions it would be worth almost any
effort on the part of the foreign company to build up a

competing interest owned and operated by nationals of the country. . . . In order to make my point I will simply ask you as a Texan what do you suppose would happen to the oil industry in Texas politically if it was entirely owned by British and Dutch capital?

"My second tentative conclusion is that it is unwise for a condition to exist in any country whereby oil rights can only be granted through a special contract with the political group which happens to be in power at the time. In other words, through concessions. It would be far more desirable for each country to have a mining law under which grants could be secured by denouncement; i.e., through a formality open to all and not requiring any special negotiation. I have not made any broad study of the legal situation but I do remember that in 1915 Cuba had such a law. It would also be desirable if denouncements of the type I suggest had to be made directly to the companies prepared to operate; in other words, if the middleman, broker or general could be eliminated.

"I remember a long time ago when Mr. Farish paid me the compliment of offering me a job with the Jersey, that during the year that it was under discussion . . . I saw Gene Holman one day and, anticipating what has since happened in Mexico, urged him to try to work out a partnership deal with the Mexican government which would satisfy their national aspirations and leave the Jersey in a position where it could ultimately retire its capital and, meanwhile, earn a reasonable return on it. Gene was adamant and replied that the matter was so important as a precedent in other areas that the company would prefer to lose everything it had in Mexico rather than acquiesce in a partnership which might be regarded as a partial expropriation. I then thought that he was wrong and afterward felt the same way. Certainly the precedent which has been established is not helpful to the company in other areas." In regard to the expropriation awards later made by Mexico, DeGolyer observed that "the award made afterward was not too far off for the strictly subsoil values, but was not great enough to include surface equipment and undrilled properties."

His book on American foreign oil policy was one of a dozen projected works that he would never complete. However, the "Preliminary Report" of the technical oil mission to the Middle East was published in the *Bulletin of the American Association of Petroleum Geologists.* Its first major finding was that "any one of the four groups now operating in the Middle East can develop and maintain within its own properties sufficient production to supply world requirements from the Middle East area for many years to come." The mission participants were listed as DeGolyer, John Murrell, C. S. Snodgrass and W. E. Wrather. The mission team left Washington in November and returned there in January, with the exception of Wrather, who was detained by illness in Arabia and who was not available for consultation in the preparation of the report.

The report and DeGolyer's later thinking about the problems of the United States' foreign oil policy aroused much debate. DeGolyer's testimony before the oil subcommittee of the House Armed Services Committee on February 6, 1948 prompted sharp attack from industry spokesmen, notably from Humble president Harry Weiss and from H. J. (Jack) Porter, president of TIPRO (Texas Independent Producers and Royalty Owners Association). Porter was particularly indignant, writing in his group's own paper, *Independent News,* on March 13 that DeGolyer's theories were "thoughtless, ill-advised, and contrary to American principles of private enterprise." Inevitably, he added: "During his entire career in the oil industry, DeGolyer has been closely connected with large oil companies. . . . He still has close personal connections, and possibly financial connections, with these people. In criticizing the last two increases in the price of crude oil, DeGolyer implies that he is in favor of price controls and regimentation. It appears that possibly the sources of DeGolyer's fees influence his judgment on any particular proposition." Since DeGolyer had argued, in the interest of national security, that the government should acquire proven domestic reserves for use in case of war, Porter observed that "this would put the government in the oil business."

But the "big companies" were no more pleased than the independents. Harry Weiss thought DeGolyer had been hypercritical of the industry and rebuked him for not using the public appearance to reassert the magnificence of the industry's contribution to the successful prosecution of World War II. To Weiss, a longtime and valued friend, DeGolyer sent a twelve-page documented letter, gently pointing out oversimplifications of the ideas he had advanced, but he was firmly, even stubbornly, unyielding about the positions he had taken in regard to the nation's future security in case of attack or declared war. He did not think that the victories of 1945 had settled very much for very long.

Above all, he was maturing new ideas for himself about this country's foreign trade policy. In his salad days in Mexico, he had watched in the operation of Mexican Eagle and Dutch Shell the meaningful cooperation between a national policy that brought political power to support private enterprise abroad. If the wave of the future after World War II indicated that monolithic governmental power structures, as in Russia and China, were

DeGolyer appearing before a Congressional hearing in 1946.

going to determine the direction of their foreign trade, then DeGolyer felt that American private enterprise would be severely penalized in the competition if it did not have available a carefully defined foreign trade policy. We obviously had none. Characteristically, DeGolyer began to meditate on a book he would write on the subject.

DeGolyer was bitterly attacked for maintaining before the committee that this country could not safely rely on its own potential oil reserves in case of wartime acceleration of oil use. Congressman Lyndon B. Johnson of Texas pressed him several times about this pessimism. At last DeGolyer said bluntly: "There are two hard facts in the oil business today, and you can like them or dislike them, but they are there and there is no question about it. . . . One of them is that the United States is the greatest consuming area in the world, and the other is that the Middle East is the area of greatest proved reserves in the world. . . . You cannot think about oil in this world without thinking about the Middle East, because there is nothing like it. I said in the report of that mission that there had not been more than 150 wildcat wells drilled in the Middle East. I did not know exactly how many had been drilled, but I was allowing an extra fifty for good measure. As a result of that drilling, they had found reserves which were equal to our reserves. At the present time, at an expense of certainly not more than 20 or 30 wildcat wells, they have increased their proven reserves to where they are perhaps almost 50 percent greater than ours."

Queried about stock-piling of oil by the government, DeGolyer said: "I have not any desire to see government in business, but I am not afraid of the fact that every time the Government does anything it is business. I don't share the apprehension of a great many of my fellow-Texans that every move the Government makes puts the Government into business."

When asked for summary recommendations, DeGolyer said he preferred to take the time to submit a careful report. This he did — at great length, time and trouble. Answering his fan mail, if one can call it that, also consumed a good deal of time. For a while after this public appearance, DeGolyer discovered in walking down the streets of Dallas that a number of oilmen he had known a few weeks before had forgotten both his face and his name. But he was not a man who held grudges, as they discovered when his point of view became accepted and they started speaking again.

In March of 1947, DeGolyer's longtime friend Sumner Pike wrote to say that one of the problems of the Atomic Energy Commission concerned raw materials, especially uranium and thorium. There had been so little demand for them in the past that no real exploration work of any magnitude had been done on either of the two elements.

"We are tentatively thinking," wrote Pike, "about an advisory committee to act as a sort of exploration brain trust to help us on this problem. The complications are endless, including military and political ones, which your imagination will quickly grasp. I know you are thoroughly sick of some kinds of Government service and are entitled to some leisure among your books and progeny, but all the same I would like to know if you would serve on a first-class committee of this sort if it were organized." He mentions other prospects: Wallace Pratt, Bill Wrather and Don McLaughlin.

DeGolyer replied yes, but he added "may I note that Wallace Pratt and myself are extremely liberal." Of Pratt, he says, "I realize this is a strange statement to make with regard to a past vice-president of the Standard Oil Company of New Jersey." To this cautionary advice, Pike replied casually, "I don't believe you and Wallace will turn out to be too liberal for present Government standards." Actually, DeGolyer was delighted to accept. He was very curious about uranium.

As early as 1940, DeGolyer and Sumner Pike had discussions about looking into the "natural gas business." Pike had what he called his "old pet idea of a big pipeline to bring some of the low priced surplus gas from Texas and Louisiana points to the big population centers north and east of Washington. The big element that hit me, however, was the tremendous progress that has surely been made in tossing around and reforming the molecular constituents of gases — thereby converting them into more valuable products."

Presently, they did more than look into the natural gas business.

17   Science and Speeches

THE CONTEXT of politics and science and commerce — fused together — in which DeGolyer spent the wartime years sharpened and broadened his mind considerably; he was led to speculate upon his increasing respect for science, his thinking became a good deal more philosophic and he was groping toward a theory that the *history* of science should be as legitimate a requirement for educated men as the history of political and military events or the history of ideas, or the history of individual nations. He began to turn nearly all his book-collecting time and energy and budget to acquiring a complete library (first editions wherever possible) of the seminal works in the development of science. This was to become the most impressive, perhaps, of all the collections he ever put together.

His mind, as his speeches and writings and letters show, was seeking to explain to himself why science was the thing that he valued most in the world, and why from his youth on, it had exercised upon him an unwavering magnetic pull. When his alma mater invited him to make the commencement address at the spring convocation in 1948, he accepted with delight. He based his address on whatever he had learned of wisdom — not homespun practical wisdom but the fruits of reflection — in sixty-two years of a multifaceted life. What he had to offer was no recipe for success, nor for happiness or tranquillity, but a method helpful in discovering truth. He titled his talk, really a sort of "summing up" of his basic beliefs, "Science — a Method, Not a Field."

The speech has a tone of humility rare in DeGolyer, as though coming from a man who in the past few years had been compelled to think upon some shaking experiences. He confesses he can say nothing new on his subject, but what he has to say he can say with authentic conviction. After rehearsing and comparing conventional definitions of science, he offers one of his own, "derived independently from speculation over a number of years": "To me, science is truth organized in order to make possible hu-

man comprehension. It is worth emphasis that all definitions of science stress systematization or classification. . . .
Most of the definitions include provision for the discovery
of truth now unknown."

Working carefully from step to step he adds to those traditional components of scientific method — observation
and experiment and proof — still another, what he calls "a
sort of anticipatory sense." This is not a gift but a virtue
acquired through the long and rigorous practice of the
other elements of scientific method; it is a habit of thought
that guides the scientist "to the most important and fruitful directions to be taken in his endeavor to extend the
frontiers of knowledge." It springs of course from what
Whitehead calls "the habit of seeking for causes and of
classifying by similarities." "It is the type of reasoning not
(yet) provable, and depending partly upon the imagination, which led Columbus to sail westward in his search
for the coast of Asia."

The built-in corrective, or at least safeguard, against
this "anticipatory sense" — and what distinguishes the man
of science as a type — is the scientific habit of impartial,
dispassionate, nonpartisan, unselfish, unprejudiced investigation. "This impartiality, as it must, leads to less regard
for authority than is true for most other fields of knowledge." In science, "there is no supreme court . . . no majority determination by election. Science is neither authori-
tarian nor democratic."

The other characteristic trait of the scientific method, he
states, is that "its perspective is of such long view that it
may be said to be timeless; it is a search for the ultimate."
And he adds, as though unconsciously recalling the war
years, in science "there is no place for the expediency
which, to my mind, controls many of the activities of the
businessman, the industrialist, and the office seeker. Nor is

there any place for the exquisite double talk of the diplomat, nor the special pleading of the lawyer defending the client he knows to be guilty, nor for the log rolling of the politician."

There is still more to get off his chest. It is not true, he argues, that science is too theoretical, as often claimed by "practical" men. "The practical man has been described, somewhat facetiously I trust, as one who follows the theories of thirty years ago. Science is based on truth, on fact, though it advances by speculation. Any scientist who is worthy of the name has spent his professional life in carefully differentiating between fact and theory and is a trained investigator. This is far more than can be said for most practical people." One would surmise that DeGolyer is working toward the conclusion that science is a kind of "purity." But no, it is not a static state — there is more to discover than has yet been discovered, former "truths" must be abandoned to yield to new, and science must serve mankind in this world. "What I have urged upon you this evening is extremely simple: to search for truth and understanding in all fields. This is the end of science and the goal is worthy of the efforts of mankind in all its affairs." Science is not one field, it is a method, a way of life. He concludes with a quotation from world-eminent historian of science George Sarton: "The acquisition and systematization of positive knowledge is the only human activity which is truly cumulative and progressive." This is not only DeGolyer's *apologia pro vita sua;* it outlines an interest which became one of the most important in his life. Its benefactor would be the campus where he made this address.

The sustained intellectual effort of the commencement address, however, was prefaced by a much more relaxed and more personal talk which DeGolyer made in April of

the same year as his response at the University of Oklahoma's first Distinguished Service Citation awards. There
were five recipients: Everette DeGolyer; the playwright
Lynn Riggs (*Green Grow the Lilacs,* the drama which inspired the musical *Oklahoma!*); Senator A. S. (Mike)
Monroney; General Raymond S. McLain and General William S. Key. DeGolyer's acknowledgment was only four
hundred words long. He said he had been asked to formu-
late his "philosophy of achievement." But, he continued,
"I have formulated no such philosophy."

The heart of the matter was simply this: "If I could have
depended on this being an audience of undergraduates,
the response would have been sure and practical. They
would have been told simply to find the right girl and
marry her, as I did. Life's most important decision was
made then, and the best possible provision laid for the solution of further problems. The family is the fundamental
unit of civilization and the wife and mother, more than any
other member, determines its character. A woman of courage and integrity to manage the so-called head of the family insures its success." The management, in his case, was
not total. Nell DeGolyer, in the audience, had not seen the
speech beforehand.

This talk itself had been preceded by another notewor-
thy one. DeGolyer was selected in 1945 to give the "appreciation address" at the presentation of the first Sidney
Powers Memorial Medal to Wallace Everett Pratt. Both
men were born in Kansas, both were geological "outcrops"
of the same area. The occasion gave DeGolyer a chance to
draw on his immense store of knowledge about the American West, and to make indirectly a point about his own
early environmental influence, with no trace of nostalgic
sentimentality.

"This was the West," he said. "The Union Pacific to the

north and the Santa Fe to the south had been built less than twenty years before. A great wave of land-hungry immigrants had swept over western Kansas; the initiation of the last and greatest land boom of our whole history as a nation. It was the west of the buffalo hunters, of the sod house, and of free range. It was the west of Wild Bill Hickock and Abilene, and Bat Masterson and Dodge City, of the Lincoln County War and Billy the Kid. It was the west of the Indian wars, of the Massacre of the Little Big Horn, and of the Battle of Wounded Knee." It was also what was known as the short-grass country, so nourishing to Longhorns. DeGolyer could not resist quoting the greatest of old Texas cowmen, Charley Goodnight: "It produces better cattle; why shouldn't it produce better men?"

Pratt, DeGolyer pointed out, found that although the plains were wide and almost limitless, they were featureless. A philosophic mind from the start, Pratt's first objective "was to find a satisfactory way of life." This had to yield first to the more practical and concrete matter of finding a way of making a living. Geology gave a harvest of both. Pratt, like Sidney Powers himself, "loved the science of geology for itself." Pratt's rarest ability, judged DeGolyer, was "to look at any situation at any time as if he had never before seen it." And he concluded by quoting a tribute to Pratt made by Eugene Holman: "He believes in the brotherhood of man. He has a host of friends in all countries of the world, regardless of creed or color. He is beloved by all."

Much of DeGolyer's analysis of the career of his friend (and ardent competitor) could apply to his own. The point is supported by an estimate of DeGolyer's central characteristic which his longtime secretary, Mrs. Ruth Castleman, made after her retirement in a note to a scholar contemplating a biography of DeGolyer. Mrs. Castleman wrote: "I have worked for Mr. DeGolyer for many years and I personally think his most important characteristic aside from the classical ones (such as industry, integrity, etc.) is his intellectual honesty. He has the ability to see things for what they are in spite of encrustations of mode, habit and all the other things that so often obscure reality."

DeGolyer took seriously the matter of honors — he was responsible for the establishment of several within the industry himself — and respected his obligations on the numerous selection committees on which he served. His attitude derived from the ancient Greek truism, attributed to Plato that "what is honored in a country will be produced there." He shared the view expressed by Dr. Carey Croneis at a Denver meeting in 1942 of the American Association of Petroleum Geologists: "Rewards often make the man. More important, in a subtle fashion, they may help make a science. It has been true in our competitor physical sciences, and it could be true for geology. Every honor-awarding society, as well as each individual honored, is enormously bettered in the layman and the administration eye; and the recipient of the medal . . . is, in most cases, not tremendously harmed by the granting of the bauble."

The decade 1938–1948 yielded a bumper crop of honors for DeGolyer. In 1938 he received the Distinguished Service Award from the Texas Mid-Continent Oil and Gas Association; in 1940 the Anthony Lucas Medal from the American Institute of Mining and Metallurgical Engineers; in 1941 the coveted John Fritz Medal awarded by the four leading national engineering societies acting in conjunction; also in 1941 election to Phi Beta Kappa at the University of Oklahoma; in 1942 initiation into Tau Beta Phi at the University of Oklahoma; honorary degrees from

Princeton (1940), the University of Washington (1942), Southern Methodist University (1945), Trinity (1947); on June 16, 1947, he was appointed to the government's Military Petroleum Advisory Committee; in 1948 he received the Distinguished Service Citation of the University of Oklahoma. Also in 1948, he was appointed a member of the advisory committee on raw materials of the United States Atomic Energy Commission.

Perhaps the most significant of the honorary awards was the John Fritz Medal, the most esteemed of engineering awards made in the United States. It was established in 1902 in memory of a great pioneer in the iron and steel industry, John Fritz of Bethlehem, Pennsylvania. The honor is awarded, "not oftener than once a year," by representatives of the four leading engineering societies: the American Society of Civil Engineers, the American Institute of Mining and Metallurgical Engineers, the American Society of Mechanical Engineers, and the American Institute of Electrical Engineers. The medal, made of gold, is presented in recognition of "notable scientific or industrial achievement, without restriction on account of nationality or sex." Awardees since its inception include Thomas A. Edison, Guglielmo Marconi, Alexander Graham Bell and George Westinghouse.

The most concise description of why DeGolyer was being so copiously honored probably was stated in the Oklahoma Distinguished Service Citation, written by Savoie Lottinville, which read: "For his contribution to the science of geology, his pioneering work in introducing geophysics into oil exploration, his diplomatic and scientific services to the nation, and his efforts to preserve the historical and literary heritage of the Southwest."

One could make a catalogue of still more honors: some large, some small, some merely, intentionally, amusing. He was also elected to the Texas Academy of Sciences and to the Texas Institute of Letters; president of the Dallas Museum of Fine Arts and of the Dallas Arboretum Club; added to the Advisory Council of the department of geology of Princeton University; elected to the Newcomen Society; appointed to a civic commission to solve the water supply problems of the city of Dallas; and in 1946, he became chairman of the Gulf Coast Area Rhodes Scholarships Selection Committee. To all these, he gave serious attention. He did not accept honorary posts which implied obligations if he did not mean to participate in the duties. (In 1943, there was a strong rumor in Washington that he was being considered for the ambassadorship to Mexico. If so, nothing ever came of it. The truth is that he refused the offer.)

As one example of the sense of obligation he felt toward "honorary" assignments, when Margo Jones organized her famous experimental "Theater-in-the-Round" in Dallas in 1945, DeGolyer agreed to be first vice-president (his close friend and business associate Eugene McDermott served as president). DeGolyer faithfully attended the many requisite organization meetings, volunteered to get twenty-one friends to match his initial gift of $1,000 (and did), labored as though it were one of his own businesses to make Margo's initial budget and business setup efficient and workable. Later, when deficits had to be covered or special money provided for new seats in the theater or other emergencies, DeGolyer came through with large checks.

Among the "amusing honors" (such as the institution of annual DeGolyer Day at the Dallas Petroleum Club), one is worth some attention. In 1948, in what was of course partially a publicity stunt for the annual State Fair of Texas, which gives prizes in many categories from cake baking and preserves to cattle breeding and oil painting, DeGolyer was awarded first prize for his chili recipe. This was also a gag to get newspaper space for a locally published book on chili, *With or Without Beans,* compiled by two chili lovers as loyal in their devotion to this Texas product as Lyndon B. Johnson.

DeGolyer was, however, a chili fanatic and his recipe is probably still unsurpassed. It turned up later in a cookbook compiled by Neiman-Marcus of Dallas, the recipes from Neiman's favorite customers, and published by Bennett Cerf (an occasional guest in the DeGolyer home) under the title of *A Taste of Texas.* The award may have been pure publicity, but DeGolyer took the matter of good chili seriously. Right after the war, he realized that his British friend, F. E. Wellings, must be hungry for chili. Wellings had married a Texas girl from Brownsville, on the Rio Grande, a place where for many years chili and enchiladas and tacos and tamales were made with dedication and art. DeGolyer sent over a big supply to the Wellings, knowing that Wellings agreed with him, as DeGolyer often said, that "chili is a seasoning superior to curry."

In the forties and fifties DeGolyer kept alive a small Dallas circle of congenial and convivial book friends, known as "the Federation," which met — when he was in town — about once a week at a "chili joint" next door to Elizabeth Ann McMurray's nationally famous Personal Book Shop. In time the Federation became a sort of unofficial welcoming committee for notable visitors to town, ranging from Clare Boothe Luce to Carl Sandburg, from James Forrestal to Alfred A. Knopf. In a very modest little "back room" reserved by the owner for the Federation, all guests (many stoutly resisted) were urged to try the *spécialité de la maison.* Since the "back room" had to be traversed by other customers who wished to wash their hands, occasionally such passers-through were invited to accept one of the delicious, fiery Mexican peppers called *jalapeños*.

DeGolyer often set the tone for a luncheon by downing, as hors d'oeuvres, whole and entire, a *jalapeño* — a heroic feat even for Mexicans conditioned to them from cradle-hood. A *jalapeño* is often defined as something which you eat first, and then vice versa. The only time DeGolyer was ever outdone in his consumption of *jalapeños* was by the number one Texas writer of the century, J. Frank Dobie. Dobie called for a whole plate of *jalapeños* and a pot of honey. Before astonished eyes, he pulverized the peppers, drenched them in honey and ate them with the air of a god enjoying nectar and ambrosia. He was promptly voted an award as the best guest in Federation history, at the suggestion of Eugene McDermott. It was one of the few Federation gatherings that DeGolyer did not seem to enjoy one hundred percent.

His attachment to *jalapeños* led him to a curious experiment late in the thirties, when he set up as a sideline, indeed, a *jalapeño* canning company in a small building with a garden lot on the outskirts of Houston. This effort to grow, can and market the celebrated Mexican specialty lasted a couple of years but won no success. The product, knowingly boiled and then marinated in a brine with olive oil and chopped onions, was offered to the public under the trade name of "Aztec Jalapeños." The American public remained indifferent. The traveler to small southwestern towns, if curious, may still occasionally find a can, by now a real antique and no doubt a danger if eaten, forlorn on some ancient grocery store shelf.

DeGolyer's good friend, Paul Seashore of Louisiana Land and Exploration, had the same idea a decade later. From his home in Houma, Louisiana, he sent DeGolyer a sample can for opinion and advice. DeGolyer responded with the most careful analysis. He thought that the batch sent him had been overcooked, so that the texture of the pepper was not sufficiently firm; the seasoning of the marinade should be corrected. From his own past failure, he suspected that the American public would buy them only with pepper seeds removed to make them milder. Nowadays there are dozens of different packs of *jalapeños* in the supermarkets — including the original favorite packed by Clemente Jacques in Mexico — and the public buys them in quantity.

So, DeGolyer's chili recipe award at the State Fair of Texas may have mollified his failure as a promoter of *jalapeños*. It certainly endowed many cookbooks with an unbeatable recipe. And the most recent book on chili, Frank Talbert's *A Bowl of Red*, is dedicated to the memory of DeGolyer, O. Henry and Joe Cooper, three top chili "experts." As DeGolyer used to say, "you can judge a southwestern town by the quality of the chili it serves." His favorite of all places to eat chili was in Tulsa, Ike's Chili Parlor, still operating in 1969, and redolent in the memory of Oklahomans, such as Savoie Lottinville, since 1914.

18   Texas Eastern Transmission

ONE OF THE BIGGEST and most successful business transactions in which Everette DeGolyer was ever involved came as a direct result of that wartime construction phenomenon, the dramatic building of the Big Inch
and Little Inch oil pipelines. The swift and successful completion by early 1943 of these arteries for fuel oil and gasoline saved the East from disaster by replacing or aug-
menting the normal tanker supply lines. This supply had
been seriously reduced by German submarine attacks and
by the fact that a sizable part of the United States tanker
fleet was on lend-lease to Great Britain. Soon after going to
Washington for the Petroleum Administration for War,
DeGolyer made several strategic public speeches insisting that the only solution to the problem was the construction of a vast inland pipeline. The government allocated
around $130 million for building Big Inch and Little Inch.

Indispensable as these pipelines had been during wartime, they presented a major problem when peace was reestablished. How would the War Assets Administration
dispose of such a considerable property, no longer usable
by the government? As in the case of other excess wartime
supplies and constructions, the lines would of course be

offered to private enterprise for bidding. This was normal procedure. But the lines posed peculiar political, social and economic problems. The army-navy board, at first, insisted their only use should be for the continued piping of oil over the 2,815-mile system from the Gulf Coast to the East, and points along the way. The board feared that the lines converted to the transportation of gas, with the alterations required, would do little to relieve a future wartime emergency.

And yet the conversion of the lines to gas transport made much sense. Gas was increasingly a favored fuel for heating and cooking, and industry was also consuming large quantities of it. Above all, such transport for gas would solve one of the most alarming of oil field problems, the terrible waste of a natural reserve when escaping gas was simply burned off at the fields in high-placed flares because there was nothing else to do with it. How to salvage this immense waste, for the gas itself could be used not merely as fuel but could also be reduced by chemical processes to gasoline, had long preoccupied leaders of the industry. Furthermore the Tennessee Gas and Transmission Company had demonstrated during the war, with spectacular success, that the gas could be saved and piped with profit commercially.

Twelve months after advertising for bids (and scores had been made), the War Assets Administration boss was still deliberating. Coal strikes and the shortage of fuel brought on by the war caused a public demand that the lines no longer be allowed to lie unused. Then the army-navy board made it clear that it did not matter whether the lines were used for oil or gas. The bidding companies were upset. They had made their bids chiefly on the basis of oil use, which would not require the expenditures that gas conversion would entail. Even so, boss R. M. Littlejohn said that the highest offer made, $110 million by the Big Inch Oil Company, headed by veteran oilman John Howard Smith, was several million dollars short of what Littlejohn regarded as a fair price.

If the army-navy board didn't care to which use the lines were put, three other groups certainly did: the railroads which transported much coal, the coalmen, and John L. Lewis' United Mine Workers Union. The competition of cheap natural gas with coal in the most thickly populated area of the nation — an area heretofore dependent on coal — was an economic menace of more than midget size. Adherents to this same opposition arose within the state governments of Texas and Louisiana. Their governors stressed that the departure of such a natural resource to the East would diminish the industrial potential of their own regions. The tanker people, of course, favored gas usage since oil could be pumped through the lines at much less cost than by shipping.

The disposal of the pipelines could not be a simple operation. It would affect too many interests: consumers, producers, regions and the economic structure. Bidding was opened again, this time clearly for the use of the lines not merely for oil but also for gas, either one. The decision was made in late January of 1947. Obviously with relief at finally getting something done, the War Assets Administration rid itself of the Big Inch and Little Inch, selling them to the highest bid among ten submitted. This was for the "whopping sum" of $143.1 million — only a couple of million less than what it had cost the government to build the lines for wartime emergency. It was a staggering $33 million more than the Smith group bid, when Littlejohn had turned down all bids because they were too low.

The purchaser was the Texas Eastern Transmission Company, headed by natural gasman E. Holly Poe, with four associates. These were DeGolyer, the two Brown brothers of Houston, George R. who would be Texas Eastern's chairman and Herman (oil and ship-building construction); and Charles I. Francis, Houston oil lawyer.

As so often in DeGolyer's career, he again linked himself with a man of identical Oklahoma background. Born in Pawnee, Holly Poe went into the oil business early. During the war, he served as director of the natural gas division of the Petroleum Administration for War. At fifty-two, he was nine years DeGolyer's junior. For a long time, Holly Poe had dreamed of using the escaping Texas gas, and had long pondered the prospect of pumping it east for fuel. He was sure of what he was doing. His new company expected to have to spend between forty and sixty million more dollars, in addition to the purchase price from WAA, to convert the lines into gas carriers. The major expense would be the installation of compressors and the construction of feeder lines. The company hoped within one year to be transporting enough cubic feet of gas to the Eastern seaboard to equal about 16,000 tons of coal daily. To finance this gigantic enterprise, the company planned to start with a four million dollar loan from Manhattan's Manufacturer's Trust, and to raise the rest of the cash required with a security issue to be handled by Dillon, Read and Company. Texas Eastern Transmission planned to pay off the government within nine months. As DeGolyer steadily observed and made into an article of faith, "what is important is to have men who are willing to take risks."

Texas Eastern Transmission Corporation, according to both *Time* and *Newsweek*, yielded the biggest business news story of the year. First of all, the transaction was reported by both weeklies to be the best deal on surplus property of the Second World War that the government had made. But it turned out that Texas Eastern had also made a tremendous deal, justifying fully its initial bold bid, 12 million dollars higher than its nearest competitor's. By the end of 1947, the company formed on January 30 of that year "appeared to be the most startlingly successful promotion of the year," said *Newsweek*. Texas Eastern, which had made $764,000 through sales of natural gas in its second quarter alone, estimated a minimum annual profit of five million dollars and anticipated a probable return of $30 to $40 million, of which more than half would be operating profit.

Although the idea had been launched by DeGolyer and his associates, it was Dillon, Read and Co., Inc., which created the real financial stir. First, they sold $120 million in first mortgages to twelve life insurance companies. Sale of the common stock, 3,564,000 shares at $9.50 per share, was completed on the first day offered. This sale was consummated to meet the November 25 deadline for payment to the government. The original investment of the organizers had been $150,000, of which $100,000 was required as evidence of good faith in making the bid. An additional five million dollars to meet guarantees and to build compressors for processing the gas, was borrowed from the original stockholders and from banks. In short, on an investment of $15,000, DeGolyer made in the first year a paper profit of one million dollars. It was, as *Time* observed, a "classic case of venture capitalism in which everybody stood to make a profit." And "the financial legerdemain had created something of benefit to the nation." Just, indeed, as the wartime oil administration had powerfully benefited the country with the original construction of the Big Inch and the Little Inch pipelines.

What baffles anyone who knew DeGolyer or who studies his career is where he found the time to turn his attention to all the multifarious things that he did. He had no patience with trivia and he did not suffer fools gladly. This would account for the widely held opinion that he was a man with an irritating lack of warmth. But he did have warmth for those he valued and he had, as the record copiously proves, a genius for friendship. Of course, a man as rich as he was could afford to make enemies and not trouble to ingratiate himself with all the self-seekers who try to free-load on celebrities.

Something drove him to keep on forever proving himself. This may have been his natural endowment of curiosity. Certainly, it was the temper of his times, and he could not escape the American worship of his generation for the "bitch goddess Success," measured chiefly in money. It would be simple to say, in quasi-Freudian style, that his impoverished boyhood and the example of his ineffectual father, which made the son the responsible "man" of the family, created in him a syndrome of insecurity which he was always fighting. Instead, perhaps, he had an inborn feeling for "style," style as determined by intellect and not by fashion, to which he was always true. He abhorred waste and what he abhorred most was the waste of intellect. It was not the habit of wealth (the early Tampico strike accustomed him to it) or any predatory instinct that drove him to ever-increasing activity; it was a seeking for excellence, defined as the mind — whether in practical or theoretical employment — realizing itself. He was probably the least lazy man that anyone in the Southwest ever knew. And when his mind finally threatened to cease to work, as he recognized in moments of lucidity, he had an answer for that.

19 Peripatetic Publisher Pursues Hobby

IN THE WARTIME DECADE of the forties, DeGolyer still found time and energy to practice his hobby of publishing, both amateur and professional. Elevated to the post of chairman of the board of the *Saturday Review*, he became the target for numerous "little" magazines and new magazine projects in search of an angel. Two of these, both regional, interested him considerably. In 1947 he subscribed for one-eighth of the stock of a San Antonio-based magazine called *Sun-Up,* and tried to interest the San Antonio oilman, Tom Slick, in buying stock. The project hardly got off the ground. And DeGolyer was sufficiently interested in a short-lived Dallas project — to give the southwestern region a slick-paper, sophisticated magazine modeled on the *New Yorker* — to get J. R. Cominsky, the business genius of the *Saturday Review,* to come to Dallas and make a considered study. *Scene* magazine was originally planned under the editorship of Stanley Walker but he withdrew. After a few impressive numbers, the magazine folded for lack of advertising support. DeGolyer, advised by Cominsky, finally rejected the idea of trying to save it.

He was not able, however, to resist book publishing, for

which he had "a passionate weakness," as he wrote Walter Stewart at Princeton. Stewart got DeGolyer interested in the new publishing firm that William Sloane established in 1948, upon pulling away from Henry Holt and Company (much of whose stock had been bought by Dallas oilman Clint Murchison) to form his own company under the name of William Sloane Associates. Bill Sloane came to Dallas and DeGolyer followed Walter Stewart's suggestion to invest in the new company. William Sloane Associates had a *succès d'estime,* as it deserved, but survived only a few years. In 1948 DeGolyer also put a sizable sum into backing publisher Henry Schuman's venture, "The Life of Science Library."

Of the Schuman "Life of Science Library," DeGolyer wrote to Dr. Jerome P. Webster, of Columbia's College of Physicians and Surgeons, that "I am so impressed with the desirability of this venture from the standpoint of the common good that I am confused as to whether or not I am making an investment or a contribution. It is intended to be an investment." He adds that Schuman needs $60,000 at once, and, "I am paying in $15,000 of the required amount. . . . I am prepared to increase my participation and will do so, but I should like to see as many people interested in it as possible." In passing, he also thanks Dr. Webster for the Trinity honorary degree of 1947: "The Trinity happenings will always remain a high spot in my life and for much or most of it, I give you thanks."

But what he enjoyed most was his own "amateur" publication from time to time of special items drawn from his own book collection or papers he himself wrote. These he issued under the imprint of the Juan Pablos Press (Juan Pablos was the first printer known to the New World, brought to Mexico from his native Spain by Bishop Zumárraga in the sixteenth century) or the Peripatetic Press, so named because its place of publication "moved about" — from Santa Fe to El Paso to Dallas to Godley (a village fifty miles west of Dallas where DeGolyer and his son-in-law Jack Maxson owned a large ranch). Some of the items issued by Juan Pablos or the Peripatetic Press were meant only for DeGolyer's friends. Others were distributed to the trade through the efforts of DeGolyer's close friend, Elizabeth Ann McMurray of Dallas' noted McMurray's Personal Book Shop, whose mail-order clientele for books about the Southwest and about oil was international (many of the foreign customers secured through DeGolyer's recommendation).

What delighted DeGolyer most in his small publishing ventures as an amateur in the field was the chance to work on the books with one of the most eccentric, colorful and gifted men in Texas, the so-called "cowboy printer" of El Paso, Carl Hertzog — whose book designing and printing make valued collectors' items. And work with Hertzog brought DeGolyer into friendship with Tom Lea of El Paso, painter and author of *The Brave Bulls* and *The King Ranch,* among other books. Hertzog and Lea belong to that disappearing breed of men who have an authentic devotion to a sense of place, in their case the American Southwest, which DeGolyer shared. This devotion, in the case of these three men, is not provincial and certainly not uncritical. It is a quality of being responsive to the daily environment and a wish to create of it something worthy of the feeling, say, of an Englishman for his downs and meadows, of a Frenchman for his rivers and canals, of an Italian for his tawny hills. It is an attitude that arises from paying fresh attention to what one sees every day, and it is perfectly compatible with a global view of things. Hertzog, for example, was born in France, grew up in Pennsylvania, came to sun-drenched El Paso for reasons of health — and has steadily refused attractive offers to move elsewhere. This feeling for place and for antiquity (for the Southwest still has its daily evidences of Indian and Spanish cultures, the latter starting a century before European transplantation to the Atlantic seaboard) was a bond among these three men in addition to their mutual love of books. Whenever DeGolyer could manage a stopover in El Paso, he always paid a visit to these nonprovincial Texans. The visit they found most memorable is recorded by Carl Hertzog in a brief memoir for this book which he calls "A Day with DeGolyer":

A DAY WITH DEGOLYER

A postcard from Elizabeth Ann gave me advance warning but the days changed and DeGolyer caught me by surprise after all. Whenever DeGolyer was involved events usually changed. The next day you are trying to figure out what happened.

The postcard said, "Dear Carl: I envy you & Mr. D for you'll soon be chatting and having fun. He leaves here Monday night on train. I thought you might like to know a little in advance to get some spare time — and still be surprised. Best, Liz." As it turned out, I didn't have to "act" surprised.

The next morning, Tuesday, Feb. 10, 1947, I called the T. & P. to be sure what time the train from Dallas would arrive — 1:30 P.M. I had all morning to clear the deck and avoid involvements that might interrupt a free afternoon.

Since I was to act surprised, I could not meet the train, nor plan anything — just had to wait it out. I skipped lunch waiting for a phone call or a taxi with DeGolyer. By 2:30 P.M. I decided he wasn't coming, missed the train, or changed his plans.

*In those days I was trying to run a shop with thirty peo-
ple and too many customers, war-time shortages and worn
down equipment, so my "free" afternoon was quickly absorbed, and the next day was so full of problems and people that I forgot about DeGolyer.*

*About 2 P.M. with a customer in my office I told our
front man that I didn't want to be interrupted. When he
stuck his head in the door, I waved him out. After waving
him out twice, he finally forced the issue by saying, "I
know you don't want to be interrupted but there is a very
important looking gentleman waiting to see you."*

*"My God! was it DeGolyer?" — waiting 45 minutes —
being treated like an unwanted peddler. I ditched my local customer and jumped out the door to see.*

*There he was, jammed up in the corner, sitting on our
iron chair especially made uncomfortable for salesmen.
Our counter built around the front door to keep wander-
ers out of the shop crowded the space. Everyone going in
and out was passing Mr. De, knee to knee.*

*Liz had told me to act surprised. I didn't have to "act." I
was embarrassed but DeGolyer was amused and he had
been entertained by observing the shop activity. He
showed his customary nonchalance, ignored my apologies,
and asked questions about the routine he had been observing.*

The first business was to go over the proofs for our book,
Across Aboriginal America: The Journey of Three Englishmen Across Texas in 1568. *He had brought the proofs,
which had been mailed to him in Dallas, but he had not
put any marks on them; he had all the corrections and alterations in his head. There were many additions, citations,
and improvements which I copied down furiously while
he just remembered.*

As we finished this discussion, DeGolyer picked up a

copy of the Twelve Travelers,* which I proudly displayed on the corner of my desk. "This is a cheap book," he said, and as I bristled, he added, "they give 'em away downtown, free."

Only part of the story unfolded at this time but I gathered that Erwin Will, who financed the book, had given a copy to Mr. DeGolyer. Mr. Will, president of the El Paso Electric Company, was chairman of the Chamber of Commerce track depression committee. In this connection he was visited by Mr. Mercier, president of the Southern Pacific, who was accompanied by Mr. DeGolyer.

As a friendly gesture Mr. Will presented a copy of Twelve Travelers to Mr. Mercier, who said, "Why don't you give one to DeGolyer, he's a book collector?" So De kidded me that "they're giving 'em away downtown." (If you are in the wake of the president of the Southern Pacific.)

When we finished our business with the proofs, I suggested a tour of the shop. I pointed out different pieces of equipment and explained photo-offset, which was new to us at that time. At 3:30 P.M. I thought it would be interesting for us to visit Tom Lea, so I said, "Let's go see Tom."

When we stepped outside, I suddenly remembered my wife had the car, but I recovered by remembering that our bookkeeper had just bought a new Chevrolet. I borrowed her car and told her that if I didn't get back in time, she could get home by driving our truck.

As Tom was living on Trowbridge Street at that time, on the outskirts of town, we had quite a ways to go. There were no pictures in his studio but there was plenty of conversation. Then we went into the house to tell stories. We were having a highball (maybe the second) when the

* Magnum opus, scarce at $125 a copy in 1955.

phone rang, and my wife told me the vice-president of the Southern Pacific had been calling, trying to locate DeGolyer. She had guessed where we were; pretty soon the VP called Tom's and interrupted DeGolyer telling a story.

The VP said, "Our train leaves for Houston at 6:30. Will you be at the depot?" DeGolyer said he would be there, came back to his chair, picked up his highball and resumed his story.

He was selling us on the idea of reprinting The Banditti of the Plains *and was dramatizing the influx of Texas gunmen into the Jackson County War. As the gunsmoke rose over the corral, the phone rang again.*

"Say, this train leaves in ten minutes. Are you coming?" DeGolyer said yes, returned to his chair and continued the Wyoming story. Tom noticed his glass was empty and asked if he would have another drink.

DeGolyer looked at the glass and said, "I believe I will," and went on telling what a good movie could be made out of the fight between the cattlemen and the nesters.

As the phone rang again, we got up to leave and I was wondering how many cops would be on my trail to the depot but DeGolyer casually lingered over the goodbyes.

I drove down Rio Grande street to avoid traffic. The train was already late. I stepped on it.

Halfway to town I thought of our bookkeeper and her car I was driving — it was an imposition. Right then I was passing her house and there was our truck parked out front.

I jambed on the brakes, told De to get in the truck while I took the keys of the Chevrolet to the front door. Two miles and five minutes later I rounded the corner of the Union Station driving the truck with Mr. DeGolyer grinning innocently.

The conductor was having a fit and two VP's were pacing the platform as Mr. DeGolyer got into his private car attached to the famous train that had never been late.

The next day I picked up the story as phone calls and letters came in.

Erwin Will phoned to ask, "Who is this guy DeGolyer who was with Mr. Mercier yesterday?"

I proudly answered, "He is the inventor of geophysics and collects royalties from all major oil companies — hundred million bucks, maybe. He came to see me about printing a book."

To which Mr. Will replied, "Do you know why he really came? The Board of Directors of the Southern Pacific met here and elected him to the Board." Oh! I was deflated but now understood why DeGolyer didn't show up that first day.

When Liz said, "Mr. De leaves here (Dallas) tonight by train," I naturally thought of the Texas & Pacific. But since he was involved with the Southern Pacific, he went to Houston the first night and came on to El Paso the following day with the vice-presidents and lawyers.

In the afternoon, I received a distinguished looking visitor who brought this note: "Dear Carl: This is to introduce John Bullington of Houston, a lover of fine printing. I know he needs no further recommendation to you. I want to tell you how much I enjoyed seeing you and your shop. I am still looking for the Gutenberg press. Meeting Tom Lea was one of the top spots of my life. Regards, De."

Then a week later: "You may have heard by now that my trip to El Paso was to meet the president of the Southern Pacific and that I have become a director of the board. While the trip may have been made for that purpose, I was the one who chose the meeting place and it was held

in El Paso in order that I might visit Tamazunchale.*
Probably I would have been better off and surer of seeing
you with a directorship on the T. and P. but half a loaf is
better than no bread."

DeGolyer sometimes, not always, measured out his independent judgment of books by his friends in the ratio in
which they could take honest criticism. One man, out-
wardly as tough as himself in the psychological sense, who
he knew could take it was Tom Lea. When Lea's *The
Brave Bulls* was published in 1949, a sort of world pre-
miere was organized for it in Dallas with autographing
parties in the stores and with Little, Brown editor Angus
Cameron in town with the author for the occasion. Frank
Dobie and other Texas celebrities flew in for a round of
parties. Dallas had staged a notable Southwest Book Fair
in 1945, for which DeGolyer organized an exhibit of
some of his rare books; the general mood of Dallas book
folk was to make an author as much a community celebrity
as a football star, or even Linda Darnell or Ginger Rogers
or Mary Martin or other famous Texans. It was a gala occasion.

On the day *The Brave Bulls* came out, DeGolyer (who
had received an inscribed advance copy) said to Tom:
"It's all good but the last line. It's cheap."

"You feel that way?" Lea asked, stabbed despite his
armor.

"Yes, I do," replied DeGolyer.

"I'm sorry as hell you take it that way," returned Lea,
and added, "I wrote the last line first. I thought it was
good enough to write a book about. In view of everything
that happened in the book, I hoped the last line might

---

* Town, Tamazunchale, near Mexico City (a pun on "Tom and
Carl").

hold a little irony." And Lea quoted the last line, " 'We'll live forever and both get rich.' "

It was DeGolyer's turn to be shaken. In its context, the last sentence is arresting; its interpretation depends on how you interpret the Mexican, or at least the bullfighter's, temperament. DeGolyer asked, "You meant that for irony? Not for a happy ending?"

"I sure as hell meant it for irony," said Lea, "and so did the bullfighter."

"Well," replied DeGolyer, "I didn't get that. Maybe I ought to read it again."

So he did, and cheerfully admitted he was wrong. Thereafter *The Brave Bulls* remained a favorite choice when he made book gifts. He may not have really felt he misunderstood that line — but he always liked a man who answered him back vigorously. More than one man found out this was the quickest way to win his esteem, or at any rate, his interest.

The book to which Carl Hertzog alludes in his sketch of DeGolyer, *Across Aboriginal America: The Journey of Three Englishmen Across Texas in 1568,* was, and is, an important footnote to American history. In his introduction to a neglected and, at one time, disbelieved historical journal, DeGolyer analyzes and documents the credibility of what he calls "a valid and important part of Texas history" in a journey made by three Englishmen who were "doubtless the first men of their blood to tread Texas soil." The first edition of Hakluyt's famous *The Principall Navigations, Voiages and Discoveries of the English Nation,* published in 1589, contained an account of the wanderings of three Englishmen in 1568 who traveled from Tampico to what is now New Brunswick. They were seamen on Hawkins' third expedition to the Indies. As a result of a misadventure at Veracruz, only one ship was left and it was both overloaded and underprovisioned. At their own request one hundred men were set ashore, of whom a score set out northward on foot. Of this group, three managed after "long travaile" and after seeing "great plaines" and many rivers to make their way to New Brunswick, where they found a French ship and sailed home. It is not known what happened to the others who started out from Mexico. One of the survivors kept a journal, "The Relation of David Ingram of Barkling," the account published in the first edition of Hakluyt. But the Elizabethans found the account hard to believe; it was dropped from subsequent editions. The English sailor, true, mixed reminiscences of Africa with his story of his New World wanderings. DeGolyer's analysis, supported by his own firsthand knowledge and personal experience of the regions traversed by the three Englishmen, points unmistakably to the credibility of the American portion of David Ingram's "Relation." Scholars have expressed gratitude at having this journal reprinted, which otherwise is preserved only in the first edition of Hakluyt, and "certified." The presentation of the original document and of DeGolyer's accompanying essay to Carl Hertzog's design (the pages from Hakluyt are in facsimile) fully matches the quality of the text. The book is the proudest achievement of the Peripatetic Press. It is a rare book now and DeGolyer the book collector is now collected in turn. The current asking price in rare-book catalogues for *Across Aboriginal America* is $250; it was published in 1947 at $5. Part of this increase, of course, is due to the cult of collecting Hertzog-designed books. But this is further proof of what De-Golyer said in accepting one of his many honors: "I have thought of a compliment that might serve as epitaph on my tombstone; it might be, 'He knew how to pick good men.'"

And not merely in his own field, although it is worth noting that of the first eleven presidents of the Society of Exploration Geophysicists, eight were from the Geophysical Research Corporation.

V

Country of the Blind

20   Joining the Cyclops Club

F OR WHAT SEEMS TO BE THE FIRST TIME, at least in his
correspondence, DeGolyer began in 1949 at age sixty-
three to think of himself as "old." In May of that year the
last fledgling left the family nest to marry in his turn. The
fledgling recalled: "He could hardly wait to get me out of
the house. It gave him my bedroom as an extra library."
Writing to Dillon Anderson soon after Everett Lee's wedding, DeGolyer said with melancholy: "The DeGolyer
family has just married off the last of its offspring, leaving
two dull old people alone in a big house. At the moment
we propose to escape it by living for two or three months
in Europe. Confidentially, this was not my idea but I expect to do my best to enjoy it." DeGolyer turned his mind
away from his black mood and chided Anderson, author
of short stories printed in the *Atlantic Monthly,* for not
pursuing an earlier vein of story telling in which the distinguished young Houston lawyer had dramatized effectively documentary aspects of Spanish and French settlement in seventeenth-century Texas. DeGolyer's absorption in the history of the American Southwest remained
steady and strong.

Nell DeGolyer, reaching back in memories, proposed a

North Cape cruise as antidote for the shock of recognition that Ev's marriage had left them rattling around in a huge house. Back in 1933, when DeGolyer was working for the government in Washington, Mrs. DeGolyer had taken their four children on a trip then much in fashion with the girls' schoolmates, the North Cape cruise of the Hamburg-America Line. She now proposed to enjoy it with De, no youngsters along. She knew her husband was worried about his eyesight. His grandmother had been stone-blind the last twenty years of her life; for some time De had been complaining that long stretches of reading caused him to "get streamers" in the vision of his right eye.

He assented to the North Cape cruise, adding that while they were on the continent he wanted to go back to Rome and Italy. From there they would return by way of London to pay a visit to their friends, Ambassador and Mrs. Lewis Douglas, and return home on the *Caronia*. Ambassador Douglas' son Peter had been trained by DeGolyer in the oil business — working in the West Texas field with James Michael; the Douglas' daughter Sharman was a close friend of Dorothy DeGolyer.

The cruise was thoroughly enjoyable, but by the time they reached Italy in August, DeGolyer's eyesight was causing him real trouble and considerable depression. For the first time in his life, as Nell DeGolyer recalls, he turned recluse. He did not want to see people or to make new acquaintances. On the other hand, he was so powerfully captivated by the church of St. Francis at Assisi that he spent the morning there and, although he was obviously sick, insisted on returning for a second visit in the afternoon. He said he would like to come back someday and make a retreat at Assisi. Nell DeGolyer was reassured by this and was not prepared for the shock she soon got.

In Venice, they engaged a chauffeur and car to drive

them to Rome. Suddenly, en route to Rome, he called out
to the driver to stop. The chauffeur pulled off the road. De-
Golyer turned toward his wife's side and said, "Nell, I can't
see. I can't even see you." But he could when he had
turned full face to her. The right eye alone had lost sight.
In her panic, she said they must fly home at once. He remained calm, and insisted they must finish their trip. It
was nearly over, and at any rate he did not want to miss
seeing old Mexican Eagle friends from England who were
now in the Royal Dutch Shell offices at The Hague. He
would not forego that nor London; in London they would
find, through Douglas, expert advice.

Nell DeGolyer was perhaps more worried than her husband. Every minor mishap of travel seemed to her an ordeal. By the time they reached The Hague both eyes were
bothering him a great deal. The second eye, he noted, was
"filled with streamers." He felt so bad there that they
missed a plane connection to Amsterdam, lost their hotel
reservation, spent a harrowing day before they reached
haven in London. Ambassador Douglas promptly made an
appointment for his friend with a famous Harley Street
specialist. The doctor's diagnosis was equally prompt: a
detached retina, requiring an operation. Douglas urged
DeGolyer to have the operation there. The doctor, sensing
DeGolyer's hesitation, volunteered to call an American
friend, one of the top eye specialists in New York and assured DeGolyer it would be all right to wait to have the
operation on home soil, if he so preferred. "Yes," said De-
Golyer, and so it was decided. Nell alerted the family before they sailed on the *Caronia*. At least, the ship wasn't
named the *Cyclops*, as a boat DeGolyer used to take between New Orleans and Tampico was.

At sea, they heard from Ambassador Douglas. He sent
the following cablegram: "Customs officers and State De-

partment will meet you at your stateroom and pilot you through immigration and customs promptly. There will be a private car on pier to take you and Mrs. DeGolyer to Waldorf-Astoria where there are reservations for you. Your appointment is with Doctor Dunnington, Eye Institute, 635 West 165th Street at 11:00 A.M. Saturday morning. Will call you late Saturday to get news. Best wishes, Douglas."

The operation took place in September 1949. It was not, as DeGolyer observed later, "particularly successful, but I am glad I had it as there would always have been a question in my mind." The question was answered, definitively. He would have to live with the use of only one eye. Many people, seeing him in the remaining seven years of his life, never knew it. His reading showed little diminution. He was back home in Dallas a month later. The doctors had advised him to obey their injunction: "be yourself but not quite so much." For the truth was that, in addition to the problem of the detached retina, he was a victim of aplastic anemia, an incurable disease so close to leukemia that only specialists can tell it apart. It was to cause him agony the remaining years of his life.

Now he could answer the hundreds of concerned letters from friends of which the reading aloud to De had occupied most of the time Nell and daughter Dorothy had spent in his hospital room. Two of these, both letter and response, may be singled out. The first was from oldtime and longtime Mexican Eagle associate Ben Belt. He had written to Nell a long letter, and concluded, "I have been thinking about you and De and we love you both." DeGolyer replied, in part: "No message that came to the hospital moved me so deeply as your letter. You and Ruth are two of my few deeply beloved friends. And a damned poor way I have had of ever showing it. It seems to me that this has been true with most of my dearest friends. Maybe it is a human failing. I hope so. Otherwise it is just my own poor cussedness. I love you too."

The other exchange was with Dwight D. Eisenhower. Eisenhower's letter of October 7, 1949, was on stationery of the president of Columbia University. He wrote:

Congratulations on your birthday.

Our mutual friend, Lew Douglas, has told me that this one will be celebrated in a hospital and — knowing the impatience of a Texan with the medics' rules, his violent rebellion against any such restraint — I urge upon you the lesson I learned this spring: There's more zest to life than ever when you are free once more. The best days lie ahead. Again congratulating you, and my best wishes for a speedy and total recovery.

> *Sincerely,*
> DWIGHT D. EISENHOWER

DeGolyer replied on October 27:

Dear General Eisenhower:

I received your cheerful letter . . . with great appreciation. I am grateful to Lew Douglas for causing you to write it.

Your experience that the best days always lie ahead inspires me to hope and believe that it will be my experience also. I have been out of the hospital two and a half weeks and am getting well back to normal.

As a classic Texan I am afraid I would disappoint you. You, I have heard, were born a Texan and became a Kansan. I was born a Kansan and became a Texan by choice.

It was fine and gracious of you to write me. I thank you and wish for you and yours the best of fortune in "the best days that lie ahead."

The two men later became good friends; when Eisenhower was elected President, DeGolyer was on occasion summoned to the White House for special consultation. He had served, in fact, on a small "confidential committee" — including some of the biggest names in government and academic circles — which was influential in persuading Ike to run for the presidency.

DeGolyer took the loss of one eye in his stride. Lewis Douglas, who had lost an eye in a fishing accident, cheerfully welcomed his friend into the Cyclops Club, observing that it had a good many unwitting and unwilling but distinguished members. DeGolyer's mood was characteristically expressed in a letter to his friend Nelson C. Works of Chicago: "If I should manage any improvement in the future it will be so much to the good and if nothing gets worse I will get along fine." And so he did until two years later when it became clear what he was suffering from. One may say that from 1949 on, he was a stricken man; after 1952 he knew it and looked at the reality with customary courage and clear-sightedness and cheerfulness of spirit, until a legitimate despondency crushed his resoluteness late in 1956.

Douglas and DeGolyer were not only business associates in several oil explorations, including a projected one in the Argentine that failed to materialize because of their distrust of the shaky Peron government, but they were also temperamentally congenial. Douglas would write to DeGolyer as "one philosophical anarchist to another." The DeGolyer girls were friends of Sharman Douglas. Indeed, when the ambassador paid the DeGolyers a visit in Dallas (they went to the Cotton Bowl football game) in the late autumn of 1950, he signed the guest book, "Lewis Douglas (father of Sharman)."

At the start of 1951, DeGolyer wrote Douglas that he had given an option on Atlatl and might sell it within the year and that "meantime I expect to embark on more wild-catting — the joy of my life — and to use Pete [Douglas] and Jimmy [Michael] in that direction." He assured Douglas of his good health, but he was back in the hospital in April. Both men were "fans" of historian Lord Acton. When DeGolyer encountered a man of action with a philosophical bent, he often advised restricting activity in the interest of rest and reading. A great partisan of the Southwest, although he spent as much time on journeys away from it as he did living in it, he counseled Douglas in 1952 to "forget about New York" and to spend more time at his home in Phoenix. Douglas, and others, might well have replied, "Look who's talking!"

On April 6, 1953 Douglas wanted to know "What would your answer be to this question?: the possibility or appropriateness of making some sort of overtures to the Mexican Government with a view to establishing a relationship under which certain of their oil fields now being operated by the Government might better be operated by a private concern and *also* under the terms of which certain rights to explore in certain areas might be acquired."

To the diplomatically framed question, DeGolyer replied directly. His answer reveals a new development in the Mexican situation. "There have been several deals made recently" he writes "by foreign groups and they have been quite successful. The type of deal which is being made is that the foreigner takes a structure all shot-out geophysically and ready to drill. He becomes responsible for the wildcat well and in case of success, for all of the development wells. The actual management of production is retained by Pemex [Petroleos Mexicanos] and until the operator gets his money back, he receives a royalty of approximately 12½ percent and one-half the remainder to apply on his investment. The sale of the oil is managed by Pemex and after the investor has his capital returned, he continues to receive the royalty oil." (The first of these "service contracts," as the Mexican government called them, was signed on March 5, 1949 with Edwin E. Pauley, Los Angeles, California, Signal Oil and Gas Company, and American Oil Company.) DeGolyer is full of praise for the excellent way in which Pemex is being managed by Senator Antonio Bermudez, "a man of the highest type in anybody's country." He adds, "I would be surprised if he would consider any kind of deal except that which I have mentioned. This is particularly true at the moment, since Pemex is being extremely successful in their operation."

When Douglas was very ill in Arizona in August of 1954, DeGolyer wrote to him, "Take good care of yourself. There are too few good men in the world for us to spare you." Six months later in February of 1955, he confided to Douglas that he was to undergo an operation he should have had four or five years earlier, the removal of his spleen. His last note to Douglas, in June of 1956, says that he and Nell plan to attend the International Geological Congress to be held in August. He did not get to make it.

Actually, the sense of caution and repose following the operation in 1949 allowed DeGolyer more time for reading than usual. Less than two months after the hospital stay he wrote a friend about reading galley proofs of a new Texas book and added, "I am slowly getting adjusted to my impaired vision and presume that I will be as good as ever in a few months, if not better." He regarded himself as "semi-retired." He explained to his long-ago Tampico

associate Charles W. Hamilton, that he would not call it
"formal retirement" since he had in the past formally retired on about three occasions. He wasn't a man who could
stay retired.

He explained to Hamilton, however, that "the important thing is to have something to do. I remember for example, T. J. Ryder, who knew nothing but business and
upon retirement was so bored that he simply curled up
and died. Ben Belt keeps talking about retiring with his
eye on the farm down in East Texas." And he mentions
that Paul Seashore, of Louisiana Land and Exploration, is
thinking about removing to Carmel, California to run a
bookstore not for the profit but "as has been said before,
one meets such interesting people."

As for himself DeGolyer reports, "I don't do anything
worthwhile any more but manage to keep interested in all
sorts of things. For the last couple of years I have been
giving a library on the early history of science to the University of Oklahoma and have been very busy collecting
the library. At the moment I am trying to make a catalogue
of about a thousand books important to the early history
of geology and mining but since I never seem to finish anything I suppose that someday in sheer exasperation I will
simply bundle up those books and send them to Norman."

To judge by his letters in which he speaks of his illness
he seems not to have suffered much. Writing to noted California bookman Lew Lengfeld, DeGolyer admits there is
"the general ball and chain effect of having to stay close
to the doctor," but "the illness itself is not at all unpleas-
ant." It even has some attractions since it allows more time
for reading. "I have read more in the last three months
[spring of 1951] than in any previous comparable length
of time and for me that is saying a good deal." In replying
to a note from Sumner Pike in regard to DeGolyer's elec-

tion in 1951 to the National Academy of Sciences, DeGolyer said he didn't know what "aplastic" meant but that in any case you recovered in a year or so if you were lucky; otherwise "you simply got filled up once a month on someone else's blood and keep going." Writing to Tom Lea just before going to Mexico for his honorary degree from the National University, DeGolyer reported "I expect to be dribbled full of blood about the end of this week in order to go."

He sent a health bulletin to F. E. Wellings, early-day British associate in the Mexican Eagle geology work, in July 1951, to report that "this has been my bad year. I have been in and out of the hospital much of the time with a case of anemia. It has involved no particular pain but has been bothersome and I live on blood transfusions." But a year later he is able to give Wellings a more optimistic report: "I have quite recovered my health. Probably the trip to Turkey did it." Though DeGolyer had gone in the same year on a trip to California for reasons of health, the visit to Turkey was special. There he got to visit his grandchildren, George and Cecilia McGhee having five children at the time. The first child of the American ambassador to Turkey and his wife had a special interest: Marcia McGhee wrote verse. Aged twelve, she had the pleasure of presenting her poems, appropriately bound, to her bookish grandfather, on his summer visit to Ankara in 1952.

DeGolyer was wrong to be cheerful about his recovery. It was fugitive, periods of the old verve and great gusto for living matched by stricken periods of wretched health. Because of his aplastic anemia, he was indeed, as he wrote Wellings, living on blood transfusions. In fact, only three months after reassuring Wellings that he had "quite recovered his health," DeGolyer confessed that after a flying trip to Spain with Nell in late October of 1952, he had

Nell and E. DeGolyer photographed at Santa Barbara. "I often wonder why people don't all try to live in California," DeGolyer mused before the big rush began.

reached New York with pneumonia. In a phrase that many of his letters from now on will echo, he writes "most of the time since has been spent in convalescence." Still, his instinctive optimism was not readily stifled. Two years later, on March 8, 1954, he again writes Wellings reassuringly but with a cautionary note added: "Let me warn you both against antibiotics. I was one who got away but not until after two years of aplastic anemia. We are getting on as well as could be expected. I am quite recovered but slowed down a bit. Nell had some heart trouble in mid-December. Spent some time in the hospital but is now up and around and we hope that except for having to take care of herself, she will be entirely recovered within a month or so." And so she was.

They were back in Spain in October 1954, in another fruitless attempt to locate oil in a country where DeGolyer would have been personally as well as professionally proud to be identified with its oil history. His associate in the Spanish ventures was his good friend Algur H. Meadows, who was later to have better luck.

21

The *Saturday Review*

O F ALL DeGolyer's haunting urges to identify tangibly with the world of books and publishing, the one association that gave him the greatest pleasure and sense of fulfillment was his connection with the *Saturday Review*. Started in 1942, interrupted by the war, resumed after that, the exhilarating association lasted till DeGolyer's final illness. He took seriously his duties as chief stockholder and as chairman of the board, the title conferred on him in February 1948.

When sufficient paper was at last available after the end of the war for the anticipated circulation growth, the *Saturday Review* quickly proved what it could do. By September of 1947 the subscription list alone, not counting newsstand distribution, had grown to 80,000, more than doubling the figure that wartime restrictions had imposed. Above all, ambitions and projects which had been maturing as plans could now be executed.

Irving Kolodin, for example, had been engaged as music editor to prepare a "Recordings" section, scheduled, at first, as a once-a-month feature. This new music section had two special "departments": Oscar Levant would contribute a column called "Scratching the Surface with Os-

car Levant," and E. L. DeGolyer Jr. would contribute a
column on imported recordings to be called "The Other
Side." Norman Cousins was fulfilling his stated intention
to convert the magazine into a genuine "review," reflecting
all aspects of intellectual and cultural activity. But he also
had even more wide-ranging plans, wildly fermenting in
the postwar period with its new go-ahead production signal. Cousins' fertile mind spawned projects in profusion.
One of his plans was a bit farfetched, however. In April
1947, under the impression that the *Atlantic Monthly* was
having difficulties, he proposed an amalgamation. But the
impression was incorrect, and the prestigious journal refused the offer.

In particular, he effected a "consolidation" with the
limping *Encore* magazine, which reprinted memorable
writing from entire literary history, and the Saturday Review Associates thus became publishers of a second "property." (DeGolyer at this time made his first acquaintance
with Richard Hofstadter's *Social Darwinism in American
Thought,* and enthusiastically urged business manager
Jack Cominsky to secure reprint rights of "this very remarkable book" for *Encore.*) DeGolyer also busied himself
with advising friends to take advertising in the *Saturday
Review;* one friend who politely declined was Stanley Marcus of Dallas' famous specialty shop.

On January 1, 1946, the *Saturday Review* put into effect
an advertising rate card based on guaranteed 60,000 circulation. Six months later, a new rate card was issued
based on guaranteed 80,000 circulation. Meantime the editorial board was dreaming up projects of the most diverse
sorts. Minor but indicative of the total enterprise was an
immensely successful *Saturday Review* George Bernard
Shaw Memorial Dinner, celebrating Shaw's ninetieth anniversary in 1946. With John Mason Brown serving as mas-

ter of ceremonies, the dinner was a resounding success and, coupled with the *Review*'s special Shaw issue, made a big dent in the public consciousness and appreciation of Shaw. (The DeGolyers delightedly flew up to New York from Dallas for the occasion.) DeGolyer was elected to the board of the *Saturday Review* in September 1946; he became chairman of the board in February 1948.

But the really major scheme was grandiose indeed. Cousins was a young man very much watched by the publishing industry; it may have been known that the *Review* could pay him only a ridiculously low salary at the time. In 1946, he was asked by Marshall Field to become editor of a new magazine project, "Project X" — which was to be a weekly magazine, *Life*-size, aiming at a minimum circulation of one million copies and to be called *USA*. Cousins was indeed tempted.

The solution he hit upon was to create a new publishing company, the Magazine Corporation of America, which would publish the *Saturday Review, Encore,* and the proposed mass-circulation new magazine. At first DeGolyer had some reservations, but finally gave his consent. On November 29, 1946, Cousins wrote DeGolyer that the decision had been made to publish *USA* as a monthly, not as a weekly. In the new organization, the *Saturday Review* group would retain control or title to 52 percent of the stock; Marshall Field would own 48 percent, investing $1,500,000 over a period of time. A dummy issue had been prepared but publication was nearly a year off, the first issue hopefully to be published in September of 1947. Cousins and Cominsky would finally have respectable salaries: $35,000 each.

In that intervening year, magazine and book publishing both nose-dived into a tremendous slump. Newsstand sales fell off sharply. And competition for paper drove the price sky-high, while printing costs rose to a new level. The slump in book sales diminished the prospects for the *Review* in book advertising. After agonizing thought, the decision was made not to try at this time to start a new mass magazine from scratch. It semed both easier and wiser, Cousins judged, to concentrate on the *Saturday Review of Literature,* developing it into a more general magazine with an expectation of 200,000 readers within a few years.

"Project X," or *USA,* was dissolved. A similar casualty was Cousins' prophetic but premature idea of the *Saturday Review*'s forming an association with moviedom, possibly with producer Walter Wanger, to make movies for television from good books. Television was well in the future but Cousins thought, quite rightly, that it would lean heavily on the movie industry. He was ahead of his time. Though still-born, this idea led to the next *Saturday Review* project, "World Literary Projects," for which DeGolyer promised $65,000 and which became in time the *Saturday Review* Syndicate Service, a package deal, highly successful, of weekly book, music and travel news and information. This was not formally established until 1949; in the meantime in June 1948, Cousins asked DeGolyer for a loan of $40,000 for the magazine, noting that the request was larger than the traditional $22,500. (Earlier in 1948, when DeGolyer accepted the chairmanship of the board, he agreed to send in a check of $67,500 "for purchase of additional stock in accordance with our agreement." He added, "It is my understanding that the note for $22,500 which I hold will be paid." The new 1948 program for expansion entailed a $125,000 increase in funding, DeGolyer's share being half the amount.)

Although the *Saturday Review* was making extraordinary progress in circulation and advertising gains, as well as in influence and prestige, it had gone back into the red.

Its problems were dual: production costs were suffering from the inflation in paper and printing prices; and book advertising, almost exclusively what the magazine carried, was at a minimum. Book publishers were experiencing the same production costs. Cousins and Cominsky saw the necessity of seeking general, not specifically book, advertising; they also saw that this change would require a much more diversified magazine, beyond the travel and recordings supplements which had been recently added. But for this proposed and ultimate diversification in editorial content, it is doubtful the magazine would have survived. It is most certainly doubtful that the pragmatic DeGolyer, however stimulating and inspiring a companion in business enterprises, would have turned out to be an "angel" geared to sink indefinite sums of money in a losing project.

A real turning point, however, came for the magazine in 1949. The admirable 25th Anniversary Issue, dated August 6, 1949, was a smash hit, selling out the original run of 150,000 copies in seventy-two hours. (The average print order for the preceding six months had been slightly over 100,000 copies.) After that, luck smiled rather than grimaced and success was assured, though it seemed at times to travel at a snail's pace. Jack Cominsky typed out a Christmas greeting for DeGolyer on December 22, 1951:

I want you to hang this on your Christmas tree:

Net profit: $23,473.52 (August, September, October, November only)
Last year, same period: Net loss: $22,174.23.

Groaned DeGolyer ironically to Dallas friends: "Why can't things like this happen in the oil business? Why, I didn't even go into the magazine as an investment at all — and here it is making money."

DeGolyer admired and shared Norman Cousins' fundamentally melioristic spirit, his blending of zest and zeal, his wish to translate thought into action. Once, in 1951, when the magazine was attacked by the reactionary columnist, George Sokolsky, DeGolyer was greatly amused. He wrote Cousins: "You seem to be lucky in having been attacked by Sokolsky. Your defense is so good that I am cynic enough to wonder whether or not you provoked the attack in order to make the defense."

Against the grain, no doubt, he even attempted to use his influence to swing "institutional" advertising in the magazine. One such appeal was made to his old friend and Amerada colleague, John M. Lovejoy. It must have been against the grain, since DeGolyer's letter merely suggests that "the public relations organization" might make "a more extended use of the *Saturday Review of Literature* than has been made." But, warming to his subject, he adds: "This is not an appeal from weakness. I have backed the SRL for something like ten years because I believe it to be a forward-looking, liberal journal. My faith has not been misplaced. The magazine seems to be fairly on its feet now and I have no concern from the viewpoint of making a profit from it."

Insofar as this researcher has been able to discover, De-Golyer's total investment over a period of fifteen years with the Saturday Review Associates (not counting repaid loans) amounted to a total of $130,000, for which, of course, he received stock in exchange. He felt it was a small outlay for what turned out to be one of the most exhilarating ventures in his versatile life and one of course that in the end proved to be most satisfying. No figurehead in the venture, he was deluged with reports from Cousins and Cominsky, wrote careful replies, sought out articles, and also book reviews and reviewers, wrote re-

views himself at a rate of $25 per assignment, coerced
friends into sending group Christmas gift subscriptions, occasionally argued vehemently with Cousins and Cominsky
— and relished their company as two of the most valued
friends he ever had in his life. He could be generous with
them as friends if not as business partners. He contributed,
for example, $5,000 to a project much dearer to Cousins'
heart than to his own, the United World Federalists. He
wrote Cousins that the contribution was a show of faith in
him, not in the organization. Their private correspondence,
incidentally, deserves someday to be separately published.
He always spoke warmly of Cousins behind his back, although he took delight in chaffing him when face to face,
with the kind of camaraderie more typical of the West
than of the East. Typical is a sentence which concludes a
letter he sent to Jack Cominsky to praise delightedly Cousins' article in the spring of 1951 titled "Conversations with
Nehru." DeGolyer writes: "I do not know what achievement Norman could make which would surprise me."

DeGolyer closed out his "proprietorship" of the *Saturday Review* in a letter to Cousins of January 27, 1955. He
was very ill, had been for six years, and for the last two
years had been compelled for reasons of health to cancel
nearly every engagement he had previously accepted.
Three months earlier Cousins had sent him a memorandum
of great importance, outlining long-term expansion programs. The estimated cost: about $100,000. So, just after
the New Year, DeGolyer answered: "I do not see that the
situation has changed . . . as compared with when I
talked to you. It seems to me that one would have to face
the necessity of continuing to put more money into the
Review for a long time and this I am not prepared to do."
He was physically sick and mentally tired. He wanted to
conserve his time and energy for his book on the history of

the oil industry. The time had come — and alas gone — when the major thing was to "subsidize" his own writing and not that of others.

So, he sold out his interest in the Saturday Review Associates to Norman Cousins — for about the sum he had posted in the crisis of 1941: $25,000. In fact, at the end of his energy, DeGolyer was beginning to close out all his accounts, emotional and otherwise. Characteristically, he refused for a time to accept any money from Cousins. He knew that Cousins, a young man with four children to educate, couldn't afford anything approaching $25,000. He wanted to turn over his stock to Cousins out of friendship. Cousins reminded DeGolyer that De had once said his original investment in the *Saturday Review* was a bet on Cousins — pure and simple. And so now Cousins asked to be allowed to pay off the bet — at least to the extent of the original amount plus some interest. DeGolyer was adamant. "Dammit," he said, "where are you going to get twenty-five thousand dollars?"

Cousins said he would borrow it from the bank.

DeGolyer replied that he himself had no use for the money and didn't want Cousins to go into debt.

Finally, Cousins used the one argument against which DeGolyer had no defense. "De," he said, "I think I'm doing what you would do if you were in my place."

DeGolyer looked at Cousins a moment, then grinned and held out his hand. "You may be right," he said, "even so, let us think about it a few days. You think about it, too. There's no point in burdening yourself unnecessarily." They spoke on the phone a few days later. Cousins said he still wanted to pay off the original bet. DeGolyer agreed. Two days later, he sent all his stock to Cousins.

A few years later the *Saturday Review* had achieved a circulation of 300,000 (and it was to go on from there) and become a resounding financial, as well as editorial, success. Toward the end of his life, DeGolyer told Cousins directly what he often had told oil cronies in Texas: "I believe I have got more fun out of the Saturday Review association than from any other business enterprise, and take more satisfaction in its success than in any oil strike."

22   Honors Mean Obligations

IF DeGolyer, like other Americans, had to flee Mexico in 1914, he was later, though much later, welcomed back with open arms. The supreme public recognition came in 1951, when he was awarded an honorary degree — that of Doctorado Honoris Causa — by the National University of Mexico, oldest university in this hemisphere, on the occasion of its celebration of its four hundredth anniversary. Long before that, Petroleum Mexicanos had engaged the consulting services of DeGolyer and MacNaughton to help solve Mexico's exploration problems after the expropriation.

Typical of the fondness and respect in which he was held is the comment of Antonio Bermudez, director of Pemex, in an interview he gave the Mexico City daily,

Excelsior, for its issue of June 18, 1947, from which this quotation is taken:

As regards exploitation, Sr. Bermudez stated that due to the happenings of 1938 certain difficulties were met with in this respect, but that at present 64 structures are pending exploration and which represent the work of a group of some of the most notable geologists in the world, headed by E. DeGaullier [another spelling of the family name in France], who, despite the fact of being an extremely wealthy man is at the service of Petroleos Mexicanos on account of his great affection for Mexico.

The immediate cause of his reentry into relationship with the oil history of Mexico, after the expropriation of 1938 (the "happenings" mentioned in the *Excelsior* interview), was of course the wartime need for the two technical oil missions to Mexico which he headed.

The doctoral award in Mexico City — the National University celebrated its fourth century of existence in three days of ceremonies — was presented with full Latin respect for ritual and punctilio. Months in advance of the September events, DeGolyer was requested to submit measurements so that he could be properly capped and gowned. The Mexican committee in charge felt obliged to verify a second time DeGolyer's stated "circumference of the head: 25 inches, hat size, 7½." The committee questioned that a five-foot, six-inch-tall man would have a head that leonine. Was one measurement or the other wrong? In the end it worked out fine. DeGolyer cherished the color photograph of himself in academic regalia as much as he did the elaborately executed diploma. "The photograph," he liked to say, perhaps to lessen the pride he took in it, and certainly

with no fidelity to accuracy, "just accents my peasant's
face."

DeGolyer's degree was awarded to a dozen "Personajes
de Todo el Mundo." Just before leaving for Mexico City
and the ceremonies, DeGolyer wrote to William D. Pat-
terson of the *Saturday Review* staff that "someone, identity not known but suspected, has sandbagged the University of Mexico for an honorary degree for me." He adds,
"since I suspect most honorary degrees are arranged in
similar fashion or derived from even baser motives, I in-
tend to enjoy and appreciate this one without inquiring
too deeply into its origin." He mentions with humor the
matter of his measurements for *"la confección de la toga"*
and confesses that "the whole thing ought to be pretty
glorious."

One of DeGolyer's minor hobbies — acquired in Mexico
— was collecting *dichos*, Spanish sayings that summarize
in tart, sharp aphorisms the collective wisdom of the people. He put together, after much sifting, a hundred or so,
perhaps intending someday to publish them in a private
edition. A more immediate use for them was to serve as
engraved adornments of a dozen silver goblets he had
bought in Mexico. He alerted all his friends who loved the
country south of the border to send him samples. He explained to Tom Lea that he wanted only the twelve outstanding "superb examples" for his silver display; he did
not want to miss anything choice. The best *dicho*, or Spanish saying, that Tom could find for DeGolyer's collection
was a local one describing the American Southwest:
"Donde no sobra otra cosa que dilatados terreños."
("Where nothing else was left over for it but wide open
spaces.") It was William Johnson, Time bureau chief in
Dallas and author of several books on Mexico, who provided him with his greatest find: *"El diablo viejo save mas*

por viejo que por diablo." DeGolyer greatly relished this
favorite *dicho* and gave it different English translations.
Johnson would chide him for poetic license and insisted
that he stick to "The old devil knows more because he is
old and not because he is a devil."

He was still pondering the book on foreign oil policy
four years later. To his old Mexican days' friend, geologist
F. E. Wellings, DeGolyer wrote on August 6, 1955, that he
had some news. "My most recent thrilling experience has
been a metamorphosis into a gas expert after a long and
calloused experience as an oil expert. I should have gone
to Brazil this fall, but the gas thing prevents." He adds
that he is "in the throes of writing a book on foreign oil
policy for the United States." He has a specific thought he
thinks would interest Iraq-experienced Wellings, namely
that states granting concessions to foreign nations should
not do so on a grand scale; the restricted area, always
granted under some type of national mining law, should
be subject to almost immediate drilling by the grantee "so
that the state itself and not some company would be the
repository for the bulk of the undrilled lands." He con-
cedes that the size of the concessions should vary in relation to the expense of operation, the more investment required the larger the concession.

This letter to Wellings was written just a year before
DeGolyer's death at age seventy. His faith in the possibility of reasonable solutions between different nationalities
seems never to have wavered. He also tells Wellings that
he has received another honorary degree, adding "but as
Mauldin's GI said, 'Give me two aspirin, I've already got
a purple heart.'" And a more personal note: "Do not be
too careless about extending invitations to visit you. I am
exceedingly anxious to see the Middle East again and particularly to have Nell see the Holy Land. Not being reli-

gious enough to regard myself as a fair subject, I am curious as to what effect it would have on her, she being a
really good Christian."

Honors, like obligations, rained down on DeGolyer after
the war — as they had indeed before. Another one in 1951
which gave him equal pride with the award from the National University of Mexico came with his election to the
National Academy of Sciences, with investiture in November at Yale University. For the first time in its history, the
academy elected to membership a mining engineer. In the
same year, in May, he was elected a Fellow of the American Academy of Arts and Sciences. The following year he
was elected by the Oklahoma Memorial Association to the
Oklahoma Hall of Fame, but the really signal professional
honor came from the American Institute of Mining and
Metallurgical Engineers. On February 20, 1952, the AIME
honored DeGolyer at its annual banquet with one of its
coveted awards, held by only twenty living men, the Citation of Honorary Membership. The citation read: "For
distinguished service to the petroleum industry through
his pioneering in the application of geophysical techniques
of oil findings, and in recognition of the many contributions he has made to our understanding of the occurrence
of petroleum and natural gas, and in grateful acknowledgment of his unselfish and patriotic service to his country,
by his leadership, sound counsel, and excellent judgment,
both in time of peace and in the face of war, which has
brought honor to himself and to the Institute."

In addition, three-hundred-word tributes were read by
Wallace E. Pratt, Rodger Denison, W. S. Morris and Paul
Weaver. Wallace Pratt did not, as might have been fore-
seen, use the occasion for conventional comments. He
characterized DeGolyer as having "eminently the psychol-
ogy of the male animal — vigorous, almost belligerent. As

an expert witness, in the rough-and-tumble of a public hearing before a Congressional committee, he is at his best. His testimony is pithy and carries conviction. It is courageous — he is in no way restrained by the realization that his recommendations will not be universally approved by his colleagues in the petroleum industry."

Pratt noted that in 1948 James V. Forrestal told him, "I am fortunate that in my official capacity here I continue to enjoy the same advice on oil problems that I learned to rely on long ago in the business world. I mean DeGolyer. In my judgment, his counsel in this field is the best the government can obtain. I have long been convinced that he is the most competent authority in the petroleum industry."

John M. Lovejoy, to be the second recipient of the De-Golyer Memorial Award of the American Institute of Mining Engineers, made the annual dinner address at the Petroleum Division meeting of the AIME in New York in 1952. Reminiscing, he recalled a conversation he had in 1919 with Mr. Skelly, who told Lovejoy that he proposed to add a geologist to the staff of Skelly Oil but "at his own personal expense," since he did not "think it proper to charge a geologist's salary to the newly organized company." Lovejoy also recalled that in 1923 DeGolyer had been named the first chairman of the new Institute of Petroleum Technologists Division of the AIME; the name was soon shortened to Petroleum Division. The first chairman of any oil committee (not division) within the AIME had been Captain Anthony F. Lucas in 1913.

Significantly, Lovejoy observed that "the exploitation of oil fields today is a truly scientific mining operation." This came about, he explained, through what was probably the most significant discovery ever made by the industry, namely that the flow of wells could be restricted without damage to the wells. This recognition allowed the conservation and total recovery program under a system of proration to develop, to be adopted voluntarily by the industry. This in turn created a new technical profession, that of petroleum engineering.

In acknowledging a copy of the talk, DeGolyer said that "your feelings, as I sit with a polished section of the core of the Backbone of the Continent taken from Amerada's first Nebraska well and note in the morning paper that Amerada jumped twenty points yesterday, are fully reciprocated by me. We might be in better financial circumstances, as I remember some of the old options, if we had hung on to our original Amerada stock and done nothing since." Yes, according to George Elliott Sweet in *The History of Geophysical Prospecting*, an original share of Amerada stock has risen "from $26 to around $1,300." This, in about forty years.

President Truman named DeGolyer to the eleven-member Scientific Manpower Advisory Committee in December 1950. In 1952, this man of varied duties and honors was appointed as member of the United States National Commission for UNESCO. But sickness forbade his attending meetings. He resigned after a year or so.

Lesser honors abounded. In 1946, DeGolyer was chosen chairman of the Gulf District Committee of Selection for the Rhodes Scholarships. His close friend, Savoie Lottinville of the University of Oklahoma, also served on the selection committee; the two would journey together to New Orleans for the annual investigation of candidates and for the final decisions. DeGolyer was proud of this assignment and, according to Lottinville, agonized over difficult decisions. He always threw his weight in favor of applicants who showed independence and a gift for self-education.

In January of 1947, DeGolyer made a new gift of books

to the University of Texas Library. For Southern Methodist University in Dallas, he contributed to the Sustentation Fund, made a $1,000 donation to its law school, and agreed to underwrite the university press's publication of a very significant work of scientific history, Professor Samuel Wood Geiser's *Naturalists of the Frontier*.

As usual he was planning a book, or several books, on his own. A new project, for which his brother Homer was engaged in magisterial research, was a history of the oil business in California. But demands on his time and attention were formidable. In early June of 1947, for example, he delivered a thirty-two-page paper before the Mid-East Conference at New York University.

There are different notions about whether DeGolyer was really a generous man with his money (the reader will find in these pages much evidence for forming an opinion), but there can be no doubt whatsoever of his extraordinary generosity in willingness, even eagerness, to share his specialized knowledge. In this regard, he had the selfless impulses of the born scholar. He never shirked local civic obligations in the city where he lived. He turned down in 1952 a suggestion that he let himself be nominated as secretary of the interior, but he agreed at the same time to serve on a committee for Water Supplies Survey for Dallas, the city suffering from a terrible drought and discovering daily that its long-range planning for adequate municipal water was derelict indeed. While serving for several years on the board of the Dallas Public Library, he was decisive in opposing censorship and securing a new library building.

DeGolyer served as president of the Dallas Museum of Fine Arts for four years, 1949–1952. He was its ninth president; his successor was Stanley Marcus. The two regimes were entirely different. DeGolyer felt very little sympathy

for contemporary art and was indeed greatly annoyed by
abstractionism and nonobjective painting. So much so, that
on one occasion when he arrived at the museum for the
preview opening of a distinctly experimental painter, he
took a look at the exhibition and in disgust sought out Cu-
rator Jerry Bywaters. "You do the honors," he said to Bywaters, "I am going home." Bywaters, a good friend, tried
a little chaffing and mentioned that everyone expected Mr.
President to say a few words of welcome. "You can say
I'm sick," replied DeGolyer, adding as a parting shot over
his shoulder, "And if you want to, you can tell them why."
He had little patience with the irrational and he was outraged when he was asked to admire it. But he had qualms.
He buttonholed knowledgeable friends for enlightenment,
but he was never persuaded. Under the directorship of
Stanley Marcus, the Dallas Museum of Fine Arts charted
another and more modern course.

One of the major collections acquired by the museum
during DeGolyer's presidency was a gift from *Life* magazine, the paintings executed by Tom Lea as part of a study
on the cattle industry — an assignment which gets partial
credit for inspiring two of Lea's books, *The Brave Bulls*
and *The King Ranch*. While illustrative and documentary,
the score or so large paintings have the authenticity and
craftsmanship to rank them in historical importance with
Remington and Russell. The collection was officially presented at ceremonies presided over by Daniel Longwell,
former chairman of the board of *Life* magazine, during the
Texas State Fair, in the autumn of 1950.

For DeGolyer, aside from its artistic worth, this acquisition was a significant triumph for the policy he favored.
He did not think it either wise or possible for the Dallas
Museum to acquire a significant and representative collection of Old Masters; he emphasized the museum's role in

fostering regional culture and providing artifacts of its growth, a program the museum later abandoned in favor of a search for modern international masters. It should be noted, however, that DeGolyer's carefully conceived program did not interpret "regional" to mean merely southwestern. He gave much time to studying possible purchases of pre-Columbian American art and of Mexican painting; he enlisted the aid of his friend Terry Duce, president of the Arabian-American Oil Company, in trying to secure an exhibition of Egyptian art. Nonetheless, his interest in art was primarily for its historical and social rather than its aesthetic import.

One member of the museum staff during DeGolyer's tenure was Margaret Milam (she resigned in 1950 to go to Japan), who was later, as Mrs. Eugene McDermott, to become the museum's thirteenth president and to mold a policy that would unite both regional and international interests.

In this swift sifting of honors that came to DeGolyer after World War II, one may be mentioned, a supreme one, that came nearly too late for him to enjoy. In April 1956, DeGolyer was made a regent of the Smithsonian Institution when President Eisenhower signed a Joint Resolution of the Senate and the House requesting his appointment.

DeGolyer could not make either of the two standard complaints about honors, that they came too late in life for real enjoyment or that they came too early and ceased so soon that the recipient lived on to be present at the burial of his own reputation. Honors came to him early and the parade never stopped. One of the most significant, the establishment by the AIME of the DeGolyer Medal of Achievement, came a decade after his death, in 1966. The first presentation of this award was made to DeGolyer me-

morially at ceremonies in New York in February 1966.
Nell DeGolyer accepted the medal for her late husband.
The second award was made to DeGolyer's lifetime friend
and former Amerada associate, John M. Lovejoy, in 1967.

23   A Writing Man

PERHAPS one reason why DeGolyer did not complete his
numerous book projects lay in the fact that he accepted
too readily invitations to read papers at conventions, to
make speeches, or to write articles and book reviews. In
the last decade of his life, he turned out a surprising number of reviews for a man so busy with other duties. This
kind of assignment he took with great seriousness. He did
not allow himself to be long-winded or rhetorical. His pref-
erence was for the compact, even the laconic. A longtime
diary keeper, he may have formed the habit of concise-
ness from this practice.

DeGolyer explained this terseness to Leonard McCollum when the latter asked him in 1952 for an opinion on a
twenty-five-page summary or draft for the use of a special
committee on oil reserves. DeGolyer reduced the report to
a single page. Reminding McCollum that they had discussed the uses of brevity before, DeGolyer clarified: "My

mania for briefness, about which I have addressed you
twice, arises out of P.A.W. experience. If we wanted a
memorandum read, we reduced it to a single page."

As a book reviewer, DeGolyer was a perfectionist, and
accepted changes in his copy with some asperity. He reviewed Jeff Dykes' *Billy the Kid: The Bibliography of a
Legend* for the June 27, 1955 issue of the *Saturday Review,*
and promptly protested the heading for his piece. "The
heading which was used, 'Hamlet on the Prairie,' seems to
me to be ridiculous. There is nothing in the review, nor so
far as I know in the Life of the Kid to suggest the Hamlet
characterization. Likewise, I do not understand why the
review had to be toned down at the end. I said: 'If one is
interested at all in this story or a story of this type, he cannot do better than read Mr. Dykes' book. I recommend it.'
It came out a lukewarm 'For a story of its type one cannot
do better than read Mr. Dykes's book.' There was a loss in
precision since this is not a story-book but the bibliography of a folk-tale; an unusual and pretty different treatment from that of the normal story-book." His vexation required a postscript: "Why the extra 's' each time the pos-
sessive of Dykes is used?"

He felt justified in complaining about casual editing because he labored over his writing. For example, one of the
most controversial reviews he ever wrote was his negative
assessment of Walter Prescott Webb's magnum opus, *The
Great Frontier.* He agreed to review this book for the *Dallas News* and, as usual, met the release date. Luckily or un-
luckily, he got the review copy nearly a month before official publication date. He read Webb's powerful — and
still greatly debated — work with the utmost respect and
the closest scrutiny. In effect, he devoted three weeks of
his life to estimating the book, as his still remaining notes
show.

Webb was a unique man in the intellectual life of Texas. A poor boy, whose homesteading West Texas parents could not offer him an education, he managed to educate himself anyway to the point of becoming the second man born and trained west of the Mississippi who was ever elevated to the presidency of the nearly century-old American Historical Association. He was, and remains through his work, one of the glories of Texas, internationally esteemed by historians.

Webb had visited in the DeGolyer home and inspected the great library of trans-Mississippi history. He had taught DeGolyer's son. In his way, he typified a kind of excellence very rare in Texas but based nonetheless on frontier qualities of character as well as mind.

Webb was, of course, greatly influenced by the magisterial work of Professor Frederick Jackson Turner on the significance of the frontier in American history; although Webb tended to minimize this influence, he is usually identified by scholars with the Turner theory and school of historians. DeGolyer early discovered in reading *The Great Frontier*, alas, that he could not accept Webb's major and daringly imaginative thesis: that the New World had served as the last great frontier, allowing immense economic expansion for an exhausted and impoverished Old World on the point of collapse when the New World windfall was discovered, conquered and exploited. For Webb, this last frontier had vanished. Therefore, the great new institutions and the thinking forged to confront the post-Renaissance world were also exhausted and had served their purpose. Human society was at a crossroads, awaiting new solutions — fresh economic, political, social and religious thinking. It was a thesis which, curiously, provoked the greatest admiration and enthusiasm from European historians, most notably from Arnold Toynbee (who made a special trip from England to Austin simply to make Webb's acquaintance) and Geoffrey Barraclough. But the book was also greeted with hoots of derision. Since a similar reception had also been given Webb's first major work, *The Great Plains,* later accepted as a classic contribution, most historians, even those in disagreement, were cautious.

DeGolyer, unlike Webb, felt that science represented a "new frontier," and that the prospect for the future was more cheerful than bleak. To insure fairness in his attack on Webb's theories, he reread the book carefully and made copious notes, along with fifty pages of extracts, all done in longhand. He reworked his review five or six times, meditated at length on the points of issue. When he turned in his review at last to the *News'* book editor, he said ruefully: "Don't ever assign me a book like that again. I really slaved over this. But don't try to pay me anything for it. If I got what I deserve for both time and concentrated work, you'd never get to put out a book page again."

Some of Webb's many disciples in the Southwest wanted to de-hide DeGolyer, writing directly to him and sending carbon copies of their letters to the *News.* But Webb, who had sustained a bitter attack on his *The Great Plains,* at a special program of the American Historical Society, was inured to disagreement. Philosophically, he pointed out that *The Great Plains* had finally won approval for its theses after much opposition; and so, he supposed, would *The Great Frontier.* In general, national reviews of the book praised the "bold imagination" and "provocative theories" of Webb, but withheld adherence to his ideas.

A number of publishers persisted in trying to get DeGolyer to write his autobiography. He steadily refused. Others proposed a biography. He declined. Norman Cousins himself had an idea. His friend Cleveland Amory had

spent some time in the American Southwest; there was an
Amory on the first board of Amerada; and *The Proper Bos-
tonians* was one of DeGolyer's enthusiasms among recent
books. Furthermore, Cleveland Amory had come to Dallas
for bookstore autographing parties and he and DeGolyer,
both possessed of minds streaked with sardonic satire, had
got along wonderfully well. Cousins proposed a discussion
between the two about DeGolyer's life story. Clip Amory
came to Dallas again, to visit the DeGolyers, in February
of 1953. He got a memorable taste of DeGolyer's skill at
gin rummy, but he didn't get a go-ahead. DeGolyer explained why in a letter to Cousins: "It was a visit that I
enjoyed very much, but I am still not convinced that the
world is waiting to hear my life story. Since I am substan-
tiated in this view by the Little Woman, it is likely to stick.
Amory is a skillful pleader, however, and instead of taking
'no' for an answer, stated that he would be back next
month. So, technically at least, the matter is still under discussion."

Once DeGolyer was persuaded he would not be imposing an unrelished chore on a friend's friend, a start was
made. But DeGolyer fell ill again (he had to cancel an important trip to Mexico in the summer of 1953 when he was
stricken just two hours before plane time), and the work
was postponed. Meanwhile, Amory received another offer
he could not refuse and which would not require his attention for too long. But DeGolyer had more bad days
than good in the last three years of his life, which precluded completion of the project. This was to him, as to
Cleveland Amory, a major disappointment.

Two special articles he wrote for the book pages of the
Dallas Morning News and the *Dallas Times Herald* reveal
the breadth of his reading and his critical taste. John Wil-

liam Rogers, book editor of the *Times Herald,* asked him
for a list, with commentary, of the ten best books he had
ever read. DeGolyer demurred at such a conventional column and offered instead to discuss a short list of great,
though little known, books which he would regret never
having encountered. More conventionally, he agreed to
prepare for the *News* a guide to the best books about Mexico. Both lists contain revelatory commentary.

Inevitably, the list of ten books that "he would hate to
have missed" opens with what was possibly his favorite
work, Andrew D. White's *A History of the Warfare of Sci-
ence with Theology in Christendom.* The list continues:
2) Apsley Cherry-Garrard, *The Worst Journey in the
World — Antarctic, 1910–1913;* 3) René Vallery-Radot,
The Life of Pasteur; 4) Edward Stucken, *The Great White
Gods;* 5) Elaine Sanceau, *The Land of Prester John;* 6)
E. A. McIlhenny, *The Alligator's Life History;* 7) John G.
Neihardt, *Black Elk Speaks;* 8) George Webb Dasent,
The Story of Burnt Njals (from the Icelandic of the Njalas
saga); 9) Eduardo Zamacois, *Roots;* 10) Honore Wilson
Morrow, *Beyond the Blue Sierra.*

He cautioned the reader that this was not a list of his
ten favorite books, simply of ten "unusual" books which he
luckily had not missed. Still, the Andrew White was a
great favorite, as was the novel by Mrs. Morrow. The story
of Scott's expedition to the Antarctic interested him chiefly
in its scientific purpose of securing eggs of the emperor
penguin, in the belief that "a study of the development of
the embryo of this most primitive of birds would throw
light upon the evolution of birds from reptiles." DeGolyer
writes that the Neihardt life story of a holy man of the
Ogalala Sioux is "impressive for the degree to which he de-
scribes the spiritual life." One might suspect him of logroll-
ing in including the book on alligators by his friend

McIlhenny, but no, DeGolyer admits the subject matter has no interest for him whatsoever, "I positively dislike alligators." But the book absorbed him by the skill with which it combined scientific observation and clear exposition. Vallery-Radot's *Pasteur* was bedside reading for DeGolyer, and a frequent gift choice for friends. On the whole, his list reflects the choices of a venturesome and scientifically oriented mind, more naturally drawn to history and personal narrative than to theoretical thought. In the language of the philosophers, he was more concerned with what is "real" than with what is "true," if indeed he would have admitted the existence of any such distinction.

The list of "best books" on Mexico had an even dozen titles. DeGolyer deplored certain gaps. Writing in 1947, he said, "I do not recall a good book in English on the colonial history of Mexico, or on its very excellent handicrafts nor a modern book on that very interesting portion of the Republic, the North and Northwest." The twelve books: 1) *Terry's Guide to Mexico* — often revised, but DeGolyer says, "I still have a great affection for the first edition, published in 1909," and he adds, "this is the best single book ever published on Mexico"; 2) *Mexico and Its Heritage,* by Ernest Gruening; 3) *Aztecs of Mexico,* by George C. Vaillant; 4) *The Ancient Maya,* by Sylvanus Griswold Morley; 5) *The Great White Gods,* by Eduard Stucken ("a magnificent historical novel . . . of the conquest — recommended instead of Prescott's *Conquest of Mexico*"); 6) *The Itching Parrot,* by José Joaquín Fernández de Lizardi ("This Mexican classic, one of the great picaresque novels, translated and with an introduction by Katherine Anne Porter, one of our best storytellers in her own right"); 7) *The United States and Mexico, 1821–1848,* by George Lockhart Rives; 8) *Mexican Empire,* by Montgomery Hyde ("best book" on Maximilian and Carlota); 9) *Leg-*

ends of the City of Mexico, by Thomas A. Janvier; 10) *Mexico South: The Isthmus of Tehuantepec,* by Miguel Covarrubias; 11) *The Peacock Sheds His Tail,* by Alice Tisdale Hobart ("an historical novel dealing wisely, and sympathetically, with the struggle over oil rights and lands"); 12) *The Story of Architecture in Mexico,* by Trent Elwood Sanford.

These lists also supply an answer to the inevitable question so often asked by first-time guests in the vast DeGolyer living room library: "But have you read all these books?" (There were about eleven thousand in that one room alone.) DeGolyer was known sometimes to have answered — depending on the questioner — "Yes, every single one"; or sometimes, "No, of course not, but many of them I have reread five or six times."

---

24   The Science Collection

O NE REASON for DeGolyer's trip to Europe in the summer of 1949 was a bit more factual than the one he gave Dillon Anderson. The trip was not simply compensation for the loneliness of the big house with no fledglings any longer living in it; DeGolyer was maturing the next great book collection he would put together, a collection to fit another major purpose. For years he had been talking casually to academic friends about the neglect of the *history* of science — not of the various fields of science but of the organic growth of the scientific way of establishing reality and truth.

Characteristically, he thought the organization and establishing of such a field of study should begin with a proper library. The ear he found most hospitable to his idea was Savoie Lottinville's. Luckily, too, the campus where DeGolyer most wanted to have his experiment started was that of the University of Oklahoma. He mapped out a tentative plan of procedure to Lottinville in 1946 on one of the latter's many visits to Dallas; and again, more precisely, in the summer of 1949, just before the DeGolyers were to set out for Europe. And so the trip acquired a second purpose: the search for books essential to a course on the history of science. In a random, unsystematic way, of course, DeGolyer had been collecting in this field all his life, but for reasons other than its centrality to the university curriculum.

DeGolyer did not let his illness diminish his devotion to the project for the University of Oklahoma. He continued to argue that it was fully as reasonable to teach the history of scientific ideas as to teach the history of political activity. Either one should have as by-product, at least, the training of the student in thinking objectively. He did not think many men in business yet shared this value. He wrote Arthur Holly Compton: "I suspect that most men who are wealthy, deep in their hearts feel that they have been very lucky and are rather afraid to throw the dice again. Consequently, with such a background, about the best one can expect is slow change to a new viewpoint instead of a radically new solution such as might occur to a man with scientific training."

The European summer trip, he observes to Compton, had yielded some priceless finds for the library collection to serve as backbone of the course. Even better, in the intervening nine months, "I have acquired the first edition of Copernicus, Napier's book on the invention of logarithms, the second edition of Boyle's *Spring of the Air*, which is the original announcement of Boyle's law, an early work of Malpigi showing some of his work with a microscope, and Volta's original announcement of his pile, as well as a copy of the first printed edition of Euclid." He explains to Compton that the University of Oklahoma is "a little short on ivy-covered walls; so the books may have a greater usefulness there than they would have elsewhere."

During the summer, Lottinville sparked a faculty committee which formulated a program, gathered curriculum information elsewhere, and made plans for positive recommendations to President George Cross. DeGolyer might be handling the matter of a required library; the university had the problem of finding a man capable of performing successfully in such a difficult assignment, interdisciplinary and demanding the widest cultural background as well as technological knowledge. The double difficulty — basic books and competent personnel — proved exhilarating to all concerned. DeGolyer was particularly engrossed; ill health, ironically, gave him the time needed.

In 1949, pursuing this favorite project, DeGolyer formally agreed with President Cross that he would collect the library to buttress a course in the history of science, lend it to the university and finally make the library a gift *if* such a course should be firmly established. Soon after, Dr. Cross started the search for a competent and distinguished professor for this project. In the whole nation there were probably scarcely a dozen men trained on the graduate level to teach such a course. There was then little or no demand for such training, and it did not appeal to specialists. As for the library itself, this became a major preoccupation for DeGolyer over the next few years. In 1953 he wrote to Dr. Chauncey Leake, then dean of the University of Texas Medical School, that the collection was deficient in medicine as a field, but that the geological section "is the best outside Europe."

The problem of finding a professor was solved in 1954 with the engaging of Dr. Duane H. D. Roller to organize the experiment. As for the books, DeGolyer began systematic purchasing as early as his talks with Savoie Lottinville in the summer of 1949, before leaving for Europe. He began ordering, by catalogue, from London dealer Raphael King in June; he continued buying very heavily from King over the next five years. He engaged one of his favorite book dealers, Jake Zeitlin of California, to begin scouting for first editions of historically meaningful scientific works. He also alerted other book friends, such as Herbert Reichner. Zeitlin performed the major service among these, but it was DeGolyer himself who put the collection together, like a mosaic structure. The inauguration of the course at his alma mater and the assembling of the background library became his major intellectual interest, so absorbing, in fact, that he was weaned away from other preoccupations, such as trans-Mississippi history, and even the *Saturday Review*. He no longer had time for everything.

Some of the larger checks to King included one for $1,307.60, dated November 1950, in payment of "the Crescentius, Wotton and Hanksbee" (3 volumes). In February of the next year, DeGolyer paid $1,373.40 for four volumes, including works of Descartes and Bacon. In April, another payment of a thousand dollars for four volumes,

one of which was Borelli's *De Motu Animallum,* followed a
week later by $182 for Pascal's *Traité de l'équilibre des
liqueurs.* In all, he found around $10,000 worth of books
he needed from King alone in the year 1952. And he
opened his book-hunting season of 1952 with a 350-pound
sterling order to King for the single volume, Luigi Gal-
vani's *De Viribus Electricitatis in Motu Musculari.*

He did not abandon his own book-writing projects.
George Brett, president of Macmillan, encouraged it seems
by Norman Cousins, persuaded DeGolyer to sign a contract on February 10, 1953 for a book to be titled "A Short
History of the American Oil Industry." His health did not
allow him to complete it, or indeed to do much more than
collect the research materials, always ably assisted in research matters by his indefatigable, loyal and marvelously
efficient younger brother, Homer. He made progress reports at intervals. He wrote to editor George Skelley at
Macmillan on November 1, 1954 that he was just back
from a trip to Europe but "I am devoting my life to history
at the present time and while I have nothing to report in
the way of manuscript, I am very satisfied with the progress I am making." He adds that he thinks "about four-
fifths of the job in writing a book is in the research," and
says he suspects the research will require another full year.
(It is interesting to note that in 1922, Macmillan editor
Harold Latham — later famous for his discovery of *Gone
With the Wind* — had written to query DeGolyer, at the
Amerada office, about writing a book on petroleum for
Macmillan.) Another transaction with Macmillan which
failed to materialize was the attempt on the part of Richard R. Smith in 1950 to interest DeGolyer in buying out
the English Macmillan's interests in American Macmillan,
at a price of about three million dollars. "No go," replied
DeGolyer, laconically.

DeGolyer's book interests included subsidy of worthwhile projects, as indicated in his offer to contribute $5,000 a year for five years in a "trial run" in order to inaugurate the publication of a "geological map of the world" survey. This offer was to assist a project of Dr. Maurice Ewing of the Lamont Geological Observatory. DeGolyer wrote that he was willing to offer his contribution in order to get the job done by private interests "in the national interest."

He took time out from the oil history to write a couple of essays: an introduction to the University of Oklahoma Press's new edition of *Vigilantes of Montana* and a brochure (1952) titled *History of Prospecting for Petroleum in Mexico Prior to 1938*, which was published in a Spanish translation by La Asociación Mexicana de Geologos Petroleros. This brochure, by the way, gives an exceedingly clear discussion of anticlinal theory; it is the lucid DeGolyer performing at the top of his gift.

At the time, 1952, DeGolyer was immensely gratified at the success of Pemex under the administration of Bermudez (and he remained gratified), and he took pride in the fact that DeGolyer and MacNaughton served as consultants for the Mexican government at the low fee of $2,000 a month. He was impelled by his enthusiasm to send Dr. Bermudez a telegram on May 26, 1953, about the bringing in of the Angostura field in the Veracruz embayment by Pemex: "I congratulate you and your staff most sincerely on this magnificent achievement. Exploration for a petroleum province requires tenacity, courage, skill and luck far beyond that required in a search for new fields, and but few men or organizations in all history have been successful in such endeavor. I congratulate the Mexican people upon this spectacular and most important result of your wise and farsighted leadership of the petroleum industry.

There is no substitute for such management in a successful enterprise."

In gratitude perhaps, Bermudez sent DeGolyer, along with his telegram announcing the Angostura success, a first edition of the old Spanish law code for the New World, *Leyes Nuevas*. Delighted, DeGolyer wrote that "this is by far the finest book in my library." No doubt De-Golyer was pleased in part because he had long ago in the early days recommended drilling the Golden Lane on a southeastern extension — a drilling not undertaken at the time — which would have included the Veracruz embayment. Not to be outdone in significant book gifts, he later sent Bermudez two volumes he particularly valued, Walter Howe's *The Mining Guild of New Spain and Its Tribunal General, 1770–1821* and a work titled *Mexico Silver and the Enlightenment*.

DeGolyer had a delicate conscience about consultation services for foreign governments. On a visit in 1952 to his son-in-law George McGhee in Turkey, DeGolyer's help was sought by Turkish officials. He replied that he could not possibly consider any relationship of Turkey with De-Golyer and MacNaughton so long as his son-in-law was American ambassador there, but he volunteered to give the officials what advice he could while there without charge. The offer was accepted.

The "DeGolyer Course in the History of Science," as it was referred to, posed the problem of finding either a historian with a knowledge of the sciences or a scientist who was a good deal more than a highly trained specialist. The university took several tentative steps before the course was finally structured in 1954. Since the DeGolyer collection was technically speaking "on loan" until final arrangements were achieved, President Cross was eager to expedite matters. In May 1950, Cross advised DeGolyer the course would be taught on the senior level — and open only to students taking honors — with the actual teaching being done in the room where the library would be housed. A year went by without definite procedure, while Dean Laurence Snyder, whose specialty was genetics, was planning the course. The plans were finally ready for the autumn of 1952, with Professor James Harlow of the Department of Physics scheduled to teach the new offering. DeGolyer volunteered to provide the money to bring in a distinguished name to inaugurate the course. Both Conant and Cohen of Harvard were approached; neither was available. DeGolyer proposed his good friend, Arthur Compton, chancellor of Washington University and winner of the Nobel Prize in Physics, who finally got the course launched with an initial lecture in February 1953. His lecture happily coincided with the university's celebration of its sixtieth anniversary and of the first decade of the presidency of Dr. Cross.

A second guest lecturer in May allowed the university to strike pay dirt. Duane Roller, an Oklahoma graduate and former associate of President Conant of Harvard and at the time technical editor for the Howard Hughes Aircraft Corporation, spoke on liberal education and its relationship to the history of science. Both the university and the speaker realized that man and plan had made a fruitful encounter. Roller accepted the curatorship of the DeGolyer science collection with the title of assistant professor of the history of science and technology. From that moment, the course and the collection went on to make history.

Meantime, in the long course of finding the right man and the right plan, the collection had lived a migrant life. DeGolyer consigned the first loan as early as November of 1949, although he reserved temporarily for his own needs a score or so of the major items for use in a special exhibition at Rice University and for display, in May 1951, at the formal opening of the new Fondren Science Building at Southern Methodist University, both occasions in celebration of benefactions from the Fondren family oil fortune which had originated in the successive development of the Spindletop area.

Pending the organization of the course, the collection was initially housed in the office of the emeritus librarian, famed bibliographer Jesse L. Rader. However, in December of 1950 DeGolyer made to the university a Christmas gift of thirty-two additional titles, valued at more than $18,000, and the continuing flow of books to the "on loan" group required enlargement of Rader's office in the basement of the library building. The permanent housing was awaiting the voting of funds by the state legislature for the purpose. But with Professor Roller's instituting of two courses in the autumn of 1954 and with further additions to the collection — DeGolyer was now supplying funds for the university to make additional selections — the DeGolyer science library replaced the university's section for rare books and became a library fully utilizable for qualified students. By 1955, a year before DeGolyer's death, the collection consisted of about ten thousand volumes. Professor Roller added two more courses, based on the materials of the expanding collection, and the field had been approved as an area study for doctoral dissertations. A checklist of the collection issued in 1953 brought an interesting revelation from the librarian of the Massachusetts Institute of Technology. He wished to buy duplicates from the University of Oklahoma; from a comparison of the great MIT history of science collection with that of the DeGolyer science library, the librarian had discovered that MIT had only sixty percent of the volumes available at Norman, Oklahoma. Oklahoma's librarian Arthur McAnally was exultant, for the checklist proved that the Southwest "was not outside the civilized area of the globe."

One distressing matter for the University of Oklahoma was occasioned by DeGolyer's career as writer, as well as reader and book collector. In preparation for his projected book on the history of the oil industry, he withheld for the time being from the University of Oklahoma gift his great private library of books specifically dealing with geology, reputed to be the best geological collection in the world. He intended, as he wrote McAnally in 1954, ultimately to add it to the science collection at Oklahoma; but he died before this part of the gift could be formalized. It now remains, then, like his third great collection, the "Southwest Collection" — history and literature, chiefly — the property of the DeGolyer Foundation. It is currently housed, on loan, at the Science Information Center of Southern Methodist University in Dallas, which also provides housing for a portion of the Southwest collection, the remainder still filling the shelves to overflowing in the DeGolyer home, destined in time to become, with the library, a gift to the city of Dallas. DeGolyer himself undertook the major task of cataloguing his geological library; furthermore, he had completed by 1954 a special annotated catalogue of the one hundred major items in this 1,400-volume collection.

What fueled this supply of energy in a man so sick and so often in the hospital in the last seven years of his three-score-and-ten span? A clue may be found in a letter he wrote to President Cross in April 1955, in which he confessed that he was "not interested just in books as science . . . the truth of the matter is that I am interested in books. . . . It seems to me that teachers, books and scholars are the fundamentals of a school. Books and scholars, or perhaps better — students, have done pretty well at times even when the student had to teach himself." And he adds this significant sentence: "Perhaps I am lonely among your alumni in feeling that I would be happier if we had a better library and even if the football team lost an occasional game."

In his way, DeGolyer wanted everybody to be happier, but typical of his pioneer heritage and his own experience, he thought this had to be earned, not given. As he often told his old servant, Lang Wingard, "I was lucky enough early in my career not to have to work any longer for a living — but I like to work." And he liked his work to have a social usefulness. He worried a good deal because his gift of books to the University of Oklahoma might be a show-case pyrotechnical display, but of little use to untrained youth. It was fine to point with pride to the rare items — some of them very costly — but what good would works in foreign languages do students who could not read them with ease? He pondered at one point the necessity of having all the rare books translated into English. He solved the problem by imposing on himself a limit of twenty percent in purchases of "rarities," for the science collection. The remainder was to be spent on works that interpreted the meaning and direction of science, on critical commentaries, even on textbooks. He wanted the library to be immediately usable. As always, he was the pragmatic, practical American of his times. Nonetheless, as in his speech on the meaning of the life of Captain Anthony Lucas — which was the central event in the fiftieth anniversary celebration of the Spindletop discovery, a speech he delivered on the Spindletop site in 1951 — he emphasized the importance of the American experiment as one that left "every man free to dream."

He valued the imagination, but only as it allowed men to prevision future reality. As a gift for his friends, he had a few paragraphs of this speech specially printed on parchment and suitably framed. He quotes, with obvious sympathy, a comment that Captain Lucas once wrote to him: "The plain fact of the matter is that I am not a trained geologist, hence do not see my way to give the proper or necessary interpretation to my — well — visions." DeGolyer infers that by "visions," Captain Lucas meant that every man was free to dream, "every man free to be wrong." "Like Napoleon's soldier, each of us carries a marshal's baton in his knapsack." This, concludes DeGolyer, is the virtue of the free enterprise system, of *free* competition. Excellence depends on effort, but failure is not dishonorable — you are free to be wrong. Success, too, should depend on effort, but success also depends, in the only kind of humility he seems to have valued, on the crowning of effort by luck. "Those who think wrongly fail but the system is many-faceted and can absorb its failures and still succeed." And therefore any system of human existence that limits choices to a single dictator is bound to fail; it can tolerate no margin for error. The virtue of democracy is that "every man is free to dream"; free competition, he thought, would insure the triumph of right ideas over wrong, or right "visions" or dreams over the false. The purpose of writing books, even in a science collection, was to record the human search for true ideas, for true "visions."

Said DeGolyer: "I have thought a lot about what men of science call 'the scientific method,' and so far as I can see, it amounts to the ages-old wisdom of proceeding by the method of trial and error. That is to say, of common sense. But there is great imagination in science too. You have to read Newton if you want to find out how men have discovered these truths about the universe. Newton had as much imagination for the great hypothesis. Or take Pasteur, and you will see again how important imagination is to science.

This portrait of DeGolyer in the academic robes of his honorary degree from Princeton was commissioned of English-born, Texas-settled Douglas Chandor by DeGolyer's associates at DeGolyer and MacNaughton as a gift for the firm's founder.

And also how in one man, as in the case of Pasteur, pure and applied science coexist."

Outstanding items in the science collection are works by Copernicus, Galileo, Newton, Bacon, Sir William Harvey, Mme. Curie, Vesalius, Malthus, Jenner, Steno, Darwin, Kepler, Hakluyt. But alongside works announcing the theory of gravitation, or the theory of the circulation of the blood, or the isolation of radium, or the origin of species, there are many others of great interest if less familiar to the layman. There is, for example, a remarkable volume by a Mexican scientist published in 1681, the *Libra Astronomica y Philosophica* of Siguenza y Gongora, in which Siguenza explains that comets are natural phenomena having no influence on the affairs of men. He was compelled to ridicule the statements of the famous religious pioneer of the Southwest, Father Kino, for medieval-minded misapprehensions that the famous comet of 1680 and 1681 presaged horrible catastrophes. Curiously enough, in New England conclusions similar to those of Siguenza were being stated by Increase Mather. DeGolyer was proud of two herbals in the collection, that of Leonard Fuchs (1501–1566), who "enjoys a verdant immortality in the beautiful group of American plants known as 'Fuchsias,'" and the *Hortus Sanitatis* printed in 1491. DeGolyer claimed this volume shows the first graphic representation of an oilman. His copy of this herbal is one of four in existence and the only one in perfect condition; it is important in the history of typography as well as in science.

25   Last Days

EVERETTE DeGOLYER fulfilled his "three-score years and ten" on October 9, 1956. He entered his seventy-first year with the prospect of having to continue to live on regular blood transfusions, with a succession of little strokes any one of which might become major; with flawed memory, and unable to read save laboriously with the help of a magnifying glass. He was not a man who could tolerate the notion of surviving as a mere vegetable. At the occasional parties he still had to attend in loyalty to friendships, he was obviously troubled by his inability to see and by the need of having Mrs. DeGolyer whisper identifications to him. One friend saw him at a reception during the Thanksgiving holidays of 1956; De mistook him for the friend's neighbor, but quickly rallied when the trend of the conversation revealed his mistake. The friend noticed that he made a signal to Nell DeGolyer, and shortly after they left the party.

Two weeks later, at dinner at the Petroleum Club, he again seemed particularly troubled by the need to have his wife identify longtime friends. He spent the rest of that night at home, wandering in and out of the library. He had lately formed the habit of going in to read at any hour of the night when he might awake, as though time were so precious he must leave nothing unread. Not infrequently, Nell DeGolyer would find him there in the library, magnifying glass in hand, as early as four-thirty in the morning. But he had, indeed, suffered from insomnia a good part of his life.

Early December in Dallas in 1956 yielded a fine spread of late Indian summer weather. The morning of December 14 was crystal clear; by work-starting time the temperature was a pleasant sixty degrees. As usual, that morning Lang Wingard drove the impeccably dressed DeGolyer (Lang always referred to him as "boss man") to the office of DeGolyer and MacNaughton, a mile or so east of the Southern Methodist University campus. DeGolyer now spent only the mornings at the office, Lang usually coming back for him just before noon.

It promised to be an untaxing and easy Friday; DeGolyer had no scheduled appointments on his calendar. No sooner had he arrived at his desk than a phone call came in from a visitor in town, Mortimer Kline, son of an old California friend of DeGolyer. The young man asked if he could pay a visit; DeGolyer consented, and Mr. Kline arrived a little before ten-thirty. DeGolyer then sent his secretary on an errand to the bank, and found some obligation to absorb the attention of his closest assistant, John Murrell. He was free to advise young Kline about a career in geology and how to succed at it.

He sent his secretary, Miss Dorothy Pitts, to a neighborhood bank to convert a thousand-dollar check into new, crisp fifty-dollar and twenty-dollar bills, for his Christmas gifts to his staff. The bank was at the moment in short supply of clean bills, so she went on to another one nearby. There, where she was unknown, she had to call in to Mr. DeGolyer to get confirmation that she was entitled to cash the check. The out-of-town guest was still in the office, and DeGolyer seemed to be enjoying a longer conversation than he had lately allowed impromptu visitors.

The visitor was still there when Miss Pitts got back; he left at about eleven-twenty. Seated at her typewriter, Miss Pitts was aware through the open door, which Mr. De-Golyer presently rose to shut, that he was absorbed in what she thought of to herself as "a brown study." She was aware that he had circled his room several times before closing the door.

She went into his office and asked him if he wasn't looking forward to the Christmas visit with his grandchildren in Washington and Virginia. He chatted a few moments about the trip. When Miss Pitts went out, he got up and closed the door tightly. She had been at her desk about a minute when she heard an odd little "popping" sound. She thought his chair had slipped off the pad as it had done once just a few days before. When she went in to see what was happening, he was slumped over his desk, bleeding profusely. Miss Pitts went quickly to the office of Mr. Porter to tell him something had happened to Mr. De-Golyer. It never occurred to her that he had shot himself. Phil Porter went into the office, came out and told Miss Pitts that Mr. DeGolyer was dead, and immediately he called the doctor. Miss Pitts supposed Mr. MacNaughton was away, but he was in his office and came out to discover what had happened. When he came out of Mr. DeGolyer's office, he said to Miss Pitts: "He shot himself; the gun is on the floor by his feet."

Mrs. DeGolyer could not be immediately reached, but young Everett was located at once and came right away. Meantime, Mrs. DeGolyer was reached and she too hastened to the office. Unprepared as she was for this tragedy, at least in her conscious mind, she knew inwardly that her husband was not the kind of man who would wait on death but would go forth to meet it. She told the children, both to comfort them and to explain, that "De had taken about all the suffering a man can take."

Justice of the Peace Glenn Byrd was summoned. He quickly returned an inquest verdict of "death by suicide." DeGolyer left no note.

The next afternoon, December 15, 1956, funeral services were held at three o'clock in the Highland Park Methodist Church, where eighteen years before DeGolyer had walked down the aisle to give his daughter Cecilia in marriage. Dr. Marshall Steel officiated at the funeral ceremonies, giving a talk so memorable and understanding that it is still recalled by the two thousand who came to pay their final respects.

The major achievements in the career of Everette Lee DeGolyer may be swiftly summarized. As a man of action and a man of science, DeGolyer is credited by nearly every technical historian as the primary and essential pioneer in establishing geophysics and seismographic detection as the indispensable tool in the evolution of the oil industry that has shaped the modern world. His accomplishment in this field was due to his fortunate combination of technical know-how and his exceptional business acumen. One must note in this connection that DeGolyer steadily insisted that he was primarily a geologist and not a geophysicist, that he himself held no patents and was not an inventor; but his vast scientific learning gave him the insight and understanding to know exactly where to throw his promotional and financial gifts to the support of inventive specialists and to help solve their problems.

As a man of action, his most important work was his central role in the formation of three of the greatest corporations in present-day economy: the Amerada Corporation, Texas Instruments, and Texas Eastern Transmission. Finally, as a man of science allied with a man of thought and culture, he put together three of the most notable private collections of books in the history of the nation — and made the three libraries available to the public. The first is the great Science Library which he gave to the University of Oklahoma, and which ranks with that of Harvard as one of the two best such libraries in this hemisphere. (In actuality, with the university's very large list of purchases since 1956, some scholars believe it to be the world's best.) The second is the Geological Library presently housed at Southern Methodist University's Science Information Center and which now numbers nearly forty thousand volumes. The third is the trans-Mississippi or Western collection of the DeGolyer Foundation, temporarily on loan to Fondren Library at Southern Methodist University, also numbering around forty thousand volumes. Under the direction of Everett DeGolyer Jr. the Foundation Library is pursuing acquisitions in fulfillment of the specific interests of its founder, adding a yearly total of three to four thousand volumes to the library that DeGolyer left at the time of his death.

The minor achievements of DeGolyer's career, enumerated in the course of this biography, are nearly all links in the chain of his three major contributions in the fields of corporate business, applied science and technology, and public benefaction through endowed libraries. There is, however, one exception. This is the fact that DeGolyer himself composed, so to speak, a fourth major achievement, that of an extraordinarily original and likable character, one with "charisma," in the modern stylish term. His ebullience, his sparkling if sardonic wit, his lightninglike responsiveness to the most diverse fields of intellectual interest, his early imitation of the suave British ways of Lord Cowdray and his entourage, never masked the fact that he was fundamentally American to the core, of the solid rock — resourceful, plucky, experimental, humorous and profoundly individualistic. Until his health failed, his presence brightened the day of everybody around him. It was perhaps this zest for living, this gusto, which won him the enduring friendship of the most diverse kinds of men, from the famous to the obscure. His achievements live on in institutions. His presence lives on in another kind of posterity, in the minds of many men.

Of the many tributes paid him in print at the time of his death, two by his scientific peers may be singled out, one by A. Rodger Denison, the other by Wallace Pratt.

Mr. Denison wrote the memorial for the National Academy of Sciences. It appeared in Volume 33 of the publication of the Academy entitled *Biographical Memoirs*. His conclusion: "With all his belief in luck, De more than any single man brought to the art of oil prospecting a series of precise 'tools' and pioneered in most cases the use and the interpretation of results. The application of these 'tools' has been responsible for the major part of the oil discoveries throughout the world in the past twenty years."

Mr. Pratt wrote in the *Proceedings* of the Geological Society of America, May 1957, that death had come for "Everette Lee DeGolyer who, for more than forty years, had stood out as the dominant figure in his profession, the busiest and most successful of petroleum geologists. . . . His achievement brought him wide acclaim as 'the father of American geophysics.'"

In their obituary notices, the *New York Times* and *Newsweek* and *Time* all noted that oilmen generally regarded DeGolyer as "the world's greatest oil geologist." *Time* ventured an explanation of his death: "Aging, one eye totally gone, he began to suffer the blood-draining anguish of aplastic anemia. He feared that somehow his mind would soon be affected, found the thought too much to bear."

As *Time* magazine observed in its obituary, there are three kinds of millionaires: 1) the "silver spoon" variety; 2) the "rabbit's foot" category; and 3) "Mr. De," in a class by himself.

The DeGolyer
Foundation Library

In the course of his lifetime, by conservative estimates, E. DeGolyer had bought or acquired nearly 89,000 volumes. By the time of his death, he had given away more than half; the remainder were in his home or on loan.

By the terms of the will of Everette DeGolyer, the De-Golyer Foundation Library is to be administered for the public good by a board of fourteen directors, of whom somewhat less than half are immediate members of the family. The instructions, or directives, for the board of governors are quite flexible. At this time (1970), the ultimate location and housing of the library are still uncertain. One of the first decisions of the board was to secure the advisory services of an eminent librarian. Lawrence Clark Powell, then director of libraries of the University of California at Los Angeles and an authority on southwestern materials, was engaged to come to Dallas and to make a study of the best possible use for the collection. Powell's conclusions were at variance with the original plan, which had been to preserve the library intact in the present home and garden estate as a self-supporting municipal gift to the city of Dallas. So long as Mrs. DeGolyer should still live in the home, the library was to be made available to the public through a special arrangement for space with the libraries of Southern Methodist University, after which time the intention was to create of the family residence a combination park, museum and library.

Dr. Powell strongly urged that the library be located in facilities normally available to a host of varied scholars and students. He declared himself in favor of emphasizing above all else the widest possible use of the books with minimum personal dislocation. In his opinion, prior attempts to maintain private libraries apart from great and active educational institutions represented a significant loss in the daily consultation of indispensable materials. (Since the site of the DeGolyer residence on White Rock Lake was actually chosen by Nell DeGolyer as a compromise for the inability to find earlier a suitable farm place in the nearby countryside, it is still a considerable drive from the heart of the city.) Powell urged concentration on book usefulness above all else. The board is quite reasonably taking its time before a final decision.

At the moment, about 40,000 books, mostly on Spanish colonial and western history and literature — plus possibly the finest railroad history collection in the nation — are spaciously but simply housed in special quarters on the third floor of Fondren Library at Southern Methodist University in Dallas, on loan. In a neighboring building, the Science Information Center, is the DeGolyer Geological Library of an equal number of volumes. Across the campus in the Southwest Legal Center Library are nearly a thousand "law-oriented" volumes which DeGolyer gave to the university's Legal Center. Some seven or eight thousand volumes of the Foundation Library remain on the shelves of the DeGolyer home; these are readily available on request and are delivered to students or scholars who want to use them at the Fondren Library location. Cataloguer and director-librarian of the Foundation Library is Dr. James Phillips, a graduate of Southern Methodist University with doctoral training at Yale and the University of Dublin, who has made himself an expert on the Southwest (one who effectively uses all the standard languages including Russian). His help to scholars is manifest in the fact that the Foundation has, despite its youth, already assembled a good shelf of published books partially or wholly indebted for source materials to the DeGolyer Foundation Library.

Whether the library will, as originally envisioned, be patterned after the nationally admired Huntington estate in Pasadena or be located on a college campus may well become the choice of Everett Lee DeGolyer Jr., who has thus far brilliantly executed his father's ideas. Up till now, his direction has revealed a steady concentration on book acquisition and continuation of journal and magazine completeness, with little waste on plush installation or decoration. It is true that the sale or lease of part of the extremely valuable lakeside property would immensely enhance the endowment money of the Foundation, which has already received several significant benefactions in the form of private collections. But as of now the plans for the future are full of promise — and provisional. Perhaps something truly original may develop. That would be in keeping with the style of E. DeGolyer.

A Bibliographical Note

I. A complete listing of the published writings of E. DeGolyer, including book reviews, will be found in the National Academy of Sciences *Biographical Memoirs,* Vol. XXXIII, pp. 65–68, Columbia University Press, New York, 1959. The memorial to DeGolyer in this case is written by A. Rodger Denison; it precedes the bibliographical listing. Other comprehensive bibliographies of the writings of E. DeGolyer may be found in: 1) *Oklahoma Geology Notes,* Vol. 17, 1957, compiled by Carl C. Branson; 2) *Bulletin,* American Association of Petroleum Geologists, Vol. 41, May 1957, accompanying a memorial notice by Lewis W. MacNaughton; and 3) *Proceedings,* Geological Society of America, Vol. 68, Part 1, 1957, accompanying a memorial by Wallace E. Pratt.

II. An excellent selected bibliography of general works on petroleum geology and geophysics is readily available in the superb study by Max Ball, *This Fascinating Oil Business,* first published by 1940 by Bobbs, Merrill and brought up to date in 1965 by Douglas Ball and Daniel S. Turner, under the same title and from the same publisher. The first edition of this book was the one general work on the oil industry that DeGolyer himself recommended to all lay readers.

A sifted list of general works in the field most useful in this biography would include the Ball work, plus Ruth Knowles' *The Greatest Gamblers: The Epic of American Oil Exploration* (McGraw-Hill, 1959), Leonard Fanning's *Foreign Oil and the Free World* (McGraw-Hill, 1954), and George Elliott Sweet's *The History of Geophysical Prospecting* (Science Press, 1966).

Among more special items, for the material on Mexico in Part I, I found invaluable John A. Spender's *Weetman Pearson* (Cassell, London, 1930), William Weber Johnson's *Heroic Mexico* (Doubleday, 1968), Anita Brenner's *The Wind that Swept Mexico* (Harper, 1943), and Robert E. Quirk's *The Mexican Revolution* (Citadel, 1963).

Other specialized or topical books of great help include Carl Coke Rister's *Oil! Titan of the Southwest* (University of Oklahoma Press, 1949), James A. Clark and Michel Halbouty's *Spindletop* (Random House, 1953), Edwin Theodore Dumble's *Geology of the Northern End of the Tampico Embayment Area* (Proceedings of the California Academy of Sciences, 4th Series, Vol. VIII), Raymond F. Mikesell and Hollis B. Chenery's *Arabian Oil: America's Stake in the Middle East* (University of North Carolina Press, 1949), Wallace E. Pratt and Dorothy Good, editors, *World Geography of Petroleum* (American Geographical Society, 1950), Eugene Victor Rostow's *A National Policy for the Oil Industry* (Yale University Press, 1948), and — a remarkably clear exposition of scientific techniques — E. E. Rosaire's *The Handbook of Geochemical Prospecting* (Subterrex, Houston, 1939), and Norman Cousins' *Present Tense* (McGraw-Hill, 1967).

III. Of the magazine articles devoted to E. DeGolyer, the ones I have found most helpful are the four mentioned above in I, accompanying the DeGolyer bibliographies, and the following: Cleveland Amory, "Mr. De of Texas," *Saturday Review of Literature,* Jan. 26, 1957; Cleveland Amory, "The Oil Folks at Home," *Holiday,* February 1957; Norman Cousins, "Life Begins at Twenty-Five," *Saturday Review of Literature,* April 24, 1965; Norman Cousins, "Retrospect and Prospect," *Saturday Review of Literature,* March 5, 1960; Carey Croneis, "E. DeGolyer, Sidney Powers Memorial Medalist," American Association of Petroleum Geologists' *Bulletin,* May 1950; and Lewis MacNaughton, "E. L. DeGolyer, Father of Applied Geophysics," *Science,* February 1957.

IV. Many other sources are cited directly in the text. The reader may safely assume that the location of documents and letters not specifically indicated is understood to be the archives of the DeGolyer Foundation in Dallas.

Index